WHEAT FIELDS

BILL SAMPSON

Flint Hills Publishing

Wheat Fields

Original cover painting by Louis Copt.
www.louiscopt.com

Cover design by Amy Albright.

Flint Hills Publishing
Topeka, Kansas
www.flinthillspublishing.com

Printed in the U.S.A.

This book is a work of fiction. Any references to historical events, real people, or real places are used fictitiously. Other names, characters, places, and events are products of the author's imagination; any resemblance to actual events or places or to actual persons—living or dead—is entirely coincidental.

ISBN Paperback: 978-1-953583-43-7
ISBN Hardback: 978-1-953583-44-4
ISBN Ebook: 978-1-953583-45-1

Library of Congress Control Number: 2022921557

1

LEAVING SALINA

Leaving Salina

Some things had moved west. Russell Stover, for decades one of Kansas City's proudest corporate names, now made and packaged its chocolates in a new manufacturing facility just west of Abilene. The Brookville Hotel had moved east. Leaving Brookville, a tiny town seven miles south of Interstate 70, it had reimagined itself in a brand new but look-alike building just north of the interstate from Abilene and had carried on for a few years before closing. But one Abilene landmark had not changed: the Eisenhower Museum. It was still the most popular place to visit in Kansas—in part because of its convenient location just south of I-70, in much larger part because of the profound achievements of the state's number one son.

Other things had stayed the same, such as the obligatory Kansas highway signs:

"Smile, your mother chose life!"

and,

"One Kansas farmer feeds 179 people — plus you!"

But Richie missed the signs. He had his head in his cell phone, reviewing the latest Facebook feed from his friends in Salina, wondering whether he'd ever see them again.

As it runs east from Abilene to Lawrence, Interstate 70 is a straight line on most highway maps. But it swings hard north for the better part of a mile just past Junction City, giving travelers a look at the bluffs to the east and the airfield to the west. Marshall Army Airfield belongs to Fort Riley, which has been a part of Kansas for a long while. Built in 1853, the post was named that same year for General Bennett C. Riley, who had led the first military escort along the Santa Fe Trail in 1829. George Armstrong Custer took command of the 7th Cavalry Regiment at Fort Riley in 1866. From 1884 until 1946, Fort Riley was the home of the U.S. Cavalry, including the 9th and 10th Cavalry Regiments, the "Buffalo Soldiers." Its horse shows and hunts and especially its polo matches, participated in by riders from the most prestigious cavalry schools in Europe, became so well known that an officer's time at the fort came to be called "the life of Riley."

Today, Fort Riley is home to the Army's First Infantry Division, The Big Red One. Boasting thirty-five Medal of Honor recipients, the Division was "first to fight" in WWI, WWII, and Vietnam. Last deployed as a division after Saddam Hussein's invasion of Kuwait, it was at the center of the success of Operation Desert Storm. Somewhere along the trail of a hundred conversations with his grandfather, who served with The Big Red One in Vietnam, Richie had heard all of this, often in his grandfather's pickup on the way to and from his games and camps and tryouts as they would drive down and back this very stretch of highway.

Richie's dad had walked away from the family when Richie was two. He had no doubt his mom loved him. But she worked at Kennedy & Coe, a fine accounting firm but one where everybody seemed to work late. She rarely got home before 6:00, and once she got home there was dinner and the other countless things that piled up for both of them, including homework for him and homework for her.

The emotional building blocks in Richie's life had been laid down by his grandfather. Granddad had a hundred stories about The Big Red One, and he told them with affection and pride and a love of country and corps that would move Richie even on the way home from a last-second loss. Richie loved his grandfather, and he loved what his grandfather stood for, so much of which had started at Fort Riley.

The trips had not slowed when his grandfather died a year ago; Richie's stock as a player was rising rapidly and, if anything, there were more of them. While he no longer had his grandfather, Richie still had this place and the memories that were tethered to it. What locked in this time as he looked up the hill at the Army's only-ever piece of nuclear-capable artillery—a 280mm cannon rusting quietly but defiantly on its concrete pad—was the thought he might never come this way again.

For a basketball junkie from Salina, I-70 was the link to the rest of the world. Salina Central's rival schools—Junction City, now nearly in the rearview mirror, and Manhattan, still a few miles ahead—were east of Salina. And the real high school basketball in Kansas was played even farther east. With the exception of a few Wichita schools, most often Heights, the state's basketball powers were all in Topeka, in Lawrence, and in Johnson County. K-State was east on I-70. So was KU, whose camp Richie attended in the summers. And Kansas City, where Richie was now playing his age-group tournaments, was also east. They were driving to Lawrence, where they would live and where Richie would enroll for his senior year of high school. The Lawrence schools, in a different conference than Salina Central and indifferent, besides, would never travel west to play the Mustangs.

The swing north along the airfield took only a minute or two at most before the road turned right toward Lawrence. Richie was already deep in thought. He missed his grandfather; he knew he was leaving his friends; he was sad, and he was getting sadder.

The highway rose up to the hillcrest, dropped down through several limestone cuts that were themselves cut for exits onto the old roads to Manhattan and Council Grove, then turned back uphill. It leveled off past cornfields fed by McDowell Creek, climbed past the rest area, then climbed still higher. This was the thick of the Konza Prairie, whose rolling limestone hills were covered with the big and little bluestem grasses that had grown here since the glaciers had retreated. Ancestors of the state bird, the western meadowlark, were the first to notice the desolate but hopeful soil, and they obliged it with the seeds they had carried in from as far away as what is now Mexico. Countless millennia later, soon after today's ranchers had finished their late-spring burns, these same grasses supported millions of head of Kansas cattle.

Richie's mom knew Exit 303 would take them to the highest point between Junction city and Lawrence, so she got off there. She stopped at the stop sign for K-18. The evening's blues and grays were coming on ahead of them, chasing the light back in their direction; they had gotten a late start. Richie's mom checked for traffic. It was unlikely here at any hour, but the occasional car racing back to campus was harder to see at sundown, and deadly if you missed it. Clear. She turned left and drove slowly to the north, stopping on the bridge between the large, rectangular openings of its concrete railing. "C'mon," she said. "Bring your phone."

Richie got out, closed the door, and walked around the front of the car. When he turned toward his mom, she was already standing at the opposite railing with her back to him. Above and all around her the western sky was painted with crimsons and garnets and ambers and gingers, and with more yellows than he had the names for. Straight ahead, the colors spread across a platform of dark cerulean that rested on the charcoal crest of the hill guarding the eastern approach to Fort Riley, the same hill they had just climbed to get here. Richie had seen some Kansas sunsets, but nothing like this. He walked to his mom's right side and stopped. He was still feeling sorry for himself, and he let his head drop. But when he lifted it again, he found he was looking ahead with his mom, the sunset washing over both of them. Richie wrapped his arm around her shoulders and breathed deeply, wanting the colors to light him up on the inside, too.

It did not take many miles for Richie to fall asleep in the front seat after they had stopped to watch the sunset. Elizabeth looked over at her son and marveled for at least the thousandth time at the brown hair now falling across his forehead, so thick it might have been chiseled into place.

She thought about the reason for this drive—about her accounting firm and how, two years ago, she had approached Kennedy & Coe about opening a special kind of office in Lawrence. She had just been elected to the executive committee. Women were important to the firm and were approaching forty percent of the partnership nationwide; but they were still underrepresented on the executive committee, and she was proud of her new position. The firm had started in Salina decades ago; it had thrived in Kansas, and it had recently done a remarkable job expanding outside of Kansas. Holding itself out as an agriculturally-centered accounting firm, it now counted multiple offices in California to accompany sister locations in Des Moines, Indianapolis, Kansas City, and other places. But Elizabeth saw a different future for accounting than the servicing of large farms and feed lots and implement manufacturers and pet food companies. The future she saw was data: collecting it from the entire ag space and not just from their clients, managing it, learning from it, and marketing what they learned to the clients they already had and to the hundreds of new companies who would want to tap into their expertise. What the firm needed, she felt, was a thought center, and she believed she could create one in Lawrence.

She had befriended a statistician at The University of Kansas, a brilliant woman from Delhi whose work fit beautifully with what she had in mind. Mini's KU team was at anyone's definition of "cutting edge" when it came to data management. She had introduced the firm's chairman, John Meyer, to Mini two years ago when they were in Lawrence for a basketball game. Never had she seen him so quiet in a meeting, or so talkative afterward.

What Elizabeth had not counted on was the time necessary to get the firm's buy-in for her idea. What she had absolutely not counted on was getting it in the spring that preceded Richie's senior year of high school. John had announced the special meeting on a Monday just three months ago in May and had set it for the same Monday's afternoon. There was no agenda—the sure sign something was up and that it was confidential. There was in fact only one matter up for consideration: Lawrence. John ramrodded both the discussion and the decision. Once the executive committee had voted in favor of the new research center there was only a slight pause before John took off his glasses, put them on the table in front of him, and smiled across at her. "Elizabeth," he said, "we would of course like you to open our new center and manage it."

She had sat through the meeting; she watched the voting; she knew it had happened. Still, she flushed with exhilaration, and pride followed right behind. This was "her baby" and everyone knew it. The meeting adjourned soon after she had nodded to John, and the conference room could have been lighted by the smiles all around as she and the other Salina partners left the space and their remote colleagues closed down their ZOOM links.

She had almost reached her office when Mary, a contemporary in the partnership and one of her best friends in the firm, asked, "How's Richie?"

"Fine," Elizabeth had responded. She wasn't being evasive; Richie *was* fine—never better. He would finish his spring honors classes with "As" but also with the profuse praise of his teachers. Elizabeth had arranged for a math tutor for Richie in seventh grade because he had already learned what the middle school might have taught him over the next two years. His current math teacher had coached him for his junior-year swing at the SAT, and both he and Elizabeth were excited at Richie's math score—a 780. He was scheduled to take the standardized test again in the fall, one of a handful of Salina Central students signed up to do so, and the math teacher was sure he would get a perfect 800 next time. Richie would play AAU basketball this summer with the same team, whose players and coach he really liked. And he had a job—two, actually. He would start with the local engineering firm in May, once school was out. Then, with the wheat harvest, he would join Annie Reinfried's custom operation as it made its way north into Kansas. Annie and her husband ran the company. Annie had grown up in Salina, she was Elizabeth's closest friend, and she treated Richie like her own son Rob—right down to the daily dose of tight schedules, tough love, and scratch biscuits. Richie reveled in the dawn-to-dusk pace, the rough-edged intimacy of the family work group, and the fact he was entrusted to drive one of the grain trucks—second only to the combines in level of responsibility.

Yes, thought Elizabeth as her face burned beneath her cheeks, *Richie was fine*. Richie also knew nothing about their moving to Lawrence. Elizabeth had not mentioned it to Richie earlier because it was only a possibility . . . and because she knew he would be hard-set against it. Now it was a reality. Now she had to tell him he would miss his senior year in Salina. Turning her face to the wall to mask its color, she thanked Mary for the support and slipped past her office door, closing it behind her and backing up against it as she caught her breath. How was she going to tell her son he would start his senior year of high school in a new city where he knew no one?

Their conversation about leaving Salina turned out to be one of the two hardest in her life, the other when she told him his father had left. But that earlier conversation, now so long ago, had all been on her former spouse. This one was on her.

She began it that evening after she had cleared the cherry pie she had spent the afternoon on. She could not focus on anything at work, Richie loved her cherry pie, and this seemed like a good time to bake one. She was running the plates under the faucet in the kitchen when the pressure that had been building throughout the meal caught up with her. "We need to talk about something, Richie," she said over her shoulder in Richie's direction.

It was an awkward start, but that's what came out when she opened her mouth. Richie, who was still at the table, was instantly wary. "OK," he said.

Their dish towels had originally been handed down from Richie's grandmother and had steadily been replaced with others like them—all-cotton, all of them plain, all of them washed a hundred times so they soaked up water like a fallow field in the middle of August. Richie's mom was still drying her hands on one as she came back into the dining room with her cup of coffee and sat down. Elizabeth had spent her professional life getting to the point, one of the keys to her success with clients and with the administration of the firm. She looked at her son and said, "We're going to move this summer—to Lawrence. The firm asked me to open an important new office there. The office was my idea—I proposed it two years ago. I told them I'd go." She wanted the last sentence back as soon as it cleared her lips. It should have been, ". . . and I told them *we'd* go." It was too late, but it hardly mattered. Richie's gaze met hers for just a moment, looking like she'd just slapped him. Then his face fell to his lap. Elizabeth did not count how many moments went by with neither of them saying anything, but it was a long time.

When it was clear Richie was not going to move and was not going to say anything either, Elizabeth spoke again. "I'm sorry, Richie. I know this is sudden, and I know this is your senior year. I . . ."

That's where she was when Richie—his head still down—pushed his chair back and stood up and placed his napkin on the table in front of him and left the room, all without a word. She could hear his boots on the stair treads as he walked upstairs, and she heard the door of his room as he closed it behind him. It would be two days before he spoke to her again.

Richie was still asleep in the front seat. She thought back to their first house in Salina—the small two-story with the side porch where Richie had gone through a bout with nightmares when he was five. He would sit up in his bed and call, "Mommy!" And if she were not right around the corner and immediately into his room he would stand up in his pajamas, toss his blanket over his little shoulders, and walk down the stairs to find her. He walked into a bridge party one evening, wide-eyed, telling everyone who would listen, "There's a lion in my room!" Elizabeth had gently introduced him to all of her friends. Then she took his hand and walked him up the stairs and lay down beside him until he fell asleep.

She thought of their move to the area around the country club when he was ten, and how excited Richie was to be so close to a swimming pool. He turned into a tow-head that summer, his brown hair bleached almost white by limitless afternoons in the glare of 100-degree suns, his growing body taking on a deep bronze. Elizabeth had had an uncle who was tall, but nothing prepared her for the succession of growth spurts that seemed to arrive every time her son changed seasons in sports. He was never into playing golf. But he was big and strong for his age and constantly around the club house, and he carried bags for the several members who were willing to pay for caddies. It was good exercise, the members were nice to him, and the money was amazing. She smiled as she remembered the first time he carried double. He was fourteen, and he was exhausted when he got home, but he made seventy-five dollars. He had never had so much money! He couldn't stop smiling, and he talked non-stop through dinner about the dozen ways he was going to spend it.

Her thoughts drifted to Abigail, Mary's daughter, who had grown up with Richie and had paired up with him at all the firm picnics and hay rack rides and Christmas parties. They would arrive at the event, scout it, find each other, and spend the rest of the time in rapid-fire conversation, often in noisy disagreement, until their parents dragged them home. That had lasted until their junior year, last year. Richie was over six feet tall and growing and was the school's star athlete; Abigail was also tall, also smart, and the captain of the dance team. For years all of their friends told them they would be the perfect couple, and then they were. Elizabeth could not have designed a better girlfriend for her son.

Richie had picked up Abigail and taken her to the Dairy Queen for a Blizzard and then driven to the country club, parking in the main lot and walking to the pool terrace, which was warm in late May but deserted as there was no water in the pool yet. They were sitting on the edge at the shallow end when Richie told her he was moving. Abigail's "No!" came out so fast she aspirated some of the ice cream and ended up coughing as violently as she was crying. Richie never was able to calm her down, so he just walked her to the car and drove her home. Elizabeth learned all of this from Abigail's mother, who felt about Richie the way Elizabeth felt about Abigail.

They had reached Topeka and were just east of Security Benefit Life on I-70 when the high beams of a west-bound semi cut through their windshield. It was a timely intrusion, and it reminded Elizabeth to stay straight for Lawrence rather than taking the curve north to Holton.

Rock Chalk Park

Richie and his mom did not make Lawrence until 11:00 p.m. There wasn't much to see other than their new apartment—on the third floor of a building that sat in a cluster of look-alikes just north of 6th Street and just east of the South Lawrence Trafficway, the roadway that led south from the Kansas Turnpike's Lecompton Exit and skirted Lawrence on its west and south sides, hooking up with Kansas K-10 east of town. They were also tired, both of them drained emotionally. So, with a minimal unpacking of clothes, they called it a night.

Richie woke up first, remembering he had left his bike on top of his mom's car. He was out of bed and to the window and pulling up the shades too fast to think about anything—just hoping it was still there, and it was. So he threw on yesterday's clothes, checked on his mom—she was still sleeping, left a note he was going to look around, and walked down the stairs and through the building's entrance door to the outside. The car was parked on the curb, straddling the black-and-yellow-striped loading area at the end of the sidewalk. They'd been too tired to notice. It was not even 6:30 yet and Richie did not think another hour would draw a parking ticket, so he untied his bike, checked his tire pressure—a habit he'd picked up from his uncle—and rode slowly north toward the cross street. Right—the street went slightly uphill past a vacant lot on the right side. Left—there were more apartment buildings like theirs, and a sign. They had moved into a complex called Hunters' Ridge. Richie headed left. When he cleared their complex he was able to see the water tower that commanded the entire area from the hill to the left. Straight ahead was a large round-about, which he circled and exited 180 degrees later. With the sun now coming up behind him he knew he was heading west, and downhill. Moving into view to the northwest was a sports complex Richie had visited many times before. Those other times he had headed straight to the basketball courts, his ear buds in and his head in his phone until his grandfather stopped in the parking lot. This time he could actually take in the tall light poles and the large buildings and the enormous parking lot that were all emerging from the north. Richie stopped at a street called George Williams Way, turned right, and headed to Rock Chalk Park.

The parking lot was just beyond the Best Western, symbiotically sited at the southeast corner of the complex. Richie rode past it and into the parking lot, working out which way to go next as he crossed it. A very large Jayhawk was emblazoned on the grey buildings that made up the tennis complex in front of him, and there was a low stadium immediately north of that. Richie rode first to the tennis complex and then into the small parking lot between the tennis building and the soccer field.

Now several years old and in constant use, the blue surface of the outdoor tennis courts looked like it might have been laid down just that month. The soccer field was the same—its natural turf so thick it looked more like a sod farm than the pitch for the very good KU women's team. A U-turn took him back into the main parking lot, where he turned north and pointed his bike at the long white building dead ahead. But before he got there, he saw what had to be a baseball or softball field on his left, so he turned west and went that way.

He could not see much of the ball field because of its high fence. But the gate straight ahead was open so Richie rode through it, coming face to face with the biggest running track he had ever seen. The field area for the shot put and javelin and discus and hammer throw was off to the right; the stands were left. Richie got off his bike and walked straight ahead onto a track he had only read about until now, a cushioned, multi-laned, laser-confirmed surface that was one of three certified 400-meter college tracks in the country.

It had been a while since he had competed in track; basketball had come to take up all of his time. But Richie Armstrong could run. A sprinter, his 200-meter time of twenty-two seconds flat during his sophomore year was the second-best among the Kansas 5A schools that spring, and Salina Central made a fuss over it. Unmoved, his AAU basketball teammates, many of them African American, had immediately dubbed him "white lightning." Richie did not compete in track his junior year because of basketball and the demands of his AP courses. And, he had grown. He went from barely six feet tall to 6'5" in his stocking feet, 6'6" in shoes. There weren't many sprinters anywhere who were 6'5". On an early August morning with nowhere else to be and nothing else to do, Richie couldn't stay off the track. He finished a lazy lap and walked over to his bike and thought to himself, *WHO gets to compete on a track like THIS?!*

He turned his bike around and rode back through the gate and east toward the same long white building he had seen a moment ago. As it was past 7:00 a.m., there were cars in its parking lot and people walking through the doors. Richie locked his bike in the bike rack and followed them. This was the part of Rock Chalk Park he knew.

Past the polished-cement entryway and its spider web of cracks was the reception desk. Behind it were the basketball courts, built a level down from the ground-floor entry. Had the courts formed a basement it would have been a gigantic walk-out. No different functionally than the basketball courts of other indoor facilities Richie had seen, these struck him like the tennis courts he had started with thirty minutes ago; they seemed brand-new. In fact they were gleaming. The walls were white and the high-gloss floors, just cleaned for the upcoming weekend, reflected at least a thousand points of the light pouring from the ceiling fixtures. There were eight full-size courts, each equipped with backboards that could be lowered along the sides to create sixteen big-enough courts. The same eight basketball courts would also convert to sixteen full-size volleyball courts. But the courts, no matter which tournament was in town, did not occupy all of the space under the longest roof Richie had seen this side of the domed football stadium in St. Louis. An eighth-mile walking/running track, a gymnastics area, a fitness room with wall-length mirrors for dancers, a cardio/weight room full of equipment—the free weights racked along the wall, meeting rooms, a snack bar, and an indoor soccer field filled it out.

As a rising-senior who played basketball, worked out with weights, jogged, ate every chance he got, and was now living only a few blocks away from this facility, Richie felt like the Orlando kids he had read about: they had grown up loving Disney movies and had awakened one magical morning to discover Davy Crockett and Donald Duck had moved in across the street.

Back in front of the reception desk, Richie asked, “How much does it cost to use this every day?”

“Are you from Douglas County?” the young man asked from behind the desk. “If you live in Douglas County, there’s no charge.”

“No,” said Richie, “Salina.”

“Then it’s five dollars a day, twenty bucks a month.”

“Thanks,” said Richie, trying to mask his disappointment. He was out the front door and almost to his bike before he remembered: *he* now lived in Lawrence, and he could come here any time he wanted. For free!

2

FREE STATE HIGH SCHOOL

Second Day

Richie slid his green and white tray along the stainless-steel tubes that formed the track to check out. *Everything in this building is green and white!* he thought to himself as he hurried past what was left of the vegetables, the cold fries, and two very well-done hamburger patties.

He was late. He had nearly missed the lunch period altogether by forgetting the entrance to the first-floor cafeteria was on the *second* floor. Richie not only had to backtrack, he had to reorient himself once he exited the stairwell on the second level. But there was a sign and he followed it, and he was soon making his way down a set of stairs he knew, to the back of the line in which he was now the only customer.

What was left to eat did not improve his mood, and he had his head down as he approached the electronic check out station. But he wasn't looking at his phone—that was in his cargo pants. He just had his head down.

"You must be the new boy everybody's talking about."

The husky baritone seemed to come out of nowhere. Richie lifted his head and found himself face to face with a middle-aged woman in a green and white smock large enough to hide a den of cub scouts.

"Yes, ma'am."

"Well," she went on, "first thing is you've got to hold your head up. Moping around won't make people not notice you; you're tall!"

"Yes, ma'am," Richie said again.

"And stop calling me 'ma'am'"!

Richie barely caught himself at "Yes."

"You hungry?"

"Yes, ma'am," slipped out before Richie could stop it.

"If you don't stop 'ma'aming' me you'll stay hungry. You got that?"

Richie nodded.

"I'm Harriet. I can see you don't have any friends here yet." Then she smiled. Her smile was so big it escaped her face and almost got caught up in her hair net. She held out her hand: "Give me your tray."

Richie lifted the tray off the rails and handed it to her.

Harriet turned back to the kitchen where there was still food, pushed through the doors, and filled Richie's green and white plastic tray almost edge to edge from the left-over containers sitting next to the stainless-steel refrigerators. Returning to the cafeteria line, she reached back behind her to the racks of potato chips and mixed nuts and assorted other junk foods next to the checkout register and swept two granola bars off their perch at the top of the rack, dropping them into the tray's single bare spot. "You look like you've been doing a ton of growing—probably get hungry in the afternoon. These'll help."

Not knowing what to say, Richie just stood there.

"See that boy over there with the god-awful yellow shirt?"

Richie turned his head. The cafeteria, nearly empty when he entered the line, was entirely empty now save the one guy in a shirt that looked like it had been tie-dyed in French's mustard and would have been easy to spot at a Taylor Swift concert.

"That's Tommy Danforth. He's a nice boy—not one of the eee-leet around here." She said the word as though "elite" status would get you electrocuted by the simultaneous discharge of a thousand hateful tweets in the parking lot after school. "You go sit next to him."

Harriett hoisted the hem of her smock, leaned in against the counter, conjured a dish towel from just over her right hip, lifted an empty serving tray out of the steam table, and let the rising plume chase her toward the kitchen. Then she stopped, her hair net slowly rotating over her right shoulder until her eyes fixed on Richie, whose eyes had never left her.

"See you tomorrow," she said, winking at him. Then she turned back left, toed the kick plate at the bottom of the swinging door, and disappeared.

Richie carried his tray to the table. Tommy Danforth was at ease within the phosphorescence of his Polo shirt, yellow radiating from him like the beams from the bug lights at the state fair in Hutchinson. He was skinny and wore a ball cap with MIZZOU-RAH on it. He looked up.

"You're the new kid."

Richie put his tray down across from the bug light. "I'm Richie—Richie Armstrong." He sat down with his back to Tommy Danforth, then swung his long legs across the bench seat as he rotated right to face him.

"Estonia?!" said Tommy, his entire body as peremptory as his question. "Really! You know the capital of Estonia! Where the hell is Tallinn?!"

"It's in Estonia," Richie said.

"Of course it is," mocked Tommy. "And what about the capital of Latvia? Riga, right?

And what about Croatia—the capital of Croatia? When Prince Ricks, who is **THE CAPTAIN OF THE FOOTBALL TEAM**, came up with Dubrovnik, anyone who had ever read **ANYTHING** about *Game of Thrones* would have thought that was **GENIUS!**

But Mr. Erickson kept looking around the room to see whether anyone else had an answer..., and *no one did.* You see anybody? Me neither. *Nobody.*

Until you raised your new-kid hand over your new-kid head and said, 'It's Zagreb.'

Were you *listening* then? Crickets! There was *no sound*! Do you know how often there is *no sound* in geography? **NEVER!** Geography is Free State's answer to *Pentecost!*

Where do you *come from*?! Did you ever *go* to high school before? Or did you have a private tutor come to your house every day and spoon-feed you all this shit?"

"Private tutor" came out hot and sharp-edged, cutting Richie exactly as Tommy had intended.

"Salina. I went to high school in Salina," Richie said, his voice low now even though they were the only two people left in the cafeteria.

"OK," Tommy went on, "Salina. Some county-seat tractor pull out in the red part of the state, no doubt. Doesn't matter. If you keep showing off like you did this morning, dissin' the other kids, it's gonna be tough even on MY sorry-ass reputation to be seen sitting with you at lunch.

Go on—eat," said Tommy, staring at Richie while he upended his can of Diet Coke to drain the last drop.

But Richie wasn't hungry anymore, and he just sat across from Tommy and stared back.

"I'm not trying to kill you, Richie Armstrong. But you have **GOT** to pay more attention in class—and I don't mean to the teacher, or this is going to be a **LONG** year for you here at Free State."

Richie had his head down again. He saw the granola bar and picked it up. When he had unwrapped it, he lifted his head. Tommy was no longer at the table. Having nearly reached the conveyor belt that took the trays back to the dishwasher, it took

Tommy only another moment to deposit his tray, look back at Richie, and shake his head. Then he was gone.

Sean Grogan

Sean Grogan described himself as "a strong five-nine" when he was playing high school sports in Quincy, Massachusetts. He built himself up to 190 his senior year and played fullback on an excellent team that made the playoffs. He had gone to Boston College to study journalism and watch Eagles football, and he had stayed in the Bay Area after graduation, working first for a suburban paper and, finally, for the *Globe*. He had never wanted to be anything but a sportswriter. He was making his way to editor when his wife left him, and the divorce hit him harder than any linebacker ever had. It cost him his house and his car, and its assault on the focus he had always brought to his columns finally threatened his job. But it didn't cost him his children. Sean and his wife had not been able to have any, which was a major part of their problem.

It was his editor who suggested he move. Sean still remembered their conversation, which went down over a cup of the *Globe's* terrible coffee in Steve's office. "Sean, you're messed up. Everybody here knows why. But until you let somebody in, nobody can help you. You won't move out of your neighborhood, you're taking the MTA to work, you eat at the same diner every night, and you don't get any sleep. You haven't written anything really good for three months and you haven't written anything really funny for six. I'm not going to fire you, but I'm going to help you move. I've checked with a friend, and I've got a place for you. It's clear across the country. But there are real sports there—college and professional, and the paper's old sports editor finally retired. They need somebody like you to get their sports page to the next level."

Steve took a long pull from a mug that said "SOX" in raised red letters and went on.

"I talked with everyone here at the paper. We love you, you know that. But we're all in agreement you need to get out of here, do something different, and we've decided to help the process. We're having a going-away party for you this Friday. Neptune—that's your favorite place in the North End, right? We've booked the back room for 7:00. Everybody's coming, even John." Steve stood up and reached out to shake Sean's hand. Sean took a while to get up out of his chair, looked at Steve for a second, then shrugged and shook hands with his boss. As he turned to leave what they called "the fishbowl" and go back to his cubicle he thought, *Must be a big deal!* John was the *Globe's* publisher. The last time he stayed in the city past 3:30 on a Friday was when the Red Sox were playing in the World Series.

There is a small space in his brain that remembers it was a great party. But right after the speeches, Sean had chased too many of "the best oysters in Boston" with too many pints of Sam Adams to recall much of it. He got there at 7:00 and it was clear the party had been rolling for a while. The speeches started at 7:30. There were one or two that were serious. Mostly it was a roast, and there were plenty of stories to choose from.

When the commotion had died down John stood up. He was still wearing his tie but had at least pulled it loose. The *Globe's* Brahmin chief executive asked everybody to be quiet, then called Sean up from where he had been leaning against the small bar in the back of the private room. John said some nice things, Sean remembered, although he could not repeat what they were. He gave Sean the obligatory going-away plaque that told his full name, position—"Senior Sportswriter," and years of service. Then he held out a small box and said, "This is from all of us, Sean: from all of your colleagues in sports and from all of your friends in the rest of the paper, right down to the guys on the presses. It's also from me and Chelsea—she sends her love—and from the company. We're all going to miss you."

The first thing Sean saw when he opened the box was a bright metal border around a familiar enameled logo. Attached to the logo was a key. Sean had always wanted the key to a Volvo; now he had one.

That was five years ago. The place Steve wanted him to try was Lawrence, Kansas; the paper was the *Journal-World.* Sean didn't make much progress on the trip the next day. But Sunday found him recovered from the party, and as he didn't have much to pack in his new car, he was on his way by noon. Steve told him he didn't need to fill out an application or call anyone—all he needed to do was show up a week from Monday. So, Sean took his time. He found some blue highways and an occasional tap in a county-seat tavern. He took walks, he got to bed early, he slept through the night for the first time in a year, and he thoroughly enjoyed himself. When he walked through the door of the paper's historically-registered brick building at 7th and New Hampshire at 8:00 sharp the next Monday morning, he felt great. He was introduced to the publisher/owner, he found his desk—it was located in an actual office with high windows that looked out the front of the building with a door that closed, and he went to work.

Sean's old-shoe manner and his encyclopedic knowledge of sports made him a quick fit in a basketball-crazed college town that was settled before the Civil War by people from Sean's part of the country. Sean knew baseball like he knew his own name, and he knew football because he had played it. The Royals weren't the

Red Sox, and maybe the Chiefs weren't yet the Patriots, but Sean quickly learned his way around both ball clubs.

The athletic department at KU was glad to see him. Sean's first few columns told the AD there was a real pro at the *Journal World*, and when they met, the AD discovered Sean was a hell of a guy. Sean was also smart, and he was good with words. It was his deft way with a keyboard and his openness to teaching the folks around him that lifted the other writers, and then the entire sports section, into prominence. They were voted the state's best sports page after Sean's second year in Lawrence, and they had "kept the trophy" every year since.

For Sean, fall sports started with high school football. It was a coin flip whose game to start with—Lawrence High's or Free State's. Free State had struggled last season, but there was a buzz around the team this summer, so Sean drove west from his downtown loft apartment to check out the Firebirds. He drove straight to the swimming pool lot on the northwest corner of the high school building. There was rarely a parking space left there on the Friday evening of a Firebird football game, but when there was one, the action was right across the street.

People who showed up for the first home game in the fall of 2009 probably expected a construction site with goal posts. There would have been a field, of course. But the rest of the complex might have been acres of bare dirt powdered by the Kansas sun and dotted with broken concrete and cement-covered 2x4s. While that would have been the case at any other high school in the state, what the Free State fans encountered that fall would have passed for the grounds of a beautiful estate owned by someone whose conspicuous consumption ran not to a lighted tennis court but to a lighted football field.

Like everything else the adoring boosters had built for the team, even the entrance columns were of beautifully laid-up Manhattan limestone. Everyone participating in the game—player or coach or student manager, cheerleader, band member, referee, home team or visitor, family or not—passed between the columns as they followed the serpentine path down into the complex. They came first to the concession facility, a large building that sat at the south end of the immaculate, natural-turf field. Built entirely of the same limestone, the building and its wide serving counters faced the field, which sat between limestone-faced stands. Opponents' parents quickly spread the rumor you had to write for ESPN to get into the limestone press box.

The stadium had been finished late in the summer, just days before the first game. As money was no object and the sprinkler system was already in place, large spruce and balsam fir and juniper were placed carefully throughout the complex, followed immediately by flatbeds of sod—only the tall fescue that grows best in northeast Kansas. Free State Football Stadium was magnificent for its first game, and for every game since.

Sean had found his parking spot opposite the entry door to the Natatorium. Its fifty-meter indoor pool struck many—especially the Lawrence High graduates who had played football for the Chesty Lions and who had fought against a second high school as their fathers had fought against the Germans—as excessive for a Kansas high school, until Free State opened it to the public on evenings and weekends. Leaving the Volvo, Sean moved carefully through the slow-moving, bumper-to-bumper traffic on the street and stepped across the far curb onto the path that led to the entry columns. His press pass swinging from the cord around his neck, Sean would not need a ticket to get in, so he merged with the upbeat crowd that already had theirs. This was proving to be a good Firebird team. It had a dynamic senior quarterback, Prince Ricks, who had thrown for two touchdowns and run for two more in Free State's first outing, a 31-0 pounding of Leavenworth High on the Pioneers' home field. Tonight's opponent, Shawnee Mission South, would be a tougher test. But nobody who followed Free State was worried.

As expansive as Sean was feeling about the crowd around him, he was just as curious about the young man straight ahead. Many young people that tall had the gait of an Ichabod Crane. But this young person was more powerfully built than Washington Irving's school teacher, and he moved with the rhythmic assurance of an athlete, so Sean caught up with him and tapped him on the shoulder and asked a question he already knew the answer to:

"Can you tell me where I can get a Diet Coke?"

The youngster had to be six and a half feet tall, and a deep Kansas summer's tan looked down at Sean as the boy's head turned to him. An aquiline nose separated his brown eyes, a rugged chin effortlessly supported the rest of his face, and ears nearly as brown as his eyes just reached a thick head of hair. Broad-shouldered and graceful, he had to be a basketball player.

"Sure," he said.

He was smiling, but it wasn't the smile Sean was used to from a high school jock going to a Friday-night game on his own campus. This young man was communicating good manners, certainly, but there was more hopefulness in the smile than self-confidence. And he was obviously by himself. Sean fell in beside him.

"Is it this big building right in front of us?" Another question Sean knew the answer to.

"Yes. The concession stand is on the other side; it faces the field."

Sean held out his hand. "I'm Sean Grogan; I'm a sportswriter for the *Journal-World*."

"Right," said Richie as he took it with his own. "I know; I recognized you. You're always wearing a Red Sox ball cap. I'm Richie Armstrong. I'm new here."

Basketball: Second Day of Practice

New kid can shoot it.

That was Jerry Fairbanks, the assistant basketball coach at Free State High School, speaking in low tones to himself and to anyone else close enough to hear him. He was standing in the corner of the gym, just getting there after a text exchange with his daughter who couldn't find the keys to the car when she got home. It was Tuesday afternoon. Fairbanks had missed the first day of practice for a dentist's appointment; this was the first time he had seen Richie Armstrong on a basketball court.

Richie had spent most of his high school career in Salina at six feet tall or less. He'd had to develop a quick release to get his shot over the guards, most of whom were as tall as he was, and especially over the "4s" and "5s", the forwards and centers, who were all taller than he was. Richie had exceptional hand-eye coordination, and he studied things. He knew how to position his hand under the ball when he shot it, and how to cradle it lightly with his left hand, and how to release the ball at the top and not on the way up, and how to move all the way through the shooting motion with his right hand—flipping his wrist and extending his fingers at the end of the follow-through. For someone his age, his mechanics were outstanding, and they had enabled him to score consistently despite his average height. That was then. Now he was 6'5", 6'6" in shoes. His release and his mechanics were the same, he still had the same 37" vertical leap, and nobody could touch him—literally. AAU opponents who had at least been able to stay with him two summers ago couldn't get near his shot last summer. And today, neither could anyone at Free State. Had Coach Fairbanks been there Monday for the introduction, the light workout, and the shoot-around, he would have seen that. He wasn't, but he saw it now.

An hour later, Fairbanks and Jason Boyer, the head coach, had worked the thirty who had shown up through free throws, layups, defense (the "ready" position; slides; moving backward; fighting through ball screens; keeping eyes on a swivel; keeping hands up), passing, and rebounding. Anyone in the stands would have heard the call of a boy's name at the front or back end of a critique. "Smith, hands up! All the time!" Or, "Bradshaw, do the layups like you mean it! Lazy in practice, lazy in the game!" Or, "Two out of ten free throws! My god, Simpson, my daughter can make two out of ten, and she's five!" But nobody in the stands would have heard "Armstrong!"

The coaches watched Richie, for sure. It hadn't sunk in for them yet, but they loved watching him. He made nine of ten free throws, and the tenth nearly went in before spinning out. Layups looked like a for-sure dunk until the very end, when Richie laid the ball softly against the glass and into the net, his hand well above the rim. Richie's defense was solid; he could thread a pass to anyone, anywhere; and he competed hard for rebounds. They spoke to him, but it was as much an acknowledgment as anything: "OK!" and "Good movement." and "D! Good D." There was no criticism—no stopping to show him how to hold the ball for a long pass or how to get in the right stance on defense or to explain why it was important to stop moving for at least a moment before shooting a free throw. There was no more point in teaching Richie Armstrong how to shoot than there was in teaching Ted Williams how to hit.

Boyer blew his whistle as the second hand swept past 4:30. “OK! Greens and Whites! I’ve got green; Prince, you’re with me. Armstrong, you’re with Coach Fairbanks; he’s got white. Billy [Billy Thompson, the manager] has the jerseys. Line up—not Prince and Armstrong, but everybody else. First guy takes green, next white, until everybody has one. Prince, Richie, you get yours, too.

OK! We’ll take one minute to see who the first five are, then it’s on. Billy—you’re the ref. Just for fun we’ll do a center jump.

McNamara [a senior and the returning center/power forward, just shy of 6’9” and well filled out at 220 pounds]—you’re a green; you’ll jump for me. Armstrong—you’ll jump for Coach Fairbanks.”

The ten guys who made their way to center court were all known to Boyer and Fairbanks—except Richie. The other nine had either played for Free State last year or had been identified by the Free State coaches on the AAU and middle-school circuits. Richie eyed Iain Finnie, a skinny redhead in a white jersey he had not met until Monday but whom he had instantly taken to. Richie whispered to Iain as they walked together: “I think I can beat McNamara to the jump ball. If I can beat him by enough I won’t just tip the ball to you—I can pass it over the heads of the guys on your side. If you cut for the basket when the ref throws the ball up, and if I’m right, I can get you the ball for a layup. Worth a try?”

“Hell yes!” said Finnie, winking back at his teammate just as Billy carried the ball into the jump circle.

McNamara was four full inches taller than Richie, and he was one of those kids with a preternatural wingspan. He wasn’t the tallest kid in 6A last year, but he had never lost a center jump and he wasn’t going to lose this one. He saw Billy look up, waited for the ball to leave the manager's hand, went up, and swiped for the ball for all he was worth. All he got was air. Richie had started his jump as soon as he saw the muscles tighten in Billy's jaw, and he caught the ball on the way up, well before it reached what might have been its apex. He didn't try to pass it to Iain—just led him well enough that Iain could catch up to it. Iain's unmolested layup made it 2-0 Whites before Billy had made it off the court. Iain was all smiles as he ran past Richie to take his defensive position on the right front of the key; Richie followed to the left front.

It was a good scrimmage. Richie got an eye-full of Prince, who was much more than a football player. He was strong, quick, savvy, a great on-ball defender, and clearly the leader of this basketball team. The coaches told them they had ten minutes, running clock, and the time flew. With thirty-three seconds left Greens were up two and everybody was dragging. They had played this full-out, just like a real game. Richie's team, which had seemed undermanned in the opening minutes as Richie refused to shoot, finally responded to his pin-point passes; his teammates had never been so wide open for jumpers and layups. But Prince was relentless on defense, and the combination of his several steals and his marksmanship from the three-point line had given the Greens a two-point lead. Time out Whites; twenty seconds on the clock; Iain to inbound the ball. Richie took the pass, streaked across the three-point line, scraped his defender off a teammate, and pulled up from deep: BAM! Whites by one. Prince calls time out.

Richie huddled his teammates and told them to pack the inbounds pass; they do. McNamara is so flustered he loses track of the time and Billy's five-second whistle forces the ball back to Richie's side. Another time out. This time Richie's teammates—and his coach—insist he take the shot, which would put the game out of reach. Richie does. A long three. Misses! Richie has charged in after his own rebound, but it caroms over his head right at Prince Ricks, who is behind the free-throw line and the closest player to the Green basket. Ricks lets the ball's momentum turn him and heads down the court for the win.

Someone might tell you Richie thought about what came next, but they'd be wrong. All he knew is what he saw with the game on the line: the ball in Prince Ricks' hand as he approached midcourt on his way to an open layup. Richie went after Prince like stopping him meant State and the Final Four and the NBA Championship all piled into one. He caught him at the free-throw line and came in from the side, not behind. They were both right-handed; Richie had one chance for a clean block, and it had to be from the side.

Prince was cruising: he never saw Richie until the new kid's forearm swept into his peripheral vision; he never felt him until the ball—which should have released sweetly over the rim—and his fingers flew sideways together, the ball bounding into the folding chairs left of the green-and-white-padded stanchion.

Absolute silence. Maybe two full seconds. Then Richie's teammates and Coach Fairbanks exploded into yelling and back-slapping and jumping up and down and running onto the court with the Firebird in the center. Even the Firebird seemed interested. Prince and Richie stood side by side beneath the basket, drained, staring at each other. "Hell of a play, man; hell of a play," said Prince. Still staring, they hugged each other—although tentatively—and turned for the shower.

Firebirds v. Trojans

Sean Grogan had come to Topeka early to have dinner at Bobo's Drive In before the game. Bobo's was a Topeka landmark, straight west of downtown on 10th Street and straight north of Washburn University on College, and it was his kind of place. The drive-in had limited in-car seating—eight drive-up stalls, which supplemented its limited indoor seating—seven stools around a horseshoe-shaped Formica counter and small booths against the outside walls. The stalls were out the back door. Unlike Sonic, there was no speaker, no sound system. Mel, third-generation owner and cook, could see your car when you pulled up. If his car hop wasn't out the door right after that, he'd turn around and yell at her. It was old-school to a fault. But it had great cheeseburgers, great fries, better rings, and an amazing apple pie that mixed julienned slices of Granny Smiths with whipped butter and cinnamon and folded it all inside a crust as good as your grandmother made. Anybody who had eaten there before ordered the pie with the soft-serve ice cream. When Sean had finished his pie and spooned up the last of the soft serve that had melted onto the battered Melamine plate, he walked out to his Volvo and drove back east to the gothic edifice on Western Street.

The game started at 7:00. Topeka High's bleachers start ten feet higher than the surface of the gym floor and protrude over the top of the team benches on both sides of the court. The sportswriters who normally work their laptops alongside the court sit above it at THS; and as the sightlines are better from there than from courtside, nobody complains.

Sean was naturally gregarious. He was as much fun on a golf course or in a sports bar as anybody. But work was work. He watched the game impassively, made a few final notes, folded up his gear, and followed the last of the crowd down the stairs to the big doors at the west end. He was back at his desk at the *Journal-World* in thirty minutes.

He would ordinarily open his laptop and piece together his story on-screen from the notes he had already left there, a process he described as "rearranging." But for special occasions he would dig his IBM Selectric out of the closet, pull a few sheets from the stash of bond paper he had brought with him from Boston, and "write" something. This was a special occasion. He had thought about the game all week. He sat down, shook out his shoulders and arms and fingers like a swimmer on the starting block, and stared at the blank page in front of him.

Grogan was no stranger to the wire services. When his report on the Topeka High game got picked up, this is what it looked like:

HAIL TO THE TROJANS!

By Sean Grogan
Lawrence, KS (AP)

If you haven't seen Topeka High School, which stands just west of the capitol building near downtown, you ought to go. Parliament and Salisbury Cathedral have their own beautiful towers. But if there is a more beautiful central tower anywhere this side of the Atlantic, I'd like to see it. Also, it's the only high school building in the country whose flagpole was once the mast of the *USS Constitution*, its rigging still a reminder of the men who fought her against the Royal Navy . . . and never lost.

The inside is impressive as well. THS has one of the largest theaters in any building in the country, still seating 3,200 for concerts and plays and school assemblies. On the east side, just inside the arched doorways and up the staircase, is the library. The main reading room has a cut-stone fireplace large enough to walk into; the upstairs alcove, which looks down on the main reading room from a series of oak-paneled smaller spaces, reminds more of Oxford than the American Plains.

On the west side, where I spent my Friday evening after an amazing meal at Bobo's Drive In (save room for the apple pie!), is the gym. Like the flagpole, the gym is one of a kind. The court is the same size as everyone else's, and the baskets are the same height. But nobody else has welded metal seating that climbs clear up to the back walls and looks like it was poured out of a gigantic erector set. Put the Trojan band in there, and the cheer squad, and the student pep squad, and the adoring thousands who still turn out for basketball even though Coach Willie Nicklin retired years ago, and you have noise like you don't get without traveling 25 miles east to Allen Fieldhouse.

The Trojans hosted the green and white from Free State High in Lawrence tonight. The game was competitive for maybe five or six minutes until "the new kid" on the Free State squad put it out of reach with passes that could have been thrown by Tom Brady. His name is Richie Armstrong—this isn't the last article you will read about him—and he had seven assists by halftime. That's only 24 minutes in 6A ball in Kansas. 24 minutes later he had 15 dimes to go with his 23 points and 10 boards. Not bad for the 2-guard. The point guard is Prince Ricks, whom you may remember from the Firebird football team. He was the quarterback of that team, and he is the quarterback of this one. If these two young men don't take Free State to the state championship in basketball, I'll eat my golf hat.

There's another spot along the Trojan hallways I did not mention—the three-story stairwell east of the tower. In the slightly longer than two-decade run-up to *Brown v. Board of Education*, that's where the Black students hung out. The space took on the name of the second basketball team at THS—"the Rambler." Black athletes could compete with whites on the football and baseball teams back then, but not in basketball. And while the Topeka High basketball varsity defended Trojan honor in the same gym I sat in tonight, the Rambler played its games at East Topeka Junior High. There weren't many road trips for any high school athletes in the '40s, but Topeka High's basketball team traveled in the school's buses and ate in restaurants and drive-ins. The Rambler made one road trip each year—to Fort Scott and Parsons and Independence. Team members and coaches stayed with Black families and took their meals in school gyms and churches, eating what the local Black community carried in for them.

Topeka High was more ready for the aftermath of *Brown v. Board* than some places. No National Guard troops had to escort young Black women up its walk and through its tower and into its long hallways. The Rambler had played its last game several years earlier, in 1949. By 1951, Topeka High's varsity basketball team included its first Black player, Bill Peterson. But if you tried to walk up or down that east-side stairwell in 1951, or 1954—the decision date of *Brown v. Board*, or 1964 for that matter, you had to move carefully. Every stair tread was filled with students—Black students. And they still called it "the Rambler."

Tonight, the gym with the warrior's helmet in the center circle saw a different ratio of Black and white. Richie Armstrong, the 2-guard from Free State, was the only white player to start the game. Guarding him for the black and gold was Tyronn Peterson—yep, Bill Peterson's great-grandson. Like Linda Brown, whose name graces the first page of the Supreme Court's decision, Bill is no longer with us.

Oh, right: the game finished 83-57, Free State. Bill Peterson was too much of a competitor to have liked the outcome of tonight's game, but he would have liked how it looked.

Gene Bennett,
Head Coach, Kansas Basketball

His given name—"Eugene"—was too formal for his home state and for Kansas, as well. His nickname was actually used in greeting by only a few close friends; to his face, most everyone else called him "coach." But when his legions of admirers in Lawrence and in every other Jayhawk hotspot spoke to one another about him, he was "Gene." Everyone knew who "Gene" was and everyone wanted to show themselves as an insider whether they were on the inside or not.

Eugene Bennett was well raised, he was a genuinely nice man, and his adult children thought he'd hung the moon for them, because he had. But when they wanted to gig him about something they would drop the "Dad" and call him "coach." Their intonation on those occasions had an edge to it—a subtle reaction to the wisp of arrogance rarely noticed beneath their father's studied, cowboy twang. The kids loved their father. But like the slave whispering in the ear of the conqueror in the triumph, they wanted their father to remember he was just a man. Just a man was okay with them.

He had been a star player in high school and in college and had gone directly to coaching. Like nearly everyone else he worked his way up: from graduate assistant to assistant coach, from assistant coach to coach of a small school, from success with the small school to success with a larger one, to the Big 10—where he had taken the Fighting Illini to consecutive conference basketball championships (his successor would take the Illinois club he built to the Final Four the season after he left) before moving to Kansas.

His Jayhawks won the Big 12 regular-season championship in his third year, then held onto it for another thirteen seasons. "14 Straight!" the banner read. No one else had done that—not even UCLA's John Wooden, whose unbreakable record of consecutive conference championships he had broken. Along the way, on a clear April night that found his team so far down with only two minutes to go that some Jayhawk fans had left the San Antonio Dome for their hotels, the kind of magic the ancient Greeks attributed to the gods reached down to touch Sherron Collins and Mario Chalmers. Their back-to-back three-pointers tied the game at the end of regulation. In the overtime, Collins and Chalmers and their aroused teammates made quick work of a stunned Memphis bunch and Gene had finally reached the summit.

There were hundreds of positive consequences of that championship. But there was one that showed Kansas just what kind of guy they had in their head coach. KU would give him a pay raise; that was understood. In addition, he was told he could ask for anything else he or his family might want and the university would gladly grant his request. He had something in mind.

Making an ask for the future of Kansas basketball, Gene told his Chancellor and his AD he wanted the facilities improved. He wanted new locker rooms with sinks and showers and shower heads that were tall enough for his players; he wanted a practice court; he wanted a special space his team could gather in just before they jogged out beneath the bleachers of Allen Fieldhouse and onto the James Naismith Court—a space to remind them what a privilege it was to play for Kansas. He wanted a convenient and private workout space for his coaches—so they would not have to stand shoulder-to-shoulder with their players in the huge and very-public Anschutz weight room doing five reps to the youngsters' fifty. He wanted a new film room, and a new rehab facility with two big hot tubs, and a new lounge for the players. He wanted a spacious storeroom/office for his managers to replace the hall closet they had been working out of for years. Finally, and most important, he wanted a new basketball dormitory—something that would put Kansas at the front of the facilities arms race with Duke and Kentucky and Carolina rather than at the back. He got all of it.

McCarthy Hall, built entirely of donor funds, is as much a symbol of the Gene Bennett era as any of the other new facilities. If it were in Venice, if it did not have its red tile roof, and if the conveyances parked alongside were renaissance carriages and not modern SUVs, it would serve as well as a Doge's Palace. Finished at a rough cost of $500,000 per occupant, McCarthy contains a small number of two- and four-person apartments. Each offers a living room, a kitchen, closets, desks, a bedroom—one for each occupant, and either one or two bathrooms. Adjacent to the lobby and visible through high glass panels is the full-scale indoor basketball half court, complete with replicas of Kansas' national championship banners and its own "Beware of the Phog" banner. There is a movie theater, a game room that overlooks the basketball court, an outdoor lounge, an indoor study room, a barber shop, and a multi-purpose room where the team can take its meals. Admittance to the hall and to all of the apartments is by fingerprint scanner.

The new practice court, boasting the jump center used in San Antonio for that national championship—Kansas bought it from the NCAA—was built adjacent to the Wagnon Student-Athlete Center on the Center's south side. Running nearly the length of the practice court, high on the north wall, is the balcony that connects to the new offices of both the men's and women's head basketball coaches. When Gene Bennett wants to see how an assistant's practice is going, or who's working on his shot, or who's playing two-on-two or three-on-three, he can open the door and step onto the balcony and find out.

Coach Bennett's office is reached at the end of a long hallway that runs south from the second-floor rotunda of the Wagnon Center. A visitor has to clear Gene's assistant first, then it's another dozen steps to the two-room suite. The hallway door admits you to a kind of reception room; just beyond it is Gene's actual office, his bathroom and shower, and the door onto the balcony.

A visitor can be fully briefed on the successes of Jayhawk hoops under Coach Bennett, can have attended most of his championship games in the Big 12 and NCAA and most of the pre-season tournaments, and can know about the other awards. All it takes for the latter is a visit to the Booth Family Hall of Athletics on the east side of Allen Fieldhouse. But the Hall of Athletics is a big space with a number of trophy cases. As Gene has his own copies of most of the hardware, walking into his office is dazzling. The polished glass and wood and silver and brass of the trophies, the artfully-milled and finished tables, the beveled-glass shelving, and the endlessly-reflecting facets of light from all of them combine in a Jayhawk answer to the Imperial War Museum in London.

Few people meet Coach Bennett for the first time in his office. But whether it's the first time or not, Gene meets you with a thousand-watt smile, a solid handshake, and a warm greeting. Like successful politicians everywhere, Gene has remembered your name, he is glad to see you, and for that moment his focus is entirely on you.

Richie Hits the Radar

Coach Bennett was sitting in the front part of his office with Brett Birmingham, his Associate Head Coach and probably the closest friend he had in Lawrence. They had been talking about Gene's assistant, Molly Kramer, who had worked with Gene for ten years—nearly as long as Brett had been with Gene at Kansas—but who had recently developed "an issue." She was jealous of the newly-hired assistant for the coach of the Kansas women's team, whose work space was in the same hallway in the Wagnon Center. Molly had found out Julie was getting two more weeks of vacation time than she was, and Molly was fuming about it. That Julie was an only child, that her mother lived in a memory-care facility in Cleveland, and that Julie was the only person the facility could count on to visit their resident was lost on Gene's assistant. The extra weeks of vacation had been Julie's only requirement for taking the job, and her resume was such the women's basketball program and the AD were glad to accommodate her. But Molly was angry about it, she had decided to stay angry, and that morning—Thursday—she had given Gene a note that if men's basketball did not add two weeks to *her* vacation package she would give her notice of resignation the next day.

Gene was not only used to Molly, he liked her. And after ten years Molly of course knew him. She knew his family, his likes and dislikes, his strengths and his idiosyncrasies, his friends, his enemies, what he wanted for lunch, and where most of the bodies were buried. But Gene thought her position was unreasonable; and Gene *really* did not like ultimatums. Gene had shared all of this with Brett and the two of them were just sitting comfortably, saying nothing. Brett liked Molly, too. But he and Gene had been down this road with other people, and he could hardly suppress the smile tugging at his mouth.

Gene stood up. "I'm gonna miss her," he said. Then he turned for the bathroom.

Brett was still sitting at the low table in the front room when Gene came back, and Brett spoke first. "Do you remember the Armstrong kid from Salina?"

Gene Bennett could not tell you what he had had for breakfast that day. But if you wanted to know about a high school prospect, even a nearly-unknown three-star junior who hailed from rural Alabama but who could shoot it, Gene was your guy. "Sure," said the coach. "Nice kid; smart kid. I remember talking with him. *Really* fast. Pretty good shot, too, but not very tall."

"He's at Free State now," said Brett. "A senior. He can still shoot. And he grew a bit. He's now 6'6".

Free State played Topeka High last week. The Firebirds won by nearly thirty; Armstrong had a triple-double. Grogan covered it; he's all over Armstrong. Sean thinks Free State will play for the state championship this year."

"What position is he playing now?" The question came out flat. Gene Bennett was being supportive of his assistant without being very interested.

"He's the '2,'" replied Birmingham.

"A triple-double?" Gene Bennett had not yet looked up from his cell phone.

"Right," said Brett.

"How many points?" Gene Bennett was still reading his incoming messages.

"Twenty-three," said Brett. And then he remembered their major disappointment of the past weekend. "I know you wanted the Murray kid from Houston, coach. Who wouldn't?! But his mom played for the Lady Wildcats at Kentucky, and we knew that might be a problem, and in the end it *was* a problem. Cal got him, and good for Cal.

But we can still use a tall guard who can shoot. Armstrong hasn't signed with anybody yet. Heck, there aren't many people who know he grew half a foot and moved to Free State! Why don't we take a look?"

"You said he had a triple-double. How many rebounds?"

"Ten—right on the money," said Coach Birmingham.

"How many dimes?"

"Fifteen. He had fifteen dimes, coach."

Gene Bennett looked up. "Where does Free State play next?"

Free State Plays at Home

The main entrance to Free State High School is on the south side, a naked flagpole providing the accent. In line with the sidewalk to the entry doors are eight parking spaces for visitors and several more handicap spaces. Farther west, twenty-six "STAFF" spaces stand side by side, undifferentiated to discourage the identification and chalking of the principal's spot.

Everyone not a visitor, everyone not part of the lucky twenty-six who drew staff parking, and everyone not going swimming enters Free State from the east where the large student lot is located. On Friday nights during basketball season the east entrance is particularly appropriate as it opens to the basketball court.

There are eight east-side entry doors: three single doors south and three north flank a lone pair, which is more or less centered beneath tall, stainless-steel letters that spell out "GYMNASIUM." The school's mascot, a pissed-off bronze eagle, arises from a column of bronze flames atop the concrete pedestal in the Firebird Courtyard. Even though ten feet in the air, the eagle's beak has been stroked so often it shows a brighter color, making the bird even more fierce than it might have been. There is more going on at Free State than sports. But a person guessing otherwise could not be faulted for the mistake.

Gene Bennett and Brett Birmingham arrived late—not more than five minutes late, but enough to let the crowd that always filled the Firebird Courtyard work its way through the doors and into the gym. Gene had learned over the years that his visits to high school games went better if his presence did not jam everything up before the game got started. He and Brett followed the hallway to the ticket counter and paid for their own tickets—another thing Gene always did as he did not want to presume upon anyone—and slowly approached the large foyer that led to the court and the stands. The hardest part was getting in without getting spotted by everyone inside and running the risk of disrupting the game. They were looking for an opening in the crowd they could walk to and sit down in without too much trouble. But Free State was playing Blue Valley Northwest, an archrival from the wine-and-cheese realm of Johnson County, the wealthiest county in the state, and the stands were packed. Gene and Brett hunched their shoulders, dropped their heads, and moved to the closest set of stair treads that headed up.

Gene Bennett had as little chance to move through a Kansas high school basketball crowd without getting noticed as a bull moose had walking into a Crested Butte coffee shop. This was especially the case at Free State: his living room was not a half a mile from the gym, and both of his kids had gone to school there. But his enormous standing had some positive effects. People rarely reached out to touch him as he moved past, and when they spoke to him they spoke quietly. Gene and Brett were able to reach seats at the top of the bleachers without too much fuss, and the first quarter was barely half gone when they sat down.

It was Firebirds' ball in the half court, score tied. Prince Ricks dribbled back and forth across the top of the key, sizing up the Blue Valley defenders like the predator he was. Richie feinted to the paint, then stepped quickly back to where he had been, creating separation from the Blue Valley player guarding him. Prince hit him as his feet cleared the three-point line. Richie up—completely unguarded. *BAM!* Never taking his eyes off the court, Brett chucked his coach on the shoulder.

Brett was a big believer in Sean Grogan and Sean obviously liked this kid. The rest of the first half went largely as Brett thought it would. Richie hit two more three-pointers on great passes from Prince Ricks and both cashed free throws like they were play money. What Brett had not anticipated was Richie's defense. The Huskies' 6'5" point guard had been All-Sunflower League last year. As Prince Ricks was just 6', the Free State coach had put Richie on the Huskies' floor leader. By the time the horn shut down the first half, Blue Valley Northwest had as many turnovers as made baskets—eleven. Prince and Richie had completely closed down the three-point line for the visitors, so all of their baskets were two-pointers. And four of the turnovers were felonies—grand theft suffered by the Huskies' point guard that led to four layups by the new kid from Salina. Richie was already close to a double-double: twenty-one points (three for four from behind the arc, four made layups out of four attempts, and four for four from the line), plus seven boards. Neither Gene nor Brett had kept track of his assists.

Gene stood up, Brett nodded, and they followed the crowd down the steps to the hallway. As the crowd milled about in front of the bathrooms and the concession stand, the two Kansas coaches quietly pushed through the doors and walked out into the parking lot. They had seen enough.

Neither spoke to the other on the way to Gene's midnight-blue Ford Explorer Platinum, one of the nice perks of being a Kansas coach. Gene got in, Brett followed, Gene hit the start button, and the twin-turbos jumped to life. But Gene did not put the big SUV in gear; he just sat there, staring at the windshield.

"Whaddya think?" asked Brett.

When Gene did not respond Brett paused for just a moment, then followed up: "Pretty good, huh? A tall white kid who can 'D' it up." Brett was a Black man.

Still nothing from Gene.

"OK," said Brett. "What's on your mind, boss?"

"You said his father is out of the picture?"

"Right," replied Brett. "For a long time. His mom moved them here from Salina last summer. She's not only the custodial parent; my sources tell me she's the only parent."

"How do we find his mom?" responded the Jayhawk head coach.

In-Home Visit

The midnight-blue SUV rolled up to the curb at 5:55. Richie's mom had asked for the late-afternoon time: she did not want Richie to miss school or basketball practice, and she had her own work to do. Her accounting firm's relationship with its academic partners was beginning to show progress. But Elizabeth knew that progress was built on her personal relationship with the two key Kansas faculty members, and her commitment to being available to them in person in the afternoon had been one of the best promises she had ever made.

Richie had been home for nearly thirty minutes. He had spent three of them changing into the slacks and loafers and button-up shirt his mom had laid out for him, and he would have spent the remaining twenty-seven pacing their living room had Elizabeth not arrived at 5:45—in time to change out of her straight skirt and jacket and harangue Richie about the condition of the same room, whose big-screen TV seemed to collect piles of discarded T-shirts and basketball shoes and drafts of homework assignments and empty potato chip bags and pop cans. When Coach Bennett and his colleague rang the doorbell at 6:00 sharp, Elizabeth and Richie were ready.

Elizabeth directed her son to one of the two chairs opposite the couch, then she turned and opened the door.

"Mrs. Armstrong?"

Elizabeth had never met the head coach of the Kansas men's basketball team. She had heard his voice in the post-game radio broadcasts, she had read about him, and she had seen as many hundreds of photos as any other Lawrence resident who did not live under a rock. Still, Gene Bennett surprised her. He was bigger than she had imagined. He was tall—probably 6'3". Intellectually, she knew how tall he was. But he seemed way bigger than that, a product of the weight he carried and an enormous set of shoulders that were cleverly draped in the blue chalk-stripe suit provided by his Wichita tailor. Elizabeth had grown up watching sports and movies with her father, and she immediately thought of Gene Bennett as a cross between Robert Redford and Dick Butkus.

Equally surprising was his manner: he would prove to be direct as well as charming, but he was polite first. After her quick, "Yes, please come in," he had replied: "May Coach Birmingham come in as well?" "Of course," she said, stepping back into her living room.

Coach Bennett moved across the threshold and stopped after a few steps. He was followed by a man just younger than he was who was wearing a sport coat and tie. "Brett, this is Mrs. Armstrong. Mrs. Armstrong, this is Brett Birmingham, our Associate Head Coach."

Brett Birmingham accompanied his head coach on all in-home visits. He set the schedule, he made the out-of-town arrangements, he researched the recruit and his family, and he knew the script—in the unlikely event Gene Bennett wandered so far away from it he got lost.

"How are you?" asked Elizabeth. "You are both welcome; please come in."

As his mother walked ahead of the coaches toward the chair next to his, Richie stood up. "This is my son, Richie," said his mother. Both visitors extended their hands in Richie's direction. Coach Bennett's was the closest, so Richie shook hands with him first, then Coach Birmingham, then he sat down again.

Gesturing to the sofa across from the two armchairs, Elizabeth said, "Please sit down. May I get you something to drink? We have soft drinks and water and some lemonade I made earlier."

Gene Bennett had been in hundreds of living rooms, he had been offered hundreds of things to eat and drink in hundreds of parts of the country, and he knew the answer to the question: "Yes; that would be very nice." The drinks were easy. The home-made edibles were the challenge. Coach Bennett had said "Yes" to a strawberry/pecan pie in Atlanta so covered in Cool Whip it looked like a snow-covered soccer ball, to petrified chicken nuggets in Provo, and to gum-drop cookies in Duluth whose "secret ingredient" proved to be CBD oil. Most of it was fine; some of it he had tasted for days. Grateful the items on today's list were few in number and liquid in form, he answered, "I'll have the lemonade—that sounds great." Birmingham opted for the same thing, and they sat down at the same time on the large sofa.

Still standing but now turned toward the kitchen, Elizabeth looked at her son. "Why don't you tell the coaches about the Firebird Spirit Award?" Then she walked out of the room to get the drinks.

Richie took a deep breath. "The Spirit Award is like the Danny Manning Award at KU," he began. "It's traditionally given to the player who best represents the school's resilient spirit. We still have several games left, and then State, but they already announced it. This year, for the first time, there are two winners. I'm one of them and Prince Ricks, our point guard, is the other one."

Elizabeth was back with the tray. "I'm sorry to interrupt, Richie," she said as she put the tray and its four glasses on the table between the sofa and the chairs. "Does anyone want sugar? This is pretty tart." There were no takers, so Elizabeth handed out three tall glasses, took one for herself, and sat down. Kansas' head coach was at the end of the sofa, directly across from her. "Go ahead, Richie," he said.

"That's pretty much it, Coach Bennett. It's a terrific award; I'm glad to be getting it, and it's cool to share it with Prince."

Elizabeth took a sip of the lemonade, put the glass down in front of her, and folded her hands in her lap.

Show time! Gene Bennett cleared his throat. "Mrs. Armstrong, thank you for letting us come by this afternoon. As you know, we've had our eye on your son for a long time—ever since he first hit the AAU circuit. He's a wonderful player, and we'd like him to be a wonderful player for Kansas."

Bennett paused for a drink of the lemonade, more to see how his audience was reacting than to see how tart it was. Mrs. Armstrong appeared comfortable, and she was paying close attention, so he leaned forward just a notch and continued.

"Richie will get more than just the Firebird Spirit Award. We think he'll be the Gatorade Player of the Year in Kansas."

Bennett glanced at Coach Birmingham, who was sitting beside him on the large couch. As he returned his attention to Richie's mother, the insider's smile he had shared with Coach Birmingham disappeared almost as quickly as it had formed, and he continued with the part of the script Brett had written for Richie's mom. "But we like more about him than just his game. Richie is an outstanding student. We have talked with our academic people, and we are confident Richie will be invited into the KU Honors Program. I'm sure you know about it, and about how the KU program is consistently rated one of the top two or three of its type in the country—whether the competing programs are at Yale, at Northwestern, or at North Dakota State." The Northwestern reference was pointed. Richie had applied to and had been accepted by the Top-Ten University in Evanston, and Kansas knew Richie's mom would regard it as a win/win for Richie to play for the Wildcats in the Big 10. "Geoff Pfeifer is one of the Honors

Program's strongest teachers, and our team's academic advisor has already approached him about taking Richie in his Honors section.

Let me speak very briefly about the financial elements of a basketball scholarship. It pays for Richie's entire tuition, of course, as well as his books and related classroom expenses. It also provides a room in McCarthy Hall, which is one of the best of our dormitories and is less than a block from Allen Fieldhouse."

Calling McCarthy "one of the best" of the KU dormitories was like calling Dale Chihuly "one of the best" of the country's glass blowers. Elizabeth knew McCarthy was the most "out-there" residence available on the KU campus or anywhere else.

Bennett continued, "And it provides meals and all the snacks Richie might want at the DeBruce Center and at the student unions.

But the Kansas scholarship package is broader than just the money and the room and board. Richie will have academic advisors at his disposal almost 24/7. He will have access to tutors in each of his courses. If he needs help in calculus, for example, he will get help from a professor or from a math graduate student who has been interviewed and approved by Kansas Athletics. He will also have what you could call an 'administrative' tutor, whose job is to make sure all of his classes are clicking, that he is on course with his major, and that he is kept informed about special opportunities such as study abroad and the application process for the Rhodes and Marshall Scholarships."

Brett's adding the Rhodes and the Marshall to the script for Richie Armstrong's mother would become one of the great moments in the history of KU basketball recruiting.

"All of this is at no cost to your son. Do you have any questions about any of these things?"

Elizabeth had gone over much of this with the faculty members whom she worked with every day. There were powerful academic scholarships at KU—the Summerfield leading the pack—but none compared with a full ride to the basketball program. As much as she was determined to be objective about this in-home visit, she had to concede the Northwestern reference was well done; the basketball program seemed to know about Richie's acceptance letter even though it had arrived just a week ago.

It was his mention of the Rhodes and the Marshall that had nearly unhinged her. She had kept that dream for her son private, like a letter to herself. Though a state school, Kansas had had remarkable success placing its finest undergraduates at Oxford and Cambridge; Elizabeth had learned that in other conversations with her KU colleagues. But she had not yet shared with her son her hope he would one day compete for such a prize. When Coach Bennett dropped the Rhodes and the Marshall into their conversation—in passing no less, as though grooming Richie for those interviews was a standard ingredient of the KU scholarship package—Elizabeth's mind drifted to her own time in high school: she was alone in her bedroom, listening to Roberta Flack. Across from her now was a man she had never met who had somehow found her letters and was reading them out loud. She forced herself back to the present; she had to get a grip on this. She took a drink of her lemonade and straightened her shoulders.

Gene Bennett was quiet, and Elizabeth concluded the KU presentation was done. She spoke next. "You have covered a lot of ground, Coach Bennett, but you have said nothing about name/image/likeness. What is Kansas' position on that as it relates to my son?"

Gene Bennett did not exactly "blush" red, but his neck was growing warm—he could feel it. NIL was new enough that his speaking about it was not yet instinctive. He had forgotten to mention it, she had called him on it, and he was taken aback—a position he was *not* used to. He was on the verge of a peremptory response when Brett Birmingham jumped in to save his boss from a moment he might regret. "That's a very important topic," Brett said hurriedly, "and something on the mind of all of our recruits and their parents."

Nearly as surprised by his colleague's taking over the conversation as he had been by Mrs. Armstrong's assertive questioning, Bennett recognized the precariousness of the moment and took immediate advantage of the softball opening Brett had left him. "That's right, Mrs. Armstrong. And excuse me for not bringing it up myself.

There are students who approach college having already made themselves household names. There are not many of them, of course; you know who they are, so I don't need to mention them. As often as not they approach their schools with commercial offers already on the table, and the school's task is not to mess things up. For the others, and Richie would find himself in this group, Kansas does two things: it facilitates the individual relationship between a business and the player they have chosen to work with, and it assures what I will call 'a general pool of revenue' that is available to *all* team members. That way, everyone will get at least some benefit from NIL. Does that answer your question?"

Elizabeth had not missed the impatience that had flared in response to her original question. But it had dissipated quickly. She was impressed with that, and Coach Bennett's eventual answer seemed straightforward. There was no hemming and hawing; there were no pie-in-the-sky promises. Bennett had thought about this, and he and his coaches and staff had come up with a program that struck her as fair. "Yes," she said. "Thank you."

Not sure he had recovered entirely, Gene Bennett opened the folder Coach Birmingham had slid across in front of him. He pulled out the four documents and placed them on the table in front of Richie's mother. "There are two important documents for a potential Kansas player, Mrs. Armstrong. The first is the Letter of Intent; the second is the Enrollment and Scholarship Agreement. While we are now into the official signing period and a Letter of Intent is not strictly required, we still like to have the student-athlete and his parent sign it. The Enrollment and Scholarship Agreement is a commitment by Richie, and by you—his parent and legal guardian—that he will enroll at KU and play basketball for us. We'd like to make Richie a Jayhawk, and we hope you will sign them. I'm leaving you two copies of each so you will have one for your file. You can read the documents at your convenience and then let us know what you and your son decide." He stopped talking, sat up a little straighter, put on his best smile, and waited.

When Richie's mother responded, "It won't be necessary for you to leave these with us," the room became so quiet Brett Birmingham could hear the garage door opening across the street. The two KU guests looked down at the same time. Neither had encountered this before. Kansas didn't sign everybody; nobody did that. But the parents would always *take* the Letter of Intent and the Enrollment and Scholarship Agreement even if they had no intention of signing them. If Birmingham had had anything to say he would still have remained quiet. This was a big-boy moment, and it was the head coach's job to get them past it. Yet Gene Bennett just sat there too, head down, saying nothing.

And so it was Richie's mother who spoke again. "You won't need to leave the documents, Coach Bennett, because Richie and I are prepared to sign them now. Richie wants to play for KU; I wanted to meet you and ask a few questions and see how things went. From my perspective, things went as well as a parent could want. You are direct, you don't pretend to have answers to everything, you have given careful attention to my son's academic future, and you seem to care about him as a person. Everyone talks about Kansas basketball's being a family. We like the idea of that, and we will be glad to be a part of it. Where would you like us to sign?"

———

They had been in Gene Bennett's Explorer for about ten minutes and were on the way to 715, a popular restaurant on Massachusetts Street where they would join the other coaches at the table being held for them in the back. They had just signed the kid, and Brett was upbeat. But the driver had yet to say anything. Anyone could speak with Gene Bennett; he was very good about that. And on a good day anyone could tease him. But only Brett Birmingham could tease him "out" of something. When it dawned on Brett that his boss had been quiet ever since they left the house, he thought about the moment when Elizabeth Armstrong had asked so pointedly about NIL, and the moment she told Coach he didn't need to leave the documents with her. *Something new each time out,* he thought to himself. Then he looked at the guy on his left. When he saw that don't-bother-me look he nearly broke up.

Brett Birmingham decided to make his play to his cell phone. Dialing up Mitch Cantfield, the video coordinator who had helped prepare the in-home pitch for Richie Armstrong's mother, he waited for Mitch's answer and then fairly shouted. "Mitch! You shoulda *been* here! Were you aware our head coach went to *law school*? Only a *lawyer* could handle the cross-examination of a basketball mom like *he* did! She asked about NIL and our coach responded with—crickets! And you should have seen his work with the *documents*! He laid them out in front of her and she told him he didn't need to *leave* them! His response to *that*? The same—*crickets*! And then she signed them, right there in her living room, just like he planned it. *Genius*! It was a Perry Mason moment, yes sir!!"

Mitch had not been there, of course, and he had no idea who Perry Mason was. But he knew Coach Birmingham loved to tease Gene Bennett, and he smiled.

Gene Bennett was finally smiling too.

State Championship

They played Wyandotte, a basketball powerhouse in Kansas City, Kansas, only thirty minutes away from Lawrence. Wyandotte's architecturally-eclectic stone and red brick building had famous twin towers. But it had equally-famous teams that had vexed the rest of the state for years. Even the legendary Danny Manning and Chris Piper, friends who started for Lawrence High and who would team up again only four years later to storm through the NCAA Tournament and beat Oklahoma for the national title, had fallen to the Bulldogs in the final game of their high school careers. Free State and Wyandotte were in Wichita now, in the INTRUST Bank Arena, but the fancy digs and the distant venue made no difference to the rivalry. They had played for thirty-five minutes, every starter was bent over with fatigue, the coaches were hoarse from yelling, and the people in the stands must have thought they had walked into a gang fight. The score had been tied a moment ago, 56-56, just as it had been tied a dozen times before that. Richie Armstrong had thirty of the Free State points. But Wyandotte had just made one of two free throws, and the Bulldogs led by one. There were thirteen seconds left.

Richie took the inbound pass from Prince and brought it up the right side against a press that wouldn't crease a Kleenex.

Everybody knew Richie would take the last shot. But the two guards in the red and white knew he wouldn't take it from the far side of half court, and the last thing they wanted was to foul the kid with the ninety-four percent free throw average. As soon as Richie crossed the half-court line the Wyandotte guards got serious, and the rest of the Bulldogs were looking his direction too. Nobody else in green and white even registered with the Wyandotte coaches; everybody knew who was going to shoot it.

McNamara had come out to the high post and Richie lobbed it to his center, squeezing his way between the two closest defenders as he did so. It was an unorthodox pick-and-roll, but it worked. When three new defenders moved up from the basket to cut him off, Richie juked to the paint, then ran to the right corner. They had only seconds left, and McNamara knew he didn't have time to wait for Richie to get there, so like a quarterback in tune with his wide receiver he threw the ball to the spot. Richie caught it over his left shoulder just as he planted his feet to avoid ending up in his manager's lap at the end of the team bench. He took enough of a dribble to get turned around without traveling, spotted Prince as he squared himself to the basket, and started to go up.

All five red and white defenders had turned toward Richie. Suddenly by himself at the top of the key, Prince Ricks had nothing but floorboards and varnish between himself and the basket. He caught Richie's eyes as Richie caught his, their nods to one another lost to the crowd. As Richie cradled the ball and released it across his outstretched fingertips, Prince broke for the basket. All of the Wyandotte players were moving, too, but it didn't seem like it. And if the 14,000 people in the arena were breathing, they didn't seem like it either.

It was Gary Fritsch of KFDI who called it first: "Armstrong goes up . . . here's that wrist flip . . . and . . . it's gonna be ***long***! No ***way*** that goes in, folks!" Across the court from Richie and in the middle of the front row, Fritsch had the right angle on the shot, and he called it correctly. But what Richie launched was not a three-pointer. It was a high-arching alley-oop intended for the one player on the court who could go up and get it. Prince speared it out of the air two feet above the rim and rammed it home.

3

KU: FRESHMAN YEAR

Summer; Boot Camp

The young men who would become the Kansas Men's Basketball Team spent June and July and August getting to know each other. Kansas' main floor in Allen Fieldhouse and the practice facility to the west let them avoid the always-surprising heat of a Kansas summer, but not the steady banter of young, same-team athletes who were nevertheless competing, feeling one another out, looking for an edge that might mean more playing time come fall. The ability to hit a deep three or a runner, or a spinning layup high off the glass to avoid the swooping arm of the defender, or to block out, or to rebound—all of this was terribly important to every one of them. Their sessions were unstructured and largely unwatched, exhilarating and joyful. Not darkened by any sort of adversity beyond a hard foul on the way to the rim, the summer days flew past.

Richie was one of three freshman scholarship players. The others were Percy Jackson, from Wichita East, and Luke Simpson, from Valley High School in West Des Moines. Richie had known Jackson for years; he had played against him in high school and with him on AAU teams, and Jackson had been the runner-up to Richie for Gatorade Player of Year in Kansas. At East, the 6'8" Jackson had played next to the basket and had developed inside moves and a soft jump hook that nobody his age could deal with. He became the city's all-time scoring leader, jumping over Antoine Carr and Ricky Ross his junior year and easing past Darnell Valentine at the end of his senior year. But his "handle"—his skills at dribbling the ball and maneuvering through the defensive traffic created by the other team—was only average, and he was not a great three-point shooter. He had weighed 200 pounds in high school, he was already up to 210, and no one knew where he would play at Kansas.

Simpson had also played the post in high school, but at 6'11" and 250 pounds there was little question that's where he would stay. The rangy center with what *The Des Moines Register* called "the wingspan of a condor" had dominated Iowa basketball since junior high and set scoring and rebounding records almost every time he walked onto the court. News of his recruitment his senior year had nearly pushed the harvest off the front page in the fall, and the New Year's Day blizzard didn't stand a chance against a new rumor that he was headed to Villanova. In the end, all of the smart money had him headed west to Spokane and to Gonzaga . . . until he didn't. When his high school sweetheart made the final cut and became a Rock Chalk Dancer, Luke signed with Kansas and followed her to Lawrence.

Richie knew the bios for the returning players like he knew his own. Billy Nixon, a senior and the point guard, looked like a dreaded-out street baller from Chicago—which he had been—until he took his shirt off. Then the 6'4", 215-pounder looked like Adonis. Maybe he was a little too keen on trashing you when he had the ball and you were the only person between him and the hoop, but he really could do anything—and he really could do it better than you. He could dribble the ball faster than most players could run, he could change direction like the ball off a ping pong paddle, and he could get his shot off before any mortal could even think about getting a hand in front of it. Richie had followed him for years and had seen him over and over on television. But seeing him face-to-face was different and guarding him was impossible. No Sports Center video could communicate that kind of speed.

Tommy Barnett, also a senior, was from Portland. He was a picture-book power forward: 6’8” tall, 255 pounds, built like an NFL nose guard. In fact one of the nicest, most helpful guys on the team, Tommy was all business on the court. It didn’t matter whether your jersey was green and gold or purple and white or any combination in between. If it was different than Tommy’s—even during practice in Allen Fieldhouse when it was the blues against the reds—he was as happy to knock you on your ass as go around you.

The third senior was Thomas Williams, the Jayhawk center. Thomas was seven feet tall, and his otherworldly wingspan made him the country’s top rim protector despite a body weight that rarely topped 225. In his junior year he was the only player in the conference to average two blocks per game, and he was guarding the basket that summer like he kept his lunch on the back iron. Richie had tried three layups his first day and Williams had rejected all three of them.

There were two walk-on juniors. But there was only one scholarship player in his third year at Kansas—Paul Preston, and most everyone believed three years would be it for the smooth-shooting wing from Fresno. At 6’7” and 230, Preston was big enough to post up inside, where his dizzying spins and his fade-aways and runners and dunks would confound all but the best defenders. If an opponent had “3s” and “4s” bigger than Paul, he would go outside the arc and torment his defender from there. Preston was a shooter. His three-point percentage, which had hovered near thirty-nine percent during the regular season, jumped to forty-four percent during last year’s Big 12 and NCAA Tournaments. Nobody faulted the media for having him gone after this season; the Kansas fans were grateful to have one more chance to watch him.

That left the two sophomore members of the team—Frank Agbani and Jeff Hanson. Hanson, the back-up point guard, was 6'1" and 175 and hailed from Fargo, North Dakota. During his last recruiting trip to the city, Gene Bennett had been caught by the Fargo television reporter as he left the Hanson home. Asked whether he would "do anything special" for Jeff and his family if the North Dakota high school legend signed with Kansas, the Kansas coach adroitly responded he could not do anything "special" for Jeff Hanson—"of course." But he allowed he had been talking with his staff about scheduling a game with North Dakota State in Fargo's new arena. Hanson may have come to Kansas anyway. But the game in Fargo was announced only days after Hanson signed his letter, and nobody was smiling bigger than Jeff's mom when the Jayhawks played the Bison to a sell-out crowd the following November. She and her husband and Jeff's five younger brothers and sisters got to watch it from the row behind the Kansas bench.

Frank Agbani was a prototypical "2": he was 6'5" tall, he was a lean 215 pounds, and he moved around the court like a seal moves through water. From Greenville, he had broken the South Carolina high school scoring record his senior year. But he was still finding his way at Kansas, and his freshman season in Lawrence had found him on the bench much more often than on the court. There had actually been some talk last spring of Frank's leaving KU and transferring to Clemson. But he was back in Lawrence this summer, he had a smile on his face, and—so far as Richie could figure it—he was always wearing the jersey for the other team! Many more times than once, as Frank had unexpectedly braked and elevated and released his jump shot over Richie's late-arriving hand, Richie had thought, *This guy plays like I do . . . only better!*

Even the weather cooperated that summer. The pounding rains that could interrupt them on the way from AFH to McCarthy Hall and drive them beneath the bullpen roof at Hoglund Field were few.

Gene Bennett's Summer Basketball Camp was a special interruption, and welcome. 500 youngsters from all over the country gathered in Lawrence, Kansas, to take instruction at "the cathedral of college basketball." The bright-eyed new kids would have been happy just to see the inside of the field house; the coaches and the KU players and the alumni, many wearing the colors of their current NBA teams, were a whole jar full of cherries on top. The experienced campers, and especially the ones who could ball, had different goals. They wanted to hone skills, learn new ones, and get noticed. More than a few campers had left Lawrence with an AAU team's invitation in their pockets.

Richie took to basketball camp like every one of his teammates—he loved it. He loved the kids; he loved the hero-worship; he loved watching them follow their coaches from station to station like pilgrims in St. Peter's. What he grew to love most, though, were the camp games. Several times a week the kids would take seats in the bleacher sections that had been pulled down while Richie and his teammates would square off for red-on-blue scrimmages. The scrimmages were monitored: they were short, and Coach Bennett and his staff watched the players carefully, using their whistles as often to calm things down as to call a foul. But the scrimmages were real; having the most points at the end mattered to every one of the young men playing. And every so often when a Mario Chalmers or a Kelly Oubre or a Wayne Selden or a Devonte Graham would don a red or blue jersey and take the court with them, magic happened.

Richie's summer ended far too quickly. August brought school, and school brought classes and homework and what KU Athletics called "academic support"—a safety net that stretched from major advising and high-level tutoring in the dozens of dedicated study spaces running between Anschutz and Wagnon to a staff member's picking you up at your dorm and accompanying you to class…all the way to your seat if it came to that. Richie was in The Honors Program, and he was a serious student besides. He didn't need a chaperone. But he had already come to appreciate the young man who ran academic support for KU basketball, Randy Brown. Randy's knocking on the door of his room in McCarthy at 9:00 a.m. on the Saturday before classes started was a surprise, but not the wheelchair Randy was sitting in. Randy had been in a chair for a long time, and he didn't let it matter. His job was to make sure every KU player succeeded in his schoolwork. They would succeed at different levels, of course; but they all had to succeed, and they did.

Because it was easier for Randy to negotiate McCarthy's large dayroom than Richie's own room, and because Richie's roommate was still asleep, they took the elevator to the first floor. Richie discovered they were both coffee drinkers, so they started with that. They might have talked about Richie's class schedule, but Richie already knew it—Randy had actually helped Richie with it that spring after Richie had committed to Kansas. They might have talked about the many levels of academic support available to all of KU's athletes, but Richie already knew them—Randy had covered them in the spring, too. Randy was there to tell Richie about his Honors 190 instructor, Geoff Pfeifer. He took maybe ten minutes, and no more than fifteen. When Randy had finished his coffee and thanked Richie for the conversation and wheeled out into an already-stifling August morning, Richie believed his Honors teacher was a cross between Aristotle and Richie's grandmother—the smartest person he would meet this fall, and the nicest. Richie was glad to be a part of the KU Honors Program and he had been ready to get started; the once-a-week class for one hour of credit met at Nunemaker on Wednesday morning. Now he was excited.

Gene Bennett knew his players had enjoyed their summer and were settling into the work of fall semester. Classes had started. When not in class they were doing their homework and meeting with their tutors. After that they were in the weight room or in their individual sessions with KU Basketball's strength and conditioning coach. After that they were in the limited one-on-one skills sessions with Gene's assistant coaches that the NCAA allowed in September. Gene did not believe in shooting hundreds of three-pointers. Gene believed in learning how to shoot one three-pointer properly, then practicing it hundreds of times. After the classes and the tutoring and the weight room and the skill building and the hot tub and the training table and the last of the homework, they were in bed. Well, maybe the freshmen were in bed.

Every so often Gene would think of the expression his dad had repeated to him: "Don't worry about the mules. Just load the wagon." Gene had asked that the words be cut into the stone with his name on it at the Basketball Hall of Fame in Springfield, Massachusetts. There had been no mules for his players to worry about that summer, and no wagon either. For the young men who would wear the crimson and blue numbers on their backs later that fall, summer basketball had been as freewheeling and fun as walking into the midway of the state fair with money in your pocket. And these first few weeks of school weren't much different; so far, this had been an easy go for all of them.

Gene Bennett had a wagon to load, of course. But Gene was also the trail boss, and the mules were his responsibility. Even though his players were as balky and as unpredictable as the critters his father had spoken about, he had to make something out of them. Gene would wait 'til September. He would start with Boot Camp. Boot Camp would be a hard wake-up call for the mules.

Monday, September 12, 5:15 a.m.

Richie was on the first floor of McCarthy having breakfast and watching the very early morning news on the flat screen that was suspended from the ceiling, just like he did every weekday. He was totally surprised when his roommate rounded the corner. 5:15 was routine for Richie; he had been getting up early as long as he could remember. Billy's getting up at 5:15 meant there had been a fire in the room, or a Martian invasion. "What are *you* up for?" asked Richie, open-mouthed at his roommate's appearance.

"Breakfast? You're eating breakfast?!" Billy was looking at Richie's plate like it had "CONDEMNED" stenciled across the top.

Richie looked down at his plate, wondering what was wrong with it. "Sure," he said. "I eat breakfast every morning. You know that."

"Bet this is the last breakfast you eat this week, Stretch."

"Stretch" was the nickname the guys on the team had come up with for him during the summer. Richie thought Stretch Armstrong sucked as an action figure and he hated the nickname. But he hoped to ditch it, and he knew any protest on his part guaranteed he would have it forever.

"Why is that?" Richie barely got the question out over the next heaping spoonful of oatmeal and milk and brown sugar and blueberries.

"Because we start Boot Camp today, dumb ass! Good luck with your healthy-choice breakfast! Boot Camp starts at 6:00. That means people in the know show up at 5:50. I'm leaving in ten minutes. You might want to come with me. You are NEVER late for Boot Camp!"

Richie was still chewing when he looked down at what was left of his breakfast—he had eaten nearly all of it. When he saw his roommate turn and walk up the stairs to their room, he was already feeling sick.

Everybody was early but there was little talking—mostly they stood around and fidgeted until Coach Bennett and his staff walked onto the James Naismith Court at the stroke of 0600. One of the managers did a quick roll call. Then there was a short talk by Coach Bennett that Richie barely heard—he was too focused on the blueberries tumbling around in his stomach. Then the players spread out across the end line. “Suicides.”

In the few seconds before the whistle, Richie looked north across the court and began to count the plastic barrels along the sidelines, so big they were lined with heavy-duty lawn and trash bags. The whistle interrupted his count. He made it to the free throw line, back to the end line, and almost to center court before he peeled left for the nearest barrel. He was not the first player to throw up; Richie learned later there was a prize for that! But he was a close second . . . and the third . . . and the fourth, until the last blueberry had been expelled and Richie was on his knees. He had been sick before, but never like this. He got back up with the help of one of the other players—he did not remember who it was; he finished the rest of the drills—he did not know how; and when it was done, he made it back to his room. He crawled into bed and pulled the cover over his eyes against the mid-morning light and stayed there past noon.

Tuesday, September 13, 5:30 a.m.

Mostly recovered from the day before, Richie got up later for the second day of Boot Camp; breakfast would wait until the weekend. He and Billy left their room together and made their way to the fieldhouse, arriving at least ten minutes ahead of 6:00. Soon after, every other member of the team had joined them on the south end line. Staring straight ahead and speaking softly, Richie asked Billy, “What happens if you’re late?”

“Special session,” Billy answered, also looking straight ahead.

“What’s that?”

“You don’t want to find out,” said the roommate.

The coaches and staff walked in. There would be no speeches this morning. To Richie’s relief he made it through the suicides without getting sick and this time actually recognized that the second round of drills was "slides"—central to playing defense. The team moved to the west sideline. Three lines of blue tape stared back at them at ten-foot intervals, the lines parallel to the north-south axis of the court. In groups of four the players would assume a "ready" position, arms out in front of them, and slide until they had crossed the first blue line, then run back, then slide to the second line, then back, then slide to the third line and be finished. "You have to cross each line with both feet," they were all told. "If your foot is on the line, you haven't crossed it." They started.

Far more obsessive-compulsive than most of his teammates, Richie had completed his first set of slides cleanly and was jogging back to where they started when he heard one of the assistant coaches yelling at Billy. The two were not twelve inches apart. They were nearly the same height but showed nothing like the same posture: Billy was already tired; the assistant coach was not. Coach Stevens literally had his back up and his arms were flailing. This was not an alert or a correction, this was raging, mean, in-your-face screaming: "BILLY! What don't you get about moving both feet ACROSS THE LINE? I catch you one more time like that and you'll get your own PERSONAL suicides at the end of this morning. You GOT THAT?!!!" Billy hung his head. "Yes, sir," he replied quietly as he hurried away from his antagonist.

Richie saw this again and again as he moved through the morning's drills. Coaches who had been nothing but good guys until now—available, helpful, always nice—were behaving like assholes. Richie didn't like it.

They finished the session like they always did—timed runs over several lengths of the court. As this was only Tuesday, Richie figured today's time would still be generous, long enough that all of the bigs could handle it easily. He was right: everyone made it and they hit the showers.

Richie did not catch up with Billy until after supper; Billy was sitting on his bed when Richie came through the suite and knocked on the door of Billy's room.

"Hey—Billy. I thought Coach Stevens was way out of line this morning, and I'm sorry you got to be the target. You OK?"

Billy looked up. If his feelings had been bruised he made no show of it. "I'm fine, Richie. You're the one who needs to do a little attitude adjusting. Stevens is a good guy, except for this week. Next week, he'll break his own arm to help you out; this week, you'd think he wanted to break yours! But that's what the coaches are trying to do this week: they want to beat you up physically so they can break you down mentally. That way when we come back—and we all *will* come back, we'll be stronger for it.

Along the way, the yelling and screaming is good for you in a different way. You'll see it when we play conference games on the road. Kansas has always—ALWAYS—been the team they love to beat. And some of the fans, especially the young ones, are every bit as fired up and nasty as Coach Stevens was this morning. We've had crazy-wild students scream at us all game long, then rush the court after beating us and run right into us. That happened at K-State a few years ago—scared everybody to DEATH! It's been a while since we've played Missouri. But the fans there used to spit at us. What we need to do in those situations is nothing! The only right reaction is not reacting at all. Coaches want to prepare us for that, too."

"OK," said Richie, finally moving away from the door and into his room.

Wednesday, September 14, 7:45 a.m.

They were just about done with "jumps"—sets of ten, one right after another, designed to mimic rebounding situations where staying with it was often as important as who was the tallest.

Richie was half done with his last set when he landed a little crooked and tweaked something on the underside of his left foot. He was sure he hadn't sprained anything, but it felt odd, and when he tried to jump again it was definitely still there. He stopped the exercise . . . and got immediately yelled at. "ARMSTRONG! Can't you COUNT?! These are sets of ten! Not sets of however many you WANT! What's WRONG with you?!"

What was wrong with Richie was the verbal abuse. He had had enough of it himself and he had seen far too much of it directed against his teammates. He was just turning to reply to the assistant coach-turned-Mr. Hyde when Tommy Barnett, the senior forward, nearly tackled him. Grabbing Richie's head with his right arm and turning him completely away from the coach—who was already bristling for a faceoff with the freshman from Salina—Tommy whispered in Richie's left ear: "You CANNOT take on a coach just because he yells at you. That's what this is ABOUT! They're SUPPOSED to yell at us. You have got to CHILL! Do you get me? Tell me 'Yes' and I'll let you go; otherwise, you'll still be in this headlock!"

They took a few more steps before Richie could manage a "Yes." There wasn't much else he could do; Tommy was 6'8" and 255 and Richie was lashed to his teammate's side by Tommy's powerful right arm. Tommy stopped walking, Richie stopped walking, and Tommy let go of Richie's head. They just looked at each other.

"Thanks," said Richie.

"No problem," replied Tommy, and then he moved off.

The players got together after their showers to talk about the rest of the week. Boot Camp was officially five days long, finishing Friday at noon. But the older players knew Coach Bennett would occasionally call it after four days, so long as people had worked hard and so long as everyone completed the run at the end of the Thursday session. For the freshmen players who felt Boot Camp had already lasted a month, the chance of an early finish was exciting. The consensus among the upperclassmen was that Boot Camp had been good so far and that Coach Bennett would end it the next day. For the first time that week, Richie left the fieldhouse with a spring in his step.

Thursday, September 15, 8:00 a.m.

There had been less yelling Thursday. Almost certainly it was because the players had their eyes on the prize; an early finish was worth working for—hitting all the marks exactly, moving through the drills with your shoulders squared and your head up. "The run" was left.

The run was longer today, but still only a quarter mile—1,320 feet. If not exhausted by four days of Boot Camp any of the KU players could have run it easily; some, like Richie, could run it really fast! But this was the end of the fourth day. And the players did not simply have to run it—they had to run it in three minutes. Here again, a quarter mile around an oval track in three minutes would have been a walk in the park for these young men. But they were tired, and they were inside Allen Fieldhouse, and that meant fifteen lengths of the James Naismith Court—at a max of twelve seconds per. For the coaches, "the run" was much more about team building than about endurance. The guards and the wings would never have a problem with it. But the bigs might.

The players knew better than to sprint down the court. Pace was important; pace meant you had something left for the thirteenth length, and the fourteenth, and the last one. So, they started together and stayed together, led as it turned out by Richie, who was a legitimate track guy. Richie had set a good pace—an easy jog that covered the eighty-eight feet in eight to nine seconds. As it was inevitable that Richie would stay somewhat in the lead, that meant he would turn first at each end of the court and be able to see how everyone else was doing. Everyone else was doing fine through thirteen lengths. Tommy Barnett was behind a little, but only a few steps.

They had started at the south end of the court. When Richie finished fourteen lengths and turned north toward the "Beware of the Phog" banner and the yellow-tape finish line put up by one of the managers, he saw Tommy was now trailing badly: he was still moving south, he had barely cleared the Jayhawk at center court, and he was laboring. Richie stopped. When he realized the teammates following him were also slowing down, he yelled, "No—no! Keep running! You're almost done." Then he spotted his roommate, grabbed him by the arm, and gestured to Tommy. The big man had barely made the south end line and had then stopped altogether. "Got to help Tommy!" Richie shouted. Billy nodded and they sprinted back to their power forward.

Tommy was holding his knees and panting. He lifted his head. "I can do this," he told them; but he dropped it again, and he was still panting, and his hands were still on his knees.

"You're right," Richie yelled at him. "But we're gonna help you."

"Billy—you take his left shoulder; I've got his right." Richie's eyes had never left Tommy.

"Have you ever run a three-legged race?"

Tommy hadn't.

Richie was still yelling: "You match your pace with the guy beside you. Just lean on us; follow our pace, don't try to set your own. Keep your head up. And don't stop! You ready?" Tommy nodded.

They had to pull him upright and pull him again to get him moving, and it was never better than clunky. But they covered the eighty-eight feet in the time they had left. Grinning, Richie and Billy turned their attention to the "attaboys" of the other players as soon as they ducked out from under Tommy's shoulders. Unsupported, the big power forward sank slowly to his knees. But he was smiling too.

Miller Hall

Twin, four-columned, buff-brick scholarship halls sit on the east side of the sidewalk between Danforth Chapel and the Chancellor's residence. The white-painted hilltop home of KU's CEO at the southeast corner of the campus commands the approach to Lawrence from the Wakarusa River to the south. Miller, the twin closer to the Chancellor, has steps down from the sidewalk to its front door. Healthy evergreens that need a haircut in every season flank the staircase and block the view of the first floor from the street. But the Ionic capitals are visible atop their columns, just beneath a strict pediment.

Miller holds down two o'clock on the traffic circle that gives access to the four buildings at the end of Lilac Lane: Miller, the Chancellor's residence (at five o'clock), Blake Hall (political science, at six o'clock), and Twente Hall (formerly the university hospital and now the home of KU's school of social welfare, at eight o'clock).

On the sun side of the stained-glass window at Danforth Chapel and just across Lilac Lane on the north side of "new" Fraser are the four sycamore trees that shaded Farieh during the early weeks of her freshman year as she turned from Jayhawk Boulevard toward her new home at Miller Hall. They gave her more than a break from the high heat of August, for they reminded her of the sycamores recently planted on Vali Asr Avenue in Tehran, along whose ample sidewalks she and her sisters had all learned to ride bicycles. A central part of that memory was her father, running alongside her, yelling “Farieh, you can do this!” Memories like this were small pieces of home for a young woman so far from hers; but the sycamores were there every day, and they helped.

Math Major

As her educational goal required a graduate degree and as she intended to achieve that elsewhere—either Oxford, where the oldest of her two older sisters was already in graduate school, or The London School of Economics, Farieh looked to the United States for college. Kansas did not have the nation's best school for the study of petroleum engineering, although its faculty was excellent. Most of the Top 10 were in Texas. But for Farieh, The Longhorn State was as long on oil-and-gas education as it was short on diversity. Louisiana and Oklahoma, whose schools boasted their own highly-rated oil-and-gas departments, were attitudinally similar. Kansas, which was well regarded academically and more moderate politically, and which had a former colleague of her father on its Business School faculty, was the winner.

She had "tested out" of her liberal arts math requirement easily enough—KU had a standardized test for that and she took it her first week on campus. Testing out of her math major was more of a challenge. She had done all the work before leaving Iran, and then some. Unlike their social peers in Tehran whose new homes boasted flat-screen TVs, Farieh's parents had a chalkboard in their library. The same library featured theater seating for their daughters, but not for movies. Only mildly comfortable—to encourage the girls' attention—the seats came equipped with retractable lapboards, not cup holders. Farieh had grown up with mathematics. She and her sisters had each mastered "the easy stuff," algebra and geometry, by the time they were ten. They had all breezed through trigonometry and had been introduced to calculus before they were teenagers. By the time they had matriculated from what would be high school in the States, they had worked their way through additional years of calculus and differential equations, linear algebra, and statistics; and their tutor had provided them a hard look at computer science. They got all of it. What the three sisters did not get were the advanced placement certificates provided by American high schools. If Farieh wanted to complete her entire math major early to make way for the cornucopia of other classes she had found on her arrival at KU, which she did, she would have to find a way to make it happen.

After stewing over it for most of September, she came up with a plan. She declared mathematics as a major, far earlier than she needed to. When the Department of Mathematics assigned Professor Don Rooney to be her advisor, almost her first question during their first meeting was whether he would give her the final he gave to his seniors in linear algebra. She said she would take it in writing or, if he wished, she would take it face-to-face as an oral exam using a chalkboard instead of a blue book. As naïve as she was enthusiastic, Farieh assumed Professor Rooney would approve her idea and then, after she had passed his test, persuade his colleagues in the math department to let her take their finals. Upon passing all of them, she would have satisfied her major requirements!

Rooney was so taken aback at the question from the fired-up young woman in the head scarf that he just stared at her. While he sensed Farieh was better grounded in math than most of his first-year mentees, he did not like her idea or her bravado. Or her head scarf. He told Farieh he would think about it and let her know.

Rooney wanted to check in with his colleagues, for two reasons. He had never done anything like this before and that made him uncomfortable. Don Rooney did not like feeling uncomfortable. And he didn't like the demeanor of the young woman in the head scarf; she was far too aggressive. He wanted to tell her "No," and he wanted backup. So, he texted the two colleagues who had the most influence over the department—Ann Garvin, the department chair, who taught differential equations, and Alan Kai, who taught the senior seminar in advanced calculus. He said he had something important and asked them to meet with him, and they met the next day.

There has been a Snow Hall at KU for over one hundred years. The original, the Snow Hall of Natural History, was named for Francis Snow, one of KU's original three professors, and housed KU's vast collection of plants, animals, and insects. Snow's assistant, Lewis Lindsay Dyche, who became a world-famous taxidermist, would later rate his own building.

KU students played basketball in the basement of the original Snow Hall. Mathematics is located in the current version, whose six stories top out on the battlements above the prominent stair tower and give it a military countenance more fitting to The Citadel than to Kansas. Snow's stone walls guard the west approach to the university's Administration Building. Chancellor Frank Strong had commissioned Snow's neighbor to be "one of the largest and most beautiful [buildings] in the state" and "the center of the University's architecture." After a shaky financial start and the scrapping of the much grander original design and long delays occasioned by quarrels over construction costs and World War I, the building finally accomplished what the Chancellor had hoped for. In 1938, four years after his death, the Administration Building was renamed Strong Hall in his honor. The stone of Strong Hall is as warm as Snow's is cold; and even attired in its final, cheaper design, Strong is as balanced and as beautiful as Snow is not.

Snow offers few modern spaces and almost no large ones. They chose Ann's office because it had a window, and a couch.

"So that's the proposal," Rooney had said when he had finished outlining what Farieh had said to him.

"What do you think about it, Don?" asked Ann. She had moved away from her desk when the two men came into the office and was sitting with Alan Kai on the couch. Rooney sat in Ann's favorite upholstered chair, which she had brought from home and had wedged between her desk and the wall.

"I don't know," said Rooney. "The student tested out of math with a perfect score. But no one in the department has ever had her in class, and her entire math education to this point has taken place in Iran."

Impressed by the audacity of Farieh's proposal, Ann was disappointed by Rooney's tepid reaction. Something else disappointed her far more. Rooney, now nearly sixty, was one of the department's good-ol'-boys. At this stage of his career he was far more likely to be at Johnny's West on a weekday evening than attending a seminar, to say nothing of presenting his own paper. His comment about Iran unveiled a prejudice she had sensed in him for some time but had not actually witnessed.

"What did her studying in Iran have to do with her freshman placement exam, Don? Those are graded anonymously, are they not? You said she made a perfect score. Who cares whether she took her classes in Tehran or in Topeka?"

Ann turned her head to Professor Kai, who was right next to her. "Alan, what about you?"

Alan Kai was thirty. He grew up in Singapore and had moved to the United States when he was a high school senior. After doing his undergraduate degree at Pitt, he took both graduate degrees at Chicago. He and his partner, a ceramics engineer, had interviewed at Kansas at the same time, both were offered jobs in Lawrence, and they had arrived two years ago. Alan was a star, and Ann really liked him.

"I think it's brilliant," said Alan. "If she passes, good for her! If she doesn't, Don and our department get major credit for their flexibility, which means everything to young people—especially the young people we are trying to attract to KU mathematics." He turned to Don.

"Don, did your student tell you why she wanted to test out of your senior-level course?"

Still smarting from his boss' upbraiding, Rooney made a reply that registered on the terse side of neutral. "Yes, she did. She wants to test out of her entire undergraduate degree in mathematics; she sees me as her first step."

"Even bolder," interjected Ann. "To Alan's point, what if we let her do that? What if all three of us gave her a problem to solve—problems demanding a solid grounding in advanced calculus, linear algebra, and differential equations? We could give them to her at the same time, with each of us present, and see how she does. There is little likelihood she will pass all three—fatigue alone almost guarantees that. But if she does pass, we will truly have something to brag about. The College marketing department will be all over it!"

Siding enthusiastically with Ann, Alan weighed in strongly for an oral exam with the proofs of her answers written on a chalkboard. Professor Rooney merely said, "OK," hoping what Ann said about the fatigue of the student's contending with three problems at the same time would prove accurate. They chose Classroom 203, an average-sized space with a huge chalkboard. And they decided to ask Farieh to consent to the attendance of a photographer from Marketing. If she passed, the photographs would be golden.

Professor Rooney texted Farieh and they scheduled the examination for the next Friday afternoon. Alan could not wait to alert Marketing and get the College on board; Ann said she would get the room.

As only Professor Rooney had actually met Farieh, her arrival at the back of 203 a week later was dramatic. Any head scarf would have been attention-getting, but the one she was wearing was bright yellow. Yellow was Farieh's favorite color, and she had many scarves in that color. She was also far taller than anyone had expected. Farieh had dressed up for the occasion; with her Manolo Blahnik heels she was the tallest person in the room at nearly six feet. Once her eyes had adjusted to the sunlight that challenged Snow's air handlers in the summer and fall, she walked steadily from behind the desks at the back of the classroom to the front. Four people waited for her—Ann Garvin, Alan Kai, Don Rooney, and Louise, the photographer. Even Rooney could not take his eyes off her; no one said a word.

"I'm Farieh," she said, breaking the brief but awkward silence. "Hello, Professor Rooney. Thank you very much for making this afternoon possible."

As Rooney was not interested in saying much of anything and was incapable of reciprocating her courtesy, Ann Garvin cut in. "You are welcome. It's 'Farieh,' is that correct?"

"Yes," replied the student.

"Well, your imaginative proposal has created quite the stir here in Snow Hall. We are all delighted to meet you, and we are excited to get started.

You may leave your jacket in the front row if you'd like." Professor Garvin gestured to one of the desks and Farieh began moving toward it. "When you tell us you're ready, we'll begin."

Responding with the same easy warmth she had felt from Professor Garvin, but so rapidly she seemed to be completing Professor Garvin's sentence and not beginning her own, Farieh answered: "I am ready now."

Each of the math professors produced a single page of paper. Rooney's was entirely filled with text; Garvin and Kai had needed perhaps half the page. Garvin collected them and held them face down. "These are questions from actual examinations, Farieh. We did not try to write the hardest problem any of us had ever seen. But I suspect each of these is the hardest problem from its respective examination. When I hand them to you, Professor Kai will note the time. You will have ninety minutes to solve the problems and to write your proofs on the chalkboard. You may use as much or as little of the chalkboard as you wish.

We will provide the same warnings our students get in an actual examination—at ten minutes, at five, and at one. When Professor Kai says, 'Time,' you will have to put the chalk in the tray and stand back from the board.

Do you have any questions?"

"Yes," said Farieh. "I did not bring any water. Is there any? May I have some?"

"Of course," said Professor Garvin. "I have a bottle of water in my backpack. Give me just a moment." She reached for the backpack, which was sitting on the desk next to her, pulled out the unopened bottle, and handed it to Farieh. "Here you go," she said. Farieh had appreciated Professor Garvin from the beginning and now liked her very much. "Thank you," she said. She drew a deep breath—the only tell of nervousness any of them would see that afternoon. "I'm ready for the problems."

Farieh took the pages from the department head and stepped forward to the desk. She scanned the three problems, then placed two of them on the desktop next to Professor Garvin's backpack. She walked to the board, picked up a new piece of chalk, and stood still before the slate as she read the third problem slowly. Then she began to write.

Her height let her use the very top of the chalkboard, and she began in the corner farthest to the left. In ten minutes, she had filled nearly two panels with the proofs of her answer to Professor Rooney's problem in linear algebra. She paused, put the chalk in the tray, took several steps back, and again stared at the page presenting the problem. She looked up and moved back to the board, picking up the eraser and removing an "equal" sign. Her chalk having filled the open space with the symbol for "equal/more than," she again stood back and read through the entire proof. Then she returned the chalk to its tray and walked back to the desk and the water.

The examinations actually used by the professors had suggested thirty minutes for each of the problems. Farieh had taken just fifteen for the first one. A person looking at Don Rooney would not know whether Farieh had solved his problem or not; he did nothing, said nothing, and sat expressionless. But Ann Garvin and Alan Kai knew. Farieh had killed it.

Farieh took a long sip from the water bottle before picking up the remaining two problems. Her head scarf did not permit a look at her entire face, but Professor Rooney noticed a slight frown that had settled just above her eyes. *Are they green?!* he thought to himself. *Why had I not noticed that before?!* But the frown delighted him.

The second problem, in advanced calculus, was Professor Kai's. Alan Kai would occasionally nod as Farieh worked her way through the proofs. When she had finished and had walked back to the desk, Alan exhaled a quiet "Bravo!"

Anne Garvin was less demonstrative than Professor Kai and soon realized she was watching Farieh almost as stonily as Professor Rooney had watched her. When she asked herself, *Why*, and after she had demanded an answer, she realized she was anxious! She wanted this compelling young woman to win this bet she had made with the three of them, and she was on pins and needles as she watched Farieh move across the front of the chalkboard.

Having taken twenty-five minutes to solve Alan Kai's problem, which she had done with hardly a wasted symbol, Farieh had forty-five minutes left for differential equations, Ann's problem. She was repeating the performance she had delivered for Professor Rooney's problem, her fingers flying across the chalkboard, when she suddenly stopped. Professor Garvin sensed this was no planned break during which Farieh might calmly check her work; there must be something wrong.

Farieh stepped farther back, then looked down at the problem she was holding in her left hand. She looked up at the board; she looked down at the problem. As Farieh once again walked back to the desk, Ann knew she had not yet finished; the calm that had accompanied the student's earlier breaks seemed absent this time. Farieh stood at the desk a long time before she surrendered to an unspoken recognition and returned to the board. This time she picked up the eraser. Looking hard at the middle panel of the three she had filled, Farieh removed its entire bottom half! Ann's uneasiness had been building since Farieh first stopped her work. Now, as Farieh deleted first one line of the proof and then the next, Ann almost gasped. There was nothing wrong with the equations that were disappearing; Farieh's proof would fail if she did not do something to reverse this. Beyond that, Farieh's time was expiring. Alan had just given the ten-minute warning, and it would take Farieh several more minutes even to replace what she had just removed.

In an interesting role reversal for her parents, it was her mother who had taught Farieh the power of mathematics. Her father introduced her to the art—how making the proofs elegant made them more accessible, and more persuasive. The equations on the central panel, like wayward paragraphs in the draft of a novel, had been in the wrong place. Farieh copied the upper portion of the panel into the space she had just created at the bottom. Then she erased the top, making space for the proofs she had erased to begin with. Ann noticed Farieh was revising them slightly as she returned them to the chalkboard, this time to the clear space at the top of the middle panel. Done!

As Alan Kai sounded the five-minute warning, Farieh stepped back, cocked her head to the side, and looked severely at the board. Satisfied, she relaxed her expression, returned her head to upright, nodded her approval, and placed the chalk in its tray. Lifting the water bottle from the desk as she walked by, she continued to the front row and sat down.

Watching all of this like she had once watched her daughter's first audition for *The Nutcracker*, Ann had not immediately understood what Farieh was doing, and she was frightened for her. But as the young woman with the yellow headscarf fit her elegant proofs into just the right places, it was clear Farieh had not merely solved the problem. Her proofs were clean; her organization was flawless; her solution was . . . beautiful. Unbidden, Ann's hands came up from her lap and applauded.

The envelope found the mailbox at Miller Hall three days later. Signed by Regents Professor Ann B. Garvin, Chair, Department of Mathematics and Computer Science, the letter inside informed Farieh she had completed the requirements for a major in mathematics in the College of Liberal Arts and Sciences. The short second paragraph continued: "When you have completed the other requirements for an undergraduate degree at the University of Kansas, you will receive a Bachelor of Science in Mathematics."

The third paragraph was still shorter: "Your degree will be awarded with highest departmental honors. Congratulations!"

The Cathedral of College Basketball

THE NOTE

The hand-written note from his publisher was on his desk when Sean rolled in on Monday, October 2. Only Sean would have recognized it as new and needing attention as it was a small thing cast onto a large pile of things of assorted sizes that passed for order in the mind of the *Journal-World*'s Sports Editor. He picked it up, smiled at the fountain-pen-crafted "Sean Grogan" standing up spiritedly from the ivory vellum—always his full name—and opened it.

Good morning, Sean.

I have a long-time friend—a sports fan—who has decided to join Mary and me in Lawrence (after years of invitations!) for a KU basketball game this fall. In our telephone call last night, I was carrying on about Allen Fieldhouse and he interrupted and said, in effect, "What's the big deal about the building?" I made an attempt to explain, a poor one as it turned out, and we went on to something else. But that portion of our conversation was very unsatisfactory to me.

Could you write up something about the field house that I can send to him?

Don't be afraid to have some fun with it; he's one of our more irreverent friends and certainly won't mind.

Thanks in advance.

Jim

Sean had marveled at Allen Fieldhouse dozens of times by now, but he had never tried to explain it to anyone. His staff meeting wasn't until the afternoon; he scheduled it that way to give his people a little extra time to sort things out after the weekend. That gave him the morning. He sat down and turned to his PC. While waiting through the booting-up process, he looked out his big windows at a morning sun that was strolling left to right along Seventh Street as though it had nothing better to do than walk by and tip its hat to him. There are moments in the life of a writer when something seems to "write itself." This was one of them.

ALLEN FIELDHOUSE

Named for Dr. Forrest C. Allen, "the father of basketball coaching," the building that houses the basketball court separately named for KU's first coach, James Naismith, who invented the game of basketball and on which KU's men and women play their games, was immediately referred to as "The house that Wilt built." More than a catchy expression, the moniker captured the enthusiasm that surrounded Dr. Allen's recruitment of the nation's finest high school basketball player—ever. In the eyes of the Kansas fans, Allen's persuading Chamberlain to leave the media-clogged high life of Philadelphia for the muted plains of Kansas was a miracle. And it soon eclipsed even the glow of the l952 NCAA championship and the Olympic championship that followed that same year. In fact, winning the NCAA and Olympic Championships was all the Kansas Legislature needed. Construction began in l952, and the first game was played in March of l955—against K-State—to a still-record crowd for basketball of 17,228. More than 20,000 people would fill it for Bobby Kennedy's visit in March of l968, when the fire marshal took the evening off and the court, the entryways, and every stair tread were packed with students.

Chamberlain was special. Gene Bennett still loves to say to his cocky one-and-dones that they will never be "the best player ever to play at Kansas." That was Wilt, whose freshman team thrashed the KU varsity and who then played two years on the varsity himself before joining the Harlem Globetrotters his senior year. Double- and triple-teamed throughout those two years at Kansas, he still *averaged* 30 points and 19 rebounds a game.

Allen Fieldhouse holds several interesting records, including the Guinness World Record for loudest indoor arena—130.4 dB! It is seen by people who don't follow the Duke Blue Devils as providing the greatest home court advantage in college basketball. And, in recent years, it has been called "the St. Andrew's of college basketball." Strictly speaking, that title rests with the YMCA in Springfield, Massachusetts, where Naismith invented the game before he came to coach it at Kansas. But Allen Fieldhouse is roundly regarded as "the cathedral of college basketball." No matter where they went to school, including Duke, the commentators for CBS and ESPN all call it that. The name stuck. Why?

It's not the physical structure. While Allen Fieldhouse is not unattractive from the outside, neither is it beautiful. It no longer sits in an empty field, for example, as it did in 1955 when it opened. And its handsome stone exterior, its landscaping, and the well-sited statues of Dr. Allen and James Naismith all disguise what might otherwise present as a gigantic Butler Building. Yet physical beauty does not make something "the" cathedral. If it did, "the" cathedral of The Anglican Communion would be Salisbury and not Westminster; Chartres would be "the" cathedral in France and not Notre Dame de Paris; and in Spain it would be the Cathedral of Santiago de Compostela and not La Sagrada Familia. What creates "the" cathedral is its visitors—the people who seek it out year after year and who fill it on the high holy days.

What has made Allen Fieldhouse "the" cathedral of college basketball is the same element—people. But Lawrence, Kansas, is a town of 100,000, not a city of millions. And the people who flock to Allen Fieldhouse on game days are mostly locals, not residents of sprawling cities like London, Paris, and Barcelona. For now more than 20 seasons in a row—more than 300 consecutive games—Allen Fieldhouse has been full. It has been full for the rivalry games against UCLA and Kentucky and Villanova and for the games that will decide the Big 12 title, of course. But it has also been full for the pre-season games against Washburn and Emporia State and Ft. Hays State and Pittsburg State. Credit goes to the two coaches who have been at Kansas since 2001. Credit especially goes to the current one, Gene Bennett, who has famously won as many conference championships at Kansas as he has lost games on its home court. His streak of fourteen conference titles in a row eclipsed the record set at UCLA by John Wooden, a record thought for decades to be unassailable. Stitched onto banners hanging from the rafters are Kansas' conference championship years—so many one ESPN commentator said, “You can’t even count them.” Also hanging overhead are the many Final Four banners. And against the north wall, just beneath the banner that warns, “**Pay Heed, All Who Enter; BEWARE of THE PHOG**,” are the national championship banners.

What do the people get when they come to a game at Kansas? First, and probably second and third besides, they get to win. Especially under Gene Bennett. People love to win. The people who buy the tickets love it, for sure. But so do the staff and the concession workers and the marshals and the maintenance crew. And so do the visitors from CBS and ESPN and every other network. If you visit Allen Fieldhouse on a game day you will see the T-shirts with the bold KU logos. But you will also see the slogans, one of which reads:

IT’S OK. EVERYBODY LOSES HERE.

What else do they get? Like the faithful at any other cathedral they get a ritual. The ritual begins as fans walk past the statues outside the field house and continues into and through the Booth Family Hall of Athletics, a museum presenting more than a century of outstanding KU athletes, conference titles, and national championships. Upstairs from the Hall of Athletics and in the center of the walkway joining the field house to the new DeBruce Center is the National Archives-quality display of the original rules of basketball, purchased for KU by the same David Booth who provided the Hall of Athletics.

Virtually all of today’s sports temples have money changers, and AFH is no exception. A large Rally House store fills the north concourse on the second level, and its numerous satellite locations follow you as you walk around just outside the arena proper. Fans pass permanent concession stands selling soft drinks and popcorn and pizza; pop-up vendors sell specialty items like barbecue and ice cream. 30 years ago, these slope-ceilinged walkways were drab. Today, as much as the cement floors and the I-beams will allow, the spaces are brightly painted and brightly lighted and festive.

But none of this prepares you for center court. The 16,300 gleaming red and blue seats do not pretend to be a record. Syracuse is still far out in front with its 50,000; both Kentucky [Rupp Arena, part of the Convention Center in downtown Lexington] and North Carolina [the Dean Dome, on campus] have more than 20,000. But it's been a long time since the Orange filled their dome for basketball. And both the Kentucky and UNC arenas are cavernous, with thousands of cushioned, theater-style seats both absorbing the sound and—inch by generous inch—pushing the fans back away from the action. Not so at Kansas, whose 16,300-seat capacity feels intimate. There are chair-back seats at center court on the second level on both the east and west sides, but they are made of hardwoods, not cushions. All the rest of the seats are benches—also hard. The seats run up and down to concrete walkways, and the fans are kept on the walkways by metal railings. The only soft surfaces in the place are found on the banners that hang from the walls and the ceiling.

Unlike the soft "Carolina blue" in Chapel Hill, KU's colors are bright: royal blues and fire-engine reds and corn yellows crowd in from everywhere. The James Naismith Court displays its name in royal blue letters and boasts a gigantic Jayhawk in the center.

A Jayhawk game at Allen Fieldhouse starts more than an hour before tip-off, and all of this is a part of the ritual. Walk in at the 75-minute mark and you will see players from both teams starting to warm up. For fans who follow the teams and who know the players, this is an exciting time. People whose seats are high in the bleachers can move down into one of the hundreds of court-side seats and watch the warmups from there.

Little by little the court fills with strength coaches and assistant coaches and the stands fill with fans and reporters and broadcasters. The Jayhawk mascots arrive—"Big Jay" and "Baby Jay"—followed by the Rock Chalk Dancers and the cheerleaders. The large pep band is already in place, and it begins to play. All of this is scripted: the fans know when to expect the cheerleaders, they know when to expect the band, and they know the tunes—they're always the same. If it looks like the band is having fun, they are! At some point the KU players do their loose-ball drill, with everyone diving face-first onto the court, and then they run off—the ones in the lead actually racing to see who can clear the northwest tunnel and make it first to the locker room.

Next up is the alma mater, usually led by a professional singer, followed by the Rock Chalk Chant, led by the cheerleaders. By now the visiting team is in its locker room and insulated from the sonorous "ROCK . . . CHALK . . . JAY . . . HAWK . . . K . . . Uuuu!" But if KU is ahead at the end of the game, they will hear it then!

After a few more cheerleader-led yells it's time for the basketball team to return. When Kansas runs through the northwest tunnel and onto the court following the very large KU banner that is run in by the largest of the male cheerleaders, the crowd is on its feet. The visiting team comes back at nearly the same time, followed by the coaches. Gene Bennett comes in last. He likes to make an entrance and he does that through the same northwest tunnel, almost always blowing into his cupped hands as though it's cold in AFH, which by now—with 16,300 screaming fans in the seats—it's not. Bennett's entrance is worth watching. The visiting head coach will be on the court and the two of them will walk toward one another for their pregame greeting. In fact friendly and outgoing and warm, Bennett is as eager to welcome most of these coaches as someone would be eager to welcome a friend into their home. He has a big smile, and he follows that up with an embrace that signals, "We know each other; I'm glad you're here!" But one or two visitors still draw a restrained welcome. Bennett greets the assistant coaches next, then he returns to the Kansas bench at the north end.

The team introductions follow the singing of the national anthem. The student sections are at the north and south ends, right behind the baskets. The tradition is for the students to hold copies of *The University Daily Kansan*, the student newspaper, in front of their faces during the visitor introductions to reflect their boredom. At the end, having booed all of the visitors, they rip up the pages and throw them on the floor.

The space between team introductions is filled by the video board, which noisily reminds the fans of how many games Kansas has won and flashes video clips of famous players and famous events, such as Mario Chalmers's three-pointer that tied the 2008 NCAA title game with John Calipari's Memphis team and sent it into overtime, when KU would win it. Ahead of the video is the voice of Larry Brown, who coached "Danny and the Miracles" to the l988 NCAA title. Coach Brown is hard to hear, but what he says of Kansas is this: "There's no better place to coach. There's no better place to go to school. There's no better place to play."

In recent years the video montage has finished with Coach Bennett. The scene is KU's game against an excellent Missouri team that led the Hawks by 19 points in the second half of the last Big 12 game Kansas played at home against the Tigers. Kansas fought back, and it sent the game into overtime when Thomas Robinson blocked the layup that would have won the game for the Tigers. Robinson's savage rejection of Phil Pressey's attempt, the greatest blocked shot *ever* in AFH, is also a candidate for greatest no-call. Missouri had a chance to win even at the end of the overtime; but when time expired before the Tigers' last shot and Kansas had finally won the game, Coach Bennett erupted from the bench with a fist pump that would have KO'd any mortal standing in front of him.

The KU announcer treats every KU starter's name as though it were multi-syllabic and every fan as though she were hard of hearing. Billy Nixon, for example, is "BIL-LY NI . . . ii . . . ii . . . XON!!!" But they are announced in good time, accompanied by dramatic gyrations from the Rock Chalk Dancers, and soon enough the game is underway. More people than Larry Brown call Allen Fieldhouse the greatest place in the country to play college basketball. They'd be right.

The cathedral of college basketball would not be complete without a sacrament—the outward and visible sign of an inward and spiritual grace. Traditionally there are seven sacraments, all of them combining well-known text with some kind of physical action. Baptism is a sacrament, as are the Eucharist and Marriage. Allen Fieldhouse offers its own sacraments. Though neither will speak, they are vividly outward in their actions and highly visible in their blue and red and yellow feathers. And if not altogether spiritual, Big Jay and Baby Jay are at least mythical. *In nomine Naismith et Allen et spiritus Jayhawk, amen.*

Emporia State

Richie was six when his mom took him to Disney World. His memory of it this evening was not of the gigantic movie characters walking around The Magic Kingdom or of the rides and their long lines or of the food. What he remembered as he sat in the locker room after Kansas' first game of the season was the beach at Cape Canaveral, and how excited he was to run out into it, and how the waves rolling in alongside the long wooden pier had stopped him cold, nearly knocking him backwards.

He ran through the Allen Fieldhouse tunnel tonight. He had run through it a hundred times in practice—to the point he didn't give it a thought. But Billy and the others had told him it would be different for a game, and they were right. The wall of noise that met him as he followed his teammates onto the court hit almost as hard as the waves in Florida. He needed a Euro-step to keep his balance and join the layup line, and his ears were still ringing after the team introductions. He remembered almost nothing of the game itself: Kansas won handily; Coach Bennett put him and the other freshmen and the non-scholarship players in for a minute or two at the end; the locker room was energized afterwards. That was it. But the noise!

Sean Grogan had made it to his seat in the front row of the east-side bleachers early. This was only an exhibition game, but it was the first game of the season and he had his laptop opened soon after the players had started to come out in ones and twos for the early warmups. Sean wanted to see the players ahead of the game. He wanted to see how they moved, how they caught a pass before they shot the ball, and whether they worked at it when it was their time to rebound. Were they pulling the ball off the backboard and making a crisp pass to the next shooter, or just hanging out—waiting for the ball to fall into their hands before making a desultory pass to the next guy? He wanted to hear the banter and learn how they interacted with their teammates. He wanted to see the new players. As much as anything, he wanted to see Richie Armstrong. Sean knew the jump from high school to the D-1 ball played at Kansas was a long one, and he wanted to see how the kid from Free State was handling it.

As exhibition games so often proved to be, this one blew neither hot nor cold. Sean wrote it up this way:

FIRST TIME OUT

By: Sean Grogan
Lawrence, KS (AP)

For 33 minutes this was a re-run of "The Gang Who Couldn't Shoot Straight." Kansas finished something like 2-for-19 behind the arc; and of the starters, only one made anything outside 12 feet. Billy Nixon, lately seen on the cover of *Sports Illustrated*, must have had the flu. Richie Armstrong, Kansas' Gatorade Player of the Year, shot twice and missed twice. And this was against Emporia State!

Asked what the game against Michigan State will be like next week, Gene Bennett reminded everyone they have "men" who look upon the basketball as "the last piece of meat on earth!"

Thomas Williams had a nice game, and Percy Jackson can play. If Percy were a sophomore and had a year's savvy and twenty pounds of muscle to go with what he already has there would be even more smiles in Lawrence. A right-hander, he made the sweetest left-handed hook shot in the lane we've seen in a while.

But it's Paul Preston who amazes you, repeatedly coming out of nowhere to rebound the ball from his 3-spot. He had 12 boards! And he made one put-back dunk off a low rebound that simply defied the laws of gravity, willing his body to levitate back to the rim after coming down with the ball. He is one pretty athlete.

Jeff Hanson looked good tonight; Frank Agbani hustled; and we were 24 for 28 from the line, which has to be a record for the Gene Bennett era. But the 19-point margin should have been 40. The upcoming match against an experienced Spartan team that is smarting from its season-opening loss to U-Conn should be an entirely different test.

Tommy Barnett did not play tonight but will be back in practice tomorrow. Jonathan Fulbright, another big, is out recovering from rotator-cuff surgery. After Williams, he was the best big man the Hawks had this summer in Europe. But Jonathan has already missed a lot, I don't believe Coach Bennett can find a place for him this season. Expect a red shirt.

Last year at this time we were wailing about how Kansas' senior guards were more interested in playing catch with the fans in the second row than getting the ball to their teammates. We have to keep things in perspective—it's November!

Michigan State:
The Flight Home, McCarthy Hall

The flight home from New York City took maybe two hours, but few team members paid attention. It was dark outside the plane and their headphones insulated them from sound and from one another. They sat quietly by twos: some of them sleeping, some of them nodding to whichever beat they liked, some of them trying to get some homework done. Even with the late night and the headgear it was a very quiet trip back to Lawrence.

Losing does that. Michigan State took it to Kansas early. Whether there were more "men" on the Spartans' roster than on the Jayhawks' was not important. Michigan State was more aggressive from the jump—they built an early ten-point lead, and they held it the entire game.

Coach Bennett was downright fatherly after the game, placing responsibility for the outcome on his lack of preparation and not on anyone's failure to box out (which was immediate and chronic, as though the Jayhawk bigs had never heard of the concept), or make free throws (the Hawks shot a meager fifty-two percent from the line), or drive aggressively all the way to the hole (the Kansas wings had the same regard for the guys in the green jerseys they must have had for their crossing guards in grade school; all the Michigan defender had to do was put a hand up and they'd stop).

The locker room conversation was as short as the break for food on the way to the airport, and then they were airborne. The conversations were even more abbreviated once they landed, relating entirely to whose stuff was whose; and the bus back to McCarthy was noiseless. When Richie and Billy pushed their roller bags past the door of their suite it was nearly 3:00 a.m.

Richie had opened his bag and was transferring clothes to the laundry hamper, so he didn't notice that Billy had already fallen onto his bed without taking off his KU ball cap or his shoes. "That was my first real game," said Richie in his roommate's direction, "and my first trip with the team, and only the second time I've been to New York City. Really sucks to lose." Billy Nixon had done everything possible to keep Kansas in it: he'd gone twelve-for-fourteen from the field with seven boards and as many assists for the game. But that was then. Now, Richie got no response from the senior point guard. Billy's eyes had closed before his ball cap hit the pillow, and he was gone.

Jacob Matthews

Jacob Matthews had been a swimmer in high school, not a middle linebacker; but he was built like the football player. His success came with the breaststroke, an event whose records seem to defy the passage of time. Taller than all of his competitors, more powerful, and far more determined, Jake's 57.9-second victory in the hundred at the state meet was so stunning the lane judge's first reaction was to hold his stopwatch to his ear and shake it, thinking it had broken. Twenty years later, Jake's name and time still looked down from the cluster of "State Meet Bests" displayed on bronze plaques behind the Golden High School diving boards.

Almost as an afterthought, he and his colleague won the state debate championship that same senior year.

In the decade or so following those luminous months, as he made his way through college, then Ireland—whose pubs he believed were "the fount of all philosophy"—then graduate school, Jake was frequently asked what his plans were when he got his degree. "Retirement," he would answer.

Jacob Matthews' Philosophy 275 class was taught in one of the few good spaces in Wescoe Hall, a large—although windowless—sloped lecture hall that could accommodate 200 students. Because the class was also available online, the classroom was rarely full. Until spring, that is, when Jake transitioned to his wildly-popular series on Epicureanism. He called it, “Epicureanism: A Rockstar Review,” riffing on the popular spring campus variety show, “Rock Chalk Review.” For these sessions, the actual class was filled with the actual students. But the online, real-time, video broadcast was pumped into every residence hall, every apartment complex, every fraternity, every sorority, and every Lawrence watering hole that had a tap and a monitor. Those not jealous of Jake estimated his online audience at over 5,000—and that was just the people in Lawrence.

Each week Jake delivered three hours of raucous but insightful titillation, pitting a contemporary rock star against the original—Samuel Clemens. Last year, students had confronted whether Taylor Swift preyed on music promoters to get ahead (no), whether she wrote her own lyrics (yes), and where she got her name (she was named for another musician, James Taylor). Whoever was “up” that year from the twenty-first century was exhaustively, ironically, and brilliantly compared with Jake’s hero from the nineteenth, whose story he relished, whose writings he thought were hilarious, whose lectures he believed to have been the best ever, and whose rescue of Ulysses S. Grant he saw as one of the greatest humanitarian acts of history.

As few students had heard of *The Innocents Abroad*, as it was about travel few of them had yet experienced, and as it was funny as hell, Jake began the third week with it. The next week was reserved for Grant.

Jake had been told in high school that *The Adventures of Huckleberry Finn* was “the great American novel.” Willing to accept that when he was a high school student, even one with some discernment—as Jake had read quite a few novels by the time he first crossed the threshold at Golden High School just west of Denver, Jake decided to test the claim after he had gotten his Ph.D.

There was a shelf of competitors by then. Jake ran the competition deliberately; Clemens won. That his boyhood literary hero prevailed did not surprise Jake. That he won in a walk did. Still, Jake did not teach about Huck and Jim. While Jake's skin was plenty thick enough to handle the controversy that had enveloped the novel, it wasn't necessary to do so.

By the time he got to Kansas, Jake was collecting not just the Mark Twain stories but the craft. He learned the scraps of paper carried in the pockets of the cub reporter in the raw, early days of San Francisco recorded not just the news but also how it sounded as it rode the jangling dialects of the speakers. Jake studied the notebooks that accompanied the older man—notebooks whose pages had filled quickly with anecdotes and observations and phrasing and sounds, all burnished by the heat of Clemens' intellect. He imagined the throngs who walked expectantly into tents and opera houses and hotel dining rooms and convention halls all across the young nation and who never left disappointed.

But past the up-from-his-beer-mug tales of The West, past the tumultuous applause dropped on his curly, white head like a waterfall of rose petals in one chataqua after another, past all the characters drawn so finely the reader recognized them at first glance—never needing an introduction, past all of that . . . was Grant.

For Jake had studied more than philosophy. He had studied history. And he had studied warfare. He knew as much about Thermopylae as the KU ROTC students knew about Afghanistan. He knew about Lepanto and Agincourt, and Trafalgar and Rorke's Drift; he knew about The Little Bighorn and about The Somme and about The Bulge. He knew about Shiloh, too, where more Americans were killed in a few hours than were lost to the attack of 9/11 and to all of the Middle East fighting since. He knew about Fredericksburg and First Manassas and Chancellorsville. He had sailed the Mississippi and had paddled the bayous surrounding Vicksburg. He had walked the Little and Big Round Tops, and the peach orchard, and the gentle upslope of Pickett's charge. He knew about the bloody angle. He had seen the Brady photographs.

And he remembered The Wilderness, another desperate clash between Americans who could barely see one another through the brush and the smoke and the fire, but who could kill each other. 25,000 casualties later, in the early evening of the third day, when Grant and his proud horse Cincinnati reached the Chancellorsville junction, both he and his army knew the question: which way would he turn? North, hugging the safe but humiliating route of the retreats of the past? Or south? When Grant tugged Cincinnati's great head toward the Spotsylvania Court House, where Lee awaited him, his soldiers leaped to their feet and cheered.

Jake knew all of this. Jake believed that after Lincoln there was but one great American of the nineteenth century—Grant. When the emperor of all diseases laid siege to Grant's throat, the General was a step away from bankruptcy. Samuel Clemens saved him. Clemens urged the general to write the two volumes of *Personal Memoirs* that are still regarded as the finest work of its kind. Clemens sat with him, he pulled up his blankets, he reviewed and edited the hand-written pages, and he arranged for their publication. At the end of the General's life, Samuel Clemens had rescued Grant and his wife and his family from personal and financial disgrace, and he had restored him to the bosom of his country.

The contemporary rock stars were necessary—for the marketing and for the intellectual counterpoint and for someone his young students could identify with immediately. But Jake was there to teach about Clemens, and Grant.

Scouting Report: Donor Atrium

There is a lot to getting ready for a basketball game. One of the most important things is to scout the opposing team and report on it to your players. The assignment is typically given to a young assistant coach, in turn assisted by the basketball staff and by such other sources as Kansas might have available. The latter could involve coaching friends whose teams had recently played the upcoming opponent. As with everything else about competitive athletics, there are some programs that are way better at this than others. Success in this area involves hours of groundwork. And once the data is collected, somebody has to make sense of it, then figure out the best way to communicate it to the room full of very young men who needed to apply it.

Gene Bennett had helped with the scouting when he was a graduate assistant and had drawn that assignment as an assistant coach at Oklahoma State. He had relished it. He loved to pore over the stats and the news articles and the messages looking for the telltales that would help his players defend against and score on the visitors. He did it for years and he got good at it. Brett Stevens was

Gene's youngest assistant coach at Kansas, promoted internally after four years as a Kansas player followed by an exceptional run-up through staff positions that included film editor and media assistant and associate director of player personnel. Brett Stevens was good at it too. Brett had a nose for news. And his ability to collect the internet reports and the newspaper articles and the posts on social media, distill it, and dole it out one player at a time so each guy had the best chance to learn it brought a smile to Gene's face every time he watched Brett do it.

Coach Bennett was heading to the media room now. One of the key items on his post-2008 championship wish list, the media room was state-of-the-art when it was added to the locker room complex in 2009 and it had been updated every other year since. Sixteen hard-bottom chairs sat four-each behind four tables, each table on its own riser, the entire space sloping down to the large video screen and white board that nearly touched one another. A rainbow of markers filled the tray of the white board on the right; the video screen gleamed black on the left above its single wireless pointer. Kansas could run the film flown in from its opponent's game in Milwaukee last night just as it could tap into its vast Opponents' Library to create five-second video proofs that the incoming point guard always wanted to go right. It could probably link to the new James Webb telescope, too, rotating its golden mirror to show the guys who was wearing what bikini on Kaanapali Beach. But that was for next year's Maui Classic!

To get to the media room Coach Bennett had to leave his office on the second floor of The Wagnon Center and make his way east to the Kansas locker room complex, which sat on the ground floor of the field house. He might take the stairs down to the north entrance of the large practice court, yet another wish-list item, and walk across it to get there. Or he could take the hallway from his office to the Donor Atrium, whose south stairs took him to the same place.

The Donor Atrium, snugged between the west wall of Allen Fieldhouse and the east wall of The Wagnon Center and roofed against the elements, was another part of the wish list, one of the several ways in which the Kansas coach had tipped his hat to the fans whose yelling in the last two minutes of regulation in San Antonio in 2008 might have lifted the roof right off a lesser building. Empty now, the space would fill on game day with a buffet line and a bar and upper-echelon Williams Fund members, all of them enjoying a convenient meal minutes from their seats. The wall hangings were modest—flat-screen TV monitors, and there was tile on the floor. The decorating budget had been reserved for the large etched windows arrayed at both ends. The one on the north end showed the campus in winter; the one on the south end showed "the shot," Mario Chalmers' three-pointer that sent the 2008 championship game into overtime.

Although walking by himself to the media room, Gene Bennett did not feel alone. Alone was where he had been the week before "the shot"—in Detroit—when there were seconds left in the Elite 8 game against Davidson. Kansas had schemed successfully to wall off Steph Curry, now an NBA superstar. But Davidson's other guard was loose and he had a shot and he took it. As it climbed and crested and fell toward the basket Gene had seen his entire life as a coach flash past him. He had never made the Final Four, and he thought the only way to get there now might be to get down on his knees. When the Davidson shot missed and he could breathe again, Gene Bennett realized he was already on his knees—face down, hugging the court at Ford Field like it was the bank of the Jordan River.

Farieh Gets a Job

Farieh pulled into the parking lot south of WheatFields at 6:00 a.m. She was not the first to arrive; the bread bakers got there at 3:00. But she was early—a habit she had picked up from her father. Farieh knew her supervisor, Elizabeth, was already there as well. Still, Farieh's work did not begin until 6:30, and as she did not want to be too early, she left the motor running and the heater on.

She had been thinking about her grandmother as she drove from her scholarship hall down the hill to Kentucky, then north to Tenth Street, then east to Vermont, then north again to the parking lot. At that time of a deserted morning the trip took no more than five minutes.

Her grandmother had taught her to cook so many things, including the Iranian breads and pastries so often laced with fruits and nuts and cinnamon and honey. WheatFields' breads were simpler as to the added items. But their crusts were old-world, like the loaves her grandmother had created, and that was what had initially drawn her to the place and to the thought of working there.

She remembered the Thursday morning in September when she had pushed through the Vermont Street door in her signature yellow head scarf and her Little Red Riding Hood basket and had asked to speak to the pastry chef. The young man across the counter from her had no idea whom she might be talking about, and Farieh had to ask him to find "the person in charge of the desserts." Elizabeth Perry looked up from behind the back counter a moment later. She saw Farieh through the large opening, smiled, made her way around to the back, then moved past the stainless-steel shaping table to the bread counter in front. Farieh knew she had a chance when Elizabeth smiled again as she asked, "How can I help you?"

"I would like to work here," said Farieh, embarrassed by the suddenness of her response. Before Farieh could follow up with something less direct, Elizabeth had smiled again.

Elizabeth was WheatFields' long-time pastry chef. She was even taller than Farieh, she was a generation older, and she had "baby-duck" hair she kept short to keep it out of the work. She was rail thin. Her skin, warmed by yet another morning in a small, heated space, was as pale as Farieh's was bronzed. Elizabeth was every bit as direct as Farieh. "I admire someone who knows what she wants," she replied. "But why should we be interested in you?"

Farieh held up her basket for a moment so Elizabeth could see it, then she said, "I can bake. I learned from my grandmother; I have baked all my life. You have the finest bakery I have seen since I have come to the United States, and I would like to work here. I have brought baklava. I thought you might want to try it."

In some respects, baklava was baklava: a mix of honey and chopped pistachios and cinnamon and sugar and maybe vanilla extract became a paste that separated layer upon layer of the thinnest pastry. But Farieh's pastry was not like anyone else's. Farieh's was the product of painstaking repetition, of buttering the phyllo dough and folding it and rolling it until it nearly tore, then buttering it and folding it and rolling it again and again until it became so thin it was almost imaginary. There is an art to most things that come out of the kitchen. Her grandmother was an artist; Farieh had been the precocious apprentice. Properly done, her grandmother had said, each layer was like the sheen on the leaf of a rose. Farieh knew the phyllo layers had to be more substantial than these words, if only just, and she had learned how to make them.

But it was the final ingredient for the paste that set apart what Farieh brought for Elizabeth. Added to the family recipe by her grandmother, the freshly-ground green cardamom did not change the taste of the baklava so much as accentuate it. It became only slightly less sweet, only slightly less honey-dominated, but brighter, and more assertive. Farieh put her basket on the bread counter, took a small step back, and waited.

Elizabeth Perry knew what good baklava tasted like. Beyond having made sheet after sheet of it herself, she liked it; she had sampled countless recipes throughout the country. But she had never tasted anything like this. The phyllo was even more delicate than her own; the ground nuts and the honey were perfect. But the cardamom . . . ! It was remarkable.

She picked up the end of the cotton apron that still boasted its morning dusting of flour, wiped the honey from her fingertips, and smiled again at the young woman standing across the counter. Farieh's head scarf gathered the green of her eyes and tossed it so it sparkled against the walls, even those at the very end of the bakery. Elizabeth spoke: "I could tell you this was delicious, young lady, but that would do it a disservice. You have brought this as a kind of portable, consumable reference. It was an imaginative idea, and a successful one. If you would like to work here, we would like to have you."

Tom Erickson

You could call Tom Erickson a "contrarian," but only if you added "lazy" at the front end. Having graduated number two in his class at Lee's Summit North High School, he decided for KU instead of Missouri, figuring most of his classmates were going to Columbia and everybody at Harpo's would soon know his tricks.

He had been a star debater for the Broncos and made state all four years, testament to his intellect and his wide-ranging vocabulary and his occasional competitiveness. An attribute never remarked upon was his appearance. No long-hair, horn-rimmed, just-out-of-the-shower look for him. He looked like the quarterback on the football team because he was a quarterback on the football team—the junior varsity, at least—his sophomore year. He wore button-down shirts, regimental-striped ties whose colors coordinated with his sport coat or suit, and he polished his shoes. Was it an act? Sure. But the parents and the business people who judged most of his debates loved the clean-cut kid who could talk, and Tom rode that for all it was worth.

State could have been another country. There, Tom's judges were debate coaches or former championship debaters and they expected a first negative to include timely citation to real research.

As timely citation to real research required work, Tom never had much of that, and he never cleared the preliminaries. That each year he dragged a colleague down with him hardly affected the young stud from the western edge of Missouri.

Unphased by the unevenness of his high school debate experience, Tom contacted the KU debate program in the spring of his senior year. He was invited to come by Bailey Hall when he got to campus, and he did—in August—when he got to Lawrence. He was greeted enthusiastically by the coaches and the team, even warmly. Tom was a handsome kid, as glib as any of them, and he exuded the same, cock-sure attitude that filled the debate team's spaces like oxygen. He was assigned a colleague and, only weeks later, found himself in his first tournament in his preferred spot—first negative. But he was no better prepared in college than he was in high school; and here, the color of his tie made not the slightest difference. Tom and his colleague went 2-6 that weekend, one of the least auspicious starts by any KU freshman team in memory. When Tom took the several stairs down to Bailey Hall's lowest level Monday afternoon and walked into the cavern everyone called "Debate," the board told him he had a new colleague.

Not really knowing this young freshman and plenty busy with the rest of his large, powerful squad, including the three teams who would all qualify in the spring for that year's National Debate Tournament, Coach Seth Daniels had not been upset over Tom's first outing. When Tom's colleague had wanted to see him that morning, he talked with her. And when she asked for a new colleague, Seth had not asked for her reasons. Neither did she offer them. The two colleagues had barely met, they were both freshmen, it was too early in the season, and a new pairing was easy to arrange. Seth broke up a team that had gone 6-2 in its first tournament but had lost in the quarterfinals, pairing Karen West, the stronger speaker, with Tom.

Karen and Tom did better: 5-3 in a highly competitive tournament at nearby Emporia State. But the next Monday morning greeted Seth with a second young woman looking for change. Karen had no trouble giving vent to why she wanted out: "Erickson is a jerk!" She forged on, barely stopping to breathe. "And maybe I could live with that. But he is also the laziest person I have ever met. He showed up with nothing. And," shouting now, "I mean NOTHING!

Do you know how many cites he offered in his entire speech? One! The Bible." There was a pause. "THE BIBLE!" Another pause. "I had to debate my ass off for us to hang with teams we should have destroyed.

At the end I was screaming at him about his not doing a thimble's-full of work to get ready. Do you know what he told me then?! He said he had several dates that week, and he had to do his laundry. Well, he can take his snarky sense of humor and shove it up his ass! I'm done with him."

First, Seth texted Erickson's original colleague and arranged to talk with her about why she had asked for a change. This second time around she told him the story—a near repeat of Karen's. Next, Seth sent an e-mail, asking Tom to see him that afternoon. Having spent almost no time in the squad rooms that fall with his teammates, Tom did not appreciate that e-mail was a little-used form of communication by "The Head Jayhawk" and one that rarely led to a cheery conversation. When Tom arrived, and after Seth had closed the door and told him to sit, his coach asked him only two questions: was the Bible his only cite, and did he attribute his lack of preparation for Emporia State—whether in jest or not—to his having several dates and needing to do his laundry. When Tom answered "Yes" to both, Seth told him he was no longer on the team.

Thanksgiving: Elizabeth

Richie slept in the Wednesday before Thanksgiving. He had no class, there was no out-of-town tournament this year, and the made-for-TV game against San Diego State at the T-Mobile Center wasn't until Saturday. The team would go through a light workout and shoot-around Thanksgiving evening, then bus into Kansas City on Friday.

He was sleeping in at his mom's new house, which she had purchased that summer. The apartment complex near Rock Chalk Park had been a good way for them to get started in Lawrence, but his mom began looking for a house early that fall, focusing first on Lawrence's eclectic, older neighborhoods. As her firm's new office had been established at Kasold and Bob Billings Parkway, just west of campus, and to maximize her availability to the KU faculty who were working with her, she ruled out Old West Lawrence and the rapidly-developing area immediately east of downtown, even though living there would have made at most a ten-minute travel difference. Where she most wanted to live was West Campus, which butted up against the west side of "the Hill" that outlined the original campus of the university. But the homes in this quiet, tree-lined area seldom came on the market. And when they did, she and her realtor would find there was an "offer pending" as soon as they could make contact with the seller. So she broadened her search to the west and finally settled on a home in Alvamar, the golf course development imagined by Bob Billings, the point guard on Wilt Chamberlain's KU basketball team, and underwritten by Bob's father and mother, Alva and Margaretta, who ran an oil company in Russell, Kansas. Not as well established as West Campus, which reminded Elizabeth of her old neighborhood in Salina, Alvamar's many homes across a wide range of styles and prices did come on the market. She chose one on Muirfield Drive. It was a trim and modest Dutch Colonial on a trim and modest lot. But the master bedroom looked out over a pergola-protected back patio, and then onto the big trees lining the golf course. It wasn't splashy—that was important to Elizabeth. But it was pretty inside and out, and she liked it.

The new house also had a dining room. It was smaller than the one Elizabeth had enjoyed in Salina, but it was there—an important change from their apartment. No dining room had prompted Elizabeth to accept her colleague's invitation for Thanksgiving dinner last year. This year she could reciprocate, and Alan and his wife Ann would join them tomorrow.

Richie told his mother she had only one speed, flat out. Elizabeth was the first one up, the first one at the office, the first one to complete a project, and—before her promotion to what she called "the research mission" in Lawrence—the first partner to have all of their clients' tax returns finished in April. She was rarely home before 7:00. Even in the fall, long after the close of tax season and its late-night and all-weekend schedules, Elizabeth would still work after dinner on a new report or a new IRS Regulation or a new client event. All of that stopped the Wednesday before Thanksgiving. Elizabeth took that day off, and she insisted that all of her reports take it off as well. The Wednesday before Thanksgiving you would find her at home—apron on and moving effortlessly in and out of the kitchen, her smile relaxed, talking to herself. Unlike the other days of the year there was no hurry; Elizabeth would flow from one task to the next. Banished too was her impatience with her son, or with anyone else.

Elizabeth's preparations for Thanksgiving dinner had moved past traditional to ritualistic. But it was her ritual, and she liked it. The turkey had to be fresh and not too large; the potatoes had to be from Idaho and firm and spotless; the roux for the gravy had to be at room temperature; the green beans had to be cut at an angle, with Maytag-brand blue cheese for the sauce; the sage for the dressing had to be real; the walnuts could not be musty; the bread for the dressing had to be sourdough—cut into dice-sized cubes and dried for at least four days. She would bake the pumpkin and apple pies Wednesday afternoon, grateful her small kitchen had two large ovens. While she selected the Granny Smith apples herself and made both of the pie crusts from scratch, she "cheated" on the pumpkin pie filling, having never been able to make one she liked better than Libby's.

Ice cream would accompany the pie. Her father had frozen her mother's homemade ice cream recipe twice a year—July 4th and Thanksgiving. Elizabeth still remembered how he would pull the paddle out of the tin cylinder when the electric motor could no longer push it and how she and her sister would dive at it with their spoons in order to have the first taste. But she did not have time to make ice cream on Thanksgiving Day, not with all the other time-sensitive dishes to attend to, and she had given up asking Richie to do it years ago. That's how Häggen-Dazs vanilla had weaseled its way onto the menu.

There were four other staples of the Armstrong-family Thanksgiving dinner: the bread, the cranberry relish, the pink salad, and the pickles. Elizabeth had gone to the Dillon's grocery store in Salina to buy Ocean Spray cranberries for her mom, and she still washed and drained and chopped the same brand—along with the orange peel—into the family recipe. The pink salad took its color and its name from the strawberry Jello that first had to set up, often outside on the deck. Next came the heavy cream, which was poured into the stiff red liquid and whipped into the pink froth that was folded around the bananas and dates and walnuts. That mixture was chilled in the refrigerator until dinner was called. Richie could barely make himself eat the stuff—he took a "courtesy bite" and no more. Elizabeth liked it, and she ate two helpings on Thanksgiving Day, carefully covering it and putting it in the refrigerator that evening. She would snack on it for days, until it began to break down, then push whatever was left into the garbage disposal.

The pickles came from Elizabeth's friend Beth, whose amazing bread-and-butters were conjured in Beth's gleaming-white kitchen in Raleigh. Each year, Elizabeth served them in the same red-and-orange serving bowl shaped like a circus clown that her mother had used for every Thanksgiving and Christmas while she was alive, although it had been used then for the cranberry relish and not for Beth's pickles.

Elizabeth thought about her mother every Thanksgiving. Mom had taught her how to cook all the foods that still made up their Thanksgiving dinner. And she had impressed upon Elizabeth how important a holiday it was, how important it was for a family to have its own rituals, and how distinctive and delicious food that someone had spent real time preparing was one of the most powerful rituals of all.

Her mother had died in Salina and the family "put everything on the sale" after the funeral. "Everything" wasn't supposed to go, of course. There were things that Elizabeth and her sister had treasured and had agreed to divide between them. Her sister got the large Red Wing water chiller with the pour spout and the almost-as-large Red Wing butter crock. Elizabeth got the clown. They agreed to flip a coin for their mother's one valuable piece of furniture—a burled-walnut, glass-front chest-on-chest that arrived in Salina roped to a covered wagon 150 years ago. Elizabeth threw the quarter in the air and had her sister, Mary, who was older, call it. "Tails!" Mary shouted. It came up "heads."

A nice farm couple from Junction City had bought their mom's house. But their wanting occupancy in only two weeks had forced such an early sale of the personal items that Elizabeth and Mary had to ask several friends to help them mark the things. So, it wasn't until the actual morning of the sale that Elizabeth realized one of the friends had put a price tag on the clown . . . and had set it out with the rest of the sale items. Her tears forming as she watched the stranger pick it up to look at it, Elizabeth stood up from her folding chair in the back of the garage, brushed her apron across her eyes, and began to pray. When the stranger put the clown back and moved on to the next table, Elizabeth rushed forward out of the shadow of the garage and saved it.

Elizabeth put the chest-on-chest in the living room of the new house in Lawrence; she put the clown on the middle shelf, right in front.

Elizabeth could make nearly anything and make it delicious. But she had never figured out bread. Moving to Lawrence had solved that problem, for Lawrence was home to one of the nation's finest artisan bakeries—WheatFields. "Discovered" by an itinerant journalist from New York City who set out to find and sample and write about the nation's finest breads, WheatFields placed first in the ranking he published at the end of his trip. But WheatFields had been making lights-out breads and pastries and cakes and cookies and pot pies and scones for years before it was discovered, and it had made them ever since. Elizabeth had gone there for lunch with a colleague from Kennedy & Coe soon after moving to Lawrence and had been impressed by the breads, by their variety, and by the unaffected competence of the people who worked there. Their Thanksgiving bread would come from WheatFields, and she knew to order it well in advance. Richie would go for it as soon as he got up.

Thanksgiving at WheatFields

The line for bread snaked north past the cash register to the tables along the north wall before turning back on itself and moving all the way back to the front. Still collecting customers, it spilled out the entrance onto the sidewalk. Richie took his place at the end and moved slowly into the bakery, then north, then alongside the tables at the north wall that overlooked 9th Street. When the line turned right toward the bread counter he noticed he had been in it for twenty-five minutes. But his mom wanted the bread, and he had no other place to be, so he bided his time as the customers in front of him were steadily attended to.

Richie was five places from the front when he noticed the young woman selling the Thanksgiving loaves was wearing a bright yellow head scarf. He was two places closer when the part of her face revealed to the public told him she was one of the most beautiful women in the world, or at least his world. When he moved up to the second spot, the tractor beam emitted from her green eyes—the first green eyes Richie had ever seen—captured him and drew him helplessly forward to the counter in front of her. That was just as well, for otherwise he would have stood like a stone in the second spot, staring at her. Now he was in the first spot, doing just that.

"Did you place an order for today?" she asked, her voice tinted with an accent as much British as Middle Eastern. Farieh's father, a banker, had been a diplomatic liaison to Iran's embassy in London, and she had spent three years there as a teenager trying her best to learn the language and to fit in at her tony "public" school.

Richie said nothing, still transfixed by the goddess in yellow in front of him.

"Excuse me," she said, this time in a tone both louder and more pointed. "Did you place an order for today?"

"Oh, yes, yes; I'm sorry," stammered Richie.

"Will you please give me your name?"

"Armstrong. Richie Armstrong." He was breathless.

"I have an Elizabeth Armstrong," said Farieh, looking down at her long alpha list for the morning. Bread sales closed at noon on Thanksgiving. "Is she a relative?"

"She's my mom," said Richie.

"OK," replied Farieh. "I have two loaves of Rustic Italian with Rosemary. Is that correct?"

Richie had no idea—he had never thought to ask his mom what kind of bread she wanted. "I'm sure that's it; that sounds wonderful. Can I have them?"

"Of course," said Farieh, "I have them just behind me." She reached around, drew two loaves from the center of the tall metal bread rack, and turned back to Richie. "Would you like them sliced?"

He and his mom had not talked about that, either. But he had heard artisan bread that was not sliced got hard after only a day or two, so he asked her to slice both loaves. She did, slipping them expertly into individual plastic bags and placing them on the counter. She was facing Richie again when she said, "That will be ten dollars and eighty-two cents."

Richie was once again staring at her, saying nothing.

Her voice rose in volume, regaining its edge of a moment before: “Ten dollars and eighty-two cents, please.”

“Oh, of course. I’m really sorry.” Richie pulled his billfold from his left rear pocket and pulled out a credit card. Not knowing what he might do if he actually touched her hand, he was careful not to; he put the card on his side of the counter. She reached across for the card, ran it, collected his copy of the receipt, and placed both card and receipt back on the counter in a series of efficient gestures. Then, as Richie continued to gaze at her, she turned her head to the right. In a voice loud enough for anyone close by to hear it, especially Richie, she said, “Next, please.”

Richie was collecting his card and receipt as the person in the second spot moved forward impatiently, cutting in front of him and brushing him back out of the way. Richie shrugged, looked down at the bread, and left the bakery. He walked west on 9th Street, past the bank and nearly to the light at Kentucky before remembering he had parked almost a block south of 9th on Vermont.

Andrew Stevenson

Andrew Stevenson had practiced law in Wichita for nearly twenty years before moving to academic life. He had thought about teaching while a law student at Kansas, where he graduated second in his class and was awarded the Mellinger Prize for scholarship, leadership, and service. But he wanted to try cases to juries; and he concluded, after as much study as he could make of it as a 3L, that Wichita offered more of a chance for that than Kansas City. He joined a prominent Wichita firm, second-chaired his first state-court trial six months later, and never looked back.

Stevenson's big frame and easy manner were natural fits for Wichita. Mentored effectively by several of the firm partners, he graciously declined the fistful of invitations to join Wichita's clubs and civic organizations whose members were the firm's clients and who recognized Andrew's energy and his natural gift for leadership. His focus was on the law, the courtroom, the judges, and the firm, and it paid off. He had arrived in Wichita at age twenty-eight, having spent three years as an Army infantry officer before going to law school. By the time he hit thirty-two he had tried a dozen cases, nine of them as lead counsel and seven of those by himself. He had lost two, both to far more experienced

Wichita lawyers. After taking their verdicts and congratulating their clients, both had made their first phone call to Andrew's managing partner to exclaim what a find he had in his young associate.

The next fifteen years had been a blur. Andrew married; he and his wife, Becky, had two children—Katherine ("Katie") and Emma ("Bugs," for her early fascination for anything that crawled), and he continued to try cases. Lots of them. The firm was hardly short of trial lawyers, but by the time he reached forty, Andrew was the lawyer every client wanted on the trial team. It wasn't necessary that he lead the team; the firm counted lawyers far more experienced than Andrew, partners whose judgment the clients were used to and whose relationships with the courts they depended upon. But when it came to setting the trial strategy, making the opening statement, and cross-examining the opposing parties and their key witnesses, especially the so-called "experts," Andrew was their guy. He was busy in the best possible way: his opinions sought not only in Wichita but by a steadily-increasing clientele throughout the Midwest, his trial skills constantly honed, his successes piling up. Becky had the girls and their schools and the family's vacations and holidays well in hand, and she had close friends—two were wives of Andrew's law partners and two were from their church.

Emma was nine when she was diagnosed with leukemia. Her doctors—Emma's pediatrician and the oncologists from The Wichita Clinic—were familiar with the juvenile strands of the disease. Even though Emma was on the older end of the juvenile spectrum, they were optimistic. But not every child does well. Emma struggled from the outset, and three months in it was apparent she was in trouble. She turned ten that July. The family celebrated her birthday with her nurses in ICU; Emma asked Katie to open her gifts because she did not have the strength to untie the ribbon. She died the next day.

Andrew survived the several weeks that followed Emma's death, but he never remembered them. His family and Becky's, who had been in and out of Wichita throughout Emma's illness, were now there full time. The law firm set up a visitation schedule so Becky would not have to prepare an evening meal until she signaled she was ready to do so. Andrew's partners had long since taken on his work; the state and federal judges, whose regard for Andrew matched that of his law firm, continued all of his trials. Everyone who could have helped the Stevensons recover did help; that's what people in Wichita did. And Andrew recovered. Almost an even month later he woke up feeling he had something he needed to do at the office, and he went.

Katie returned to school at Robinson that fall, Andrew was already back to work, their parents had returned to their own homes, and Becky told her many friends at the law firm they could stop with the meals—she was all right. But she wasn't. Depression walked into Becky's life the day the door closed to Emma's, and it unpacked its bags.

Andrew and Becky tried to make things work for a year, and then another as Becky at last seemed to be getting stronger. But whatever strength she was gaining was steeling her against her husband, whom more and more she resented. Becky conceded to her friends, and even to her priest, that Andrew was no more to blame for Emma's death than the mailman. She tried to like him again; she certainly didn't dislike him. She tried to hide the bad times, tried to push them into deep places where the light of the present couldn't reach them. But too often, being around Andrew brought them back. Finally, even hearing his voice was too much. She filed for divorce at the end of the third year, and Andrew let her go. Katie, who had just started at East High, stayed with her mom; Andrew moved into a condo a few blocks from the firm.

Stephen Clark watched all of this from Green Hall in Lawrence. Clark had tried cases as an AUSA in the Southern District of New York right out of Columbia. Thinking a job "out west" would be fun, he joined the law faculty at Kansas at the start of Andrew Stevenson's 3L year. Stephen taught the new Trial Tactics course, and the many gifts brought to the class by this confident young infantry officer were the highlight of Stephen's first semester. As Andrew's three years of military service made them the same age, Stephen became Andrew's friend as well as his teacher. It was Stephen who had listened to Andrew weigh the pros and cons of Kansas City against those of Wichita, and it was Stephen who had encouraged him to stay in Kansas. Stephen was now the Dean of the law school at Kansas, and it was clear to him that Andrew again had pros and cons to weigh. He called Andrew and invited him to dinner: Stephen would drive to Wichita if Andrew would buy the meal. Andrew accepted.

Dinner was at Chester's, the steakhouse close to Andrew's condo and to Stephen's hotel. They took a table in the back overlooking the small lake, ordered Kansas City strip steaks and a bottle of cabernet, and were deep into what was going on with Andrew before the server returned with their menus. Mostly it was Andrew who talked. But Stephen wanted the evening to close on two points, and he waited until just after Andrew had paid the check to make them: Andrew had a gift for all aspects of litigation, including teaching it; if Andrew ever wanted to teach litigation at KU, there was a place for him. It would be another year before Andrew called Stephen to accept the offer. But when he accepted it, he was ready.

Kentucky Comes to Allen Fieldhouse

By Sean Grogan
Lawrence, KS (AP)

THE ANXIETY

Kansas plays one of the toughest non-conference schedules in the country as a warmup for playing the toughest conference schedule in the country. But there is always a marquee game in Allen Fieldhouse—the ticket everyone keeps for themselves. It might be Villanova, or it might be Michigan, but it's big. This year it was Kentucky. If there is a Kansas-killer of the past decade, it's the crew from horse country.

A win against the Wildcats is hard to come by. Kentucky had no trouble with a really good Kansas team in the 2012 NCAA Championship game in New Orleans, letting Gene Bennett's friend John Calipari take home the trophy. And they beat another good Kansas team in a recent SEC/Big 12 match in Lexington. Now the Wildcats were coming to Lawrence. If you checked in with a fan walking the sidewalk along Massachusetts, you'd hear the kind of surface optimism you'd expect. But something different lived just beneath the surface—the fear Kentucky might be able to work the same kind of voodoo here in AFH.

THE GAME

FIRST HALF

3-point shooting is the fools' gold of college basketball. It looks great and feels great and can sustain you until crunch time at the assay office. Then you need to find something else if you want some spending money for the weekend.

A made 3 may be even more of an adrenaline high than a dunk. A dunk is something you're supposed to make; a 3-pointer is different. In a game where you're guarded, they're all difficult—as though nobody really expects the shooter to make them. But when he does it's great!

Kansas went 5-for-8 from behind the arc in the first half against Kentucky. What put Kansas in such a good position to make 3-pointers in that delirious first half was crisp passing. The Jayhawk shooters were as close to open as a Gene Bennett-coached offense could get them, and they responded. Billy made the first one; when Percy Jackson followed quickly behind him Kansas was off to the races. On the very next defensive possession, a charged-up Jackson stole the ball and got it ahead to Preston, and the Wildcats had to foul Paul to stop the layup. Ball to Kansas; Percy again. Again benefiting from excellent ball movement, the Wichita freshman makes two more on a nice jumper. Kentucky to a zone. No matter. Percy and Billy Nixon cut it up and Williams scores on a nice left-handed hook. When Frank Agbani drains another 3,

Kansas has fought back from its early 10-4 deficit and leads 21-17.

It would be all Kansas from then until the break. Superb ball movement on offense, made shots, and the best perimeter defense of the season carried the Jayhawks to the half-time locker room. Thomas Williams did not have an overall-outstanding half, but he fronted the Wildcats' seven-foot lottery pick—Jacob Spetzal—and harassed the inlet pass and made him work. With 6:42 left, Williams got a piece of the pass intended for young Mr. Spetzal [he's a freshman] and tipped it to Jackson. Preston, already ahead of the Wildcats on the break, took Percy's pass and laid it in. Kansas up 10. In what seemed only two more ticks off the clock—three max, Billy and Paul hit back-to-back 3s to put Kansas up 33-19. Now fired up, Preston used his length to talk his man out of the 3-pointer he had been drawing up and stopped that next shot before it even happened!

The Kansas scoring ended on a bellwether play from Agbani. With only single-digit seconds left Frank drove the baseline, nearly collided with Kentucky's seven-footer, then lofted a lovely right-handed runner as he went by him to the left that gave Kansas a 39-21 halftime lead.

Kansas' ball-hawking, forcing-through-screens effort had made it harder for the Wildcats to get the ball to the paint. Inside, the Hawks were doing a nice job helping one another on Spetzal and on Dallas Bakunov, Kentucky's other seven-footer. [Yes—they have two!] Thoroughly frustrated by most of those first 20 minutes, Kentucky's #55—Damon Hoy, their all-east-of-the-Mississippi 6'5" combo guard—drove it in past a mostly-admiring Kansas defense and jammed it home to end the half. No one wearing red and blue seemed to appreciate what that might signal for the second half.

SECOND HALF

I will say this about our team . . . we can screw up a good time about as well as anybody I've ever seen.

Gene Bennett

Another ragged start for Kansas, and by the 15:30 mark it was all Wildcats. Kansas was losing track of the ball too often, then missing the shots it took. Kentucky, meanwhile, had found the range at the south basket and their guards were exploiting Billy Nixon's fatigue—a product of Jeff Hanson's not playing because of a tough case of turf toe. [There's no "turf" in basketball, of course. But its hard surface is just as unyielding as an artificial football field, and the hyper-extension that results is the same.]

Kansas had stopped driving the ball, taking away the kick-outs that had led to many of the first-half 3s. Kentucky, in turn, had done a better job getting the ball inside, then back out to its shooters. On defense, the Wildcats were an entirely different team. Preston made a nice move to the basket from the right side and was stuffed; Billy drove it the next time, but into so much traffic he could barely see the rim, much less hit it. Preston's runner was picked up by the Wildcats' seven-foot picket line and intercepted. Pretty soon the lead had dwindled to four.

Percy Jackson soared for the next offensive board and ended up with it. But like Billy and nearly everyone else in white, Percy just could not get the ball in the hole. When his first hook shot was blocked he gamely got the rebound. But he missed the next one, too, as did Preston on his next try and Agbani on his.

What else was going on that second half? Did we mention #55? The senior guard from clear across the country—LA, of course—had been the SEC conference player of the year last year and was a pre-season second-team All-American this time around. Hoy, who had made the frustration-induced throw-down to end the Wildcats' scoring the first half, contributed the lion's share of it in the second. And it was Hoy who took the most advantage of a tired Billy Nixon. When Hoy made two free throws at the 5:32 mark he had 25, and it was a 2-point ball game.

Big moment. Who will answer?

Percy tried, but Spetzal's defense forced a far more difficult layup than Jackson had in mind, and he missed. When Hoy blew past a clearly tired Billy Nixon—and got fouled and made both—it was a tie.

Percy spins and is stripped. Hoy leads the break and makes a no-look pass to Spetzal, who is running with him (!), and the seven-footer lays it in. Having outscored Kansas 34-14 this half, Kentucky now leads 55-53.

"First one to 60 wins!" a grumpy Gene Bennett said to anyone listening.

Clock down to 3:34; Kansas ball; Percy. Spins again—this time into a double team; stripped again.

But Billy digs down and finds something there and drives it the other way, gets fouled, and makes both. Tied again. Gene Bennett has been watching as well as talking to himself. Preston hasn't been moving well. Time out. When the trainer indicates a leg cramp, Bennett subs in Richie Armstrong and rotates the taller freshman to defend Hoy in place of Nixon. This is not a fix that would have lasted even four minutes at the start of the half. But there are two minutes left, Armstrong is fresh, Nixon needs a break, and the novelty of it and Armstrong's length slow down Hoy for at least a moment.

Next possession, second bellwether play: Richie Armstrong. When the freshman spots an opening and drives it in from the right side of the free throw line, Spetzal and Bakunov see him and move his way, certain they can stop him in time. But Armstrong stops himself just after his runner climbs over the two Cane-tuck redwoods, and then it falls through the cords.

The next 90 seconds are a blur of back and forth until Tommy Barnett, in to spell a flagging Williams, rips down a rebound and starts the break . . . by dribbling it off his ankle. Wildcat ball beneath their basket. The inbound play is to Hoy, of course, and the All-American candidate beats everybody for a layup almost before the timer can start the clock. Tie game.

Hawks ball; nothing. Kentucky rebounds and brings the ball up. Spetzal sets a great pick on Armstrong, Frank is too far away to close the other side of the ball screen, and Hoy lays it in so by himself he looks like he's on probation. Wildcats up two; Kansas ball; 22 seconds left.

NEW KID

Everybody knew Gene Bennett had called the play for Billy Nixon. Even the servers at the concession stands who had walked around their counters and were watching the game on their overhead monitors knew the drill. Nixon would run the clock down to eight or nine seconds then drive like hell down the lane and put up a shot that would either go in or draw a foul. Vintage stuff; everybody had seen the tape.

Kentucky's Hall-of-Fame coach had seen the tape too. As the clock passed 12 seconds and Nixon started his move toward the foul line he was blocked by the Wildcats' point guard on Billy's left side. Spetzal, who had snuck up from the base line, closed on his right. Billy had absolutely nowhere to go; and when he gave up his dribble you could hear the gasps from the fans in the front-row. Five seconds left.

The double had left Richie Armstrong alone in the corner. Billy Nixon must have sensed his roommate was open because he sure couldn't see him, so he jumped as high as he could and pitched the ball in the freshman's general direction in the hope Armstrong was watching.

Richie Armstrong was watching. With an elite athlete's sixth sense, he not only knew where to look for the ball but also knew he had to move to his right—away from the basket and well behind the three-point line—in order to catch it. When Nixon's pass reached Armstrong's hands it looked like the youngster from Free State had been waiting for it his entire life. The movements that followed—taught and practiced in sweltering Kansas summers, reinforced by hundreds of AAU and high school events, and refined under the tutelage of his current coaches and teammates—were seamless. Armstrong was up in a heartbeat, his hands ratcheted into the shooting position as he neared the top of his jump, and his right-hand follow-through kissed the ball off his extended fingers the instant before the horn sounded. A food-truck junkie could not have squeezed a street taco through the space between Armstrong's hand and the ball when the red lights flashed around the backboard.

The 16,300 people who had been screaming the instant before stopped screaming . . . and waited. Also waiting were the players and the coaches, and the refs, and the broadcasters and the sportswriters, and the cheerleaders and the Rock Chalk Dancers and the band. Big Jay was frozen on the sidelines while Baby Jay, always in character, impishly held her hands over her eyes. The ball climbed up its parabola and crested and started down. And when it whistled through the cords as though cuing the band for "I'm a Jay, Jay, Jayhawk," everything went crazy.

"Pillow Talk": Kentucky

That was some kinda shot, little bro!

Billy Nixon had just climbed into bed and was about to close out of his iPhone, but he had to give his roommate some love before lights out.

"Thanks, Billy," said Richie. "But you got the ball to me, and I still don't know how you did that."

"Desperation is the mother of invention!"

"Maybe so," Richie responded, "but it was one heck of a pass for a guy who was locked down that tight. In any event, we got out of there with a 'W,' and that's what counts the most."

"You can save that humble-pie shit for ESPN. That was the kick-ass three ball of the season. You need to *like* it for a while—put your arms around it—at least 'til tomorrow morning. See you then." And with that Billy set his alarm, put his phone down, rolled over, and was asleep in five seconds—just like always.

Richie lay back on his bed watching the light from Oliver's parking lot spilling through the windows and across the ceiling, the room quiet. Quite the change from the locker room after the game where the noise and the jumping around and the chest bumps and the back slaps might have gone on forever if Coach Bennett had not walked in with a frown on his face. Ever-focused on their coach's mood, Richie and his teammates got quiet in a hurry as they waited to find out what was up. It didn't take long.

"Richie!" Gene Bennett had raised his voice and he still seemed serious. All eyes turned to the youngster who had just ended the Jayhawks' long night against the Wildcats from Kentucky. "If I'd known you could shoot like that, I'd have put you in for two minutes in the first half!" And with that the bedlam started up again.

There was nobody to see it now, but Richie was smiling as big as he had ever smiled in his life. He was smiling at the joy of his shot falling through the net and the noise (!) that exploded when it did. Mostly he was smiling about how he had felt about the guys in the locker room, and about coach when he had walked in and kidded him, and about how everything seemed so much more familiar when he had showered and walked down the hallway filled with the photographs of the Kansas players whose names were known by everyone. He had pushed through the south door of the field house and had looked across the baseball field and had seen McCarthy Hall, and for the first time it did not seem like a destination, a place he was aspiring to. McCarthy Hall was home now.

Richie Armstrong was a Jayhawk.

Andrew and Geoff Walk to the Union

W*hat's up with your point guard?*

Andrew Stevenson's imposing torso filled the door frame in a Harris tweed jacket and a blue Ralph Lauren button-down shirt. His question was addressed to his closest academic colleague, Geoff Pfeifer, whose office in the Nunemaker Center's south wing lay just past the receptionist. Nunemaker was the home of the KU Honors Program; Andrew's office was at Green Hall, the law school's building, just down the hill.

Inside Geoff's office door were floor-to-ceiling book shelves filled not with books but with pre-Columbian pottery of every shape and size, photographs of family and the myriad of friends and admirers Geoff had cultivated throughout the academic world, leather-bound dissertations gifted to him from adoring graduate students, two of his own paintings—as modest and restrained as Geoff, two Robert Sudlow prints of the Stull Road west of Lawrence, and an immodest trove of KU basketball memorabilia. The senior Marshall Scholar on the KU campus, Geoff was a student and a teacher of history. He was the duty stand-in when the university needed a Dean for the College of Liberal Arts and Sciences but was still in the process of selecting a permanent replacement. And, some years ago, he had been acting Chancellor. Geoff was erudite, he was articulate, and he was kind. He could speak in depth about topics ranging from world peace to Renaissance art to the importance of tenure to a university. But Geoff was also a Jayhawk. As much as anything, he liked to talk about KU basketball.

The point guard Andrew had in mind was Richard "Richie" Armstrong, a 6'6" freshman from Lawrence's Free State High by way of Salina South, who was as capable academically as he was with a three-pointer and who had been part of Geoff's ten-student Honors Seminar first semester.

What Andrew knew was that Richie had gone 0-for-5 from beyond the arc the night before. He wasn't benched for that; KU's coach knew anyone could have a bad night shooting the ball. He'd been benched after several defensive breakdowns that had come early in the second half.

What Andrew did not know was that Richie had a girl problem. Geoff's grapevine reported Richie was infatuated with a freshman from Iran but felt wrong-footed in every encounter with her. As Richie had in fact scheduled an appointment with Geoff for tomorrow, Geoff assumed what was up was the girl. But his conversation with his student about Richie's personal life would be private, so Geoff talked hoops instead.

"Can't play defense. Gene will let a guy have a bad night shooting. Even on defense, he knows anybody can lose his man once in a while. But twice in a row would have gotten Frank Mason benched when Frank was a junior; Richie's just a freshman."

"Gene" was the Hall-of-Fame basketball coach at Kansas. He had a last name, but the people who knew him or knew of him could be grouped into two camps, and neither was inclined to use it.

In the first camp were the people who actually knew Gene Bennett and who knew him well: the assistant coaches; the senior staff in the Athletic Department and The Williams Fund, the donor organization; the senior administration for the University; the Chancellor; a small number of faculty; and his friends—often former KU players or people who had grown up with him in college or who had become important to him at the several schools he had coached before he came to Kansas. Geoff was in the first camp. He was a faculty member who had taught Gene's daughter when she was a KU Honors student. When she told her dad it was like taking class from her grandfather, Geoff became a made man in Gene's eyes.

In the second camp were the many thousands of members of "Jayhawk Nation" who fiercely loved KU basketball and who fiercely believed they had the best coach in the country. If they actually encountered the Kansas coach around town, on campus, in Kansas City or Wichita or Dodge City, or at a post-season tournament, they would respectfully—even adoringly—address him as "Coach." But when referring to him among their friends and business colleagues he became "Gene." He was thus "Gene" to thousands of people who had never so much as shaken hands with him. But that was OK. Such familiarity may have offended the French; but around Lawrence, Kansas, it was an important part of the lubrication that made things work.

"You're right," said Andrew. "That first time I didn't notice it." Andrew and Geoff were season-ticket holders and missing a game was something that happened when they were out of town on business. Family events and vacations, arranged with the basketball schedule carefully in mind, did not conflict. "But the second time, Richie's guy went by him like Richie was looking for popcorn, and it was a layup and two points before Richie knew he needed salt."

"We did OK, though," responded Geoff. "Won by twenty points. That's still my definition of a good KU game!"

"Roger that," said Andrew. "We're good; no question. When he's on, Richie is a pretty special long-range shooter. I know Gene would like to be able to count on him once we get into the conference schedule."

"You hungry?" asked Geoff.

"Yep," said Andrew. "It's a beautiful winter day—what say we walk to the Union?"

"Done," said Geoff, standing up from behind the Biedermeier writing desk that was too fancy by half for Nunemaker, or nearly any other building on campus. Geoff had found it in Stuttgart in the 1980s when he managed KU's academic exchange program with The University of Heidelberg. He had fallen for it despite the many digits on its price tag, and he bought it on the spot. He justified its astronomical price to his wife by telling her it "spoke to him" when he walked into the shop. Elizabeth, Geoff's wife of now close to fifty years, was not without a sense of humor. She was really not put out by the cost of the piece; it was not like she had never purchased anything expensive herself! But she did not like its size; she did not like its nineteenth-century style; and she did not like its mirrored finish. So, she found an old microphone used by the campus radio station, one that had KANU welded to the base in large letters, and she set it on top of the desk the week it arrived from Germany. When Geoff protested, Elizabeth told him that if he wanted to keep "that glistening monstrosity" in "my house," it had "better start talking!"

Geoff and his wife were a popular couple because the warmth that moved between them enfolded everyone who wandered into their space. But just as Geoff held sway over their relationship with the university, Elizabeth ruled their home. Not able to speak up for itself, or for anyone else, the Biedermeier was soon exiled to Geoff's office at Nunemaker.

Geoff gathered the jacket that hung from its hook at the end of the bookcase and followed Andrew out the door. As it was semester break, Andrew could pick up Geoff. Ordinarily it was

Geoff who would pick up Andrew. He would make his way down Daisy Hill from his office, announce himself to Doris—who served as the receptionist for the Dean of the School of Law as well as Mother Superior to the new crop of 1Ls, then wander up and down the rows of display cases housing announcements and trophies and donor lists and the most recent faculty publications while he waited for Andrew. The faculty publications were the most interesting to Geoff, as he knew a fair number of the law school teachers. Among the many statistics the law school dean would visit upon you in any given faculty senate meeting or cocktail reception was how the law faculty "blew the doors off" the other university faculties in sheer academic output. That some of it was pedestrian stuff published by law reviews desperate for content was not common knowledge. But Andrew—himself a contributor to the most prestigious journals in the fields of civil procedure and trial practice—knew it, and he had shared it with Geoff when Geoff asked about the dean's cocktail-party preaching.

Geoff would have just retraced his steps past the long list of donors when Andrew would hurry down the back stairs and around the corner. "Sorry!" He always exhaled loudly as he tried to catch his breath around the exclamation. "Are you ready?" Andrew's salutation was always the same, no matter how many minutes had elapsed since Doris had first summoned him from the quiet of his third-floor office; it always tickled Geoff to hear it. "Yes," Geoff would reply smartly in the direction of his newly-arrived Modern Major General; "Ready!" Their real conversation then swung into full flow not two steps closer to the front door, and it would surge back and forth between them until they had reached the small receptionist stand at The Impromptu Café, tucked almost out of sight at the top of the staircase in the Union.

This time they walked down the hill together, skirted Green Hall on its north side, and walked next past the Tai Chi—the blocky, modern, bronze statue gifted to the School of Law by former Chancellor W. Clarke Wescoe to help salve the law school's feelings after its failure to move the Daniel Chester French. Decades before, French had captured the law school's original Dean, James Woods "Uncle Jimmy" Green, for a space in front of its original building. French could convey the emotionality of his subject in either stone or bronze. Just as he had captured the exhausted resolve of the sitting figure in The Lincoln Memorial, French had identified the two poles of the first law dean's personality. Green was magisterial—tall, ramrod-straight, his flared coat and vest accenting the ready position of his lower body. But he was also encouraging—his right arm draped affectionately across the back of the student standing next to him, his outstretched left arm urging the young man to take the bold path. Like its predecessor at the west end of The Mall in Washington, D.C., there was nothing about the Kansas sculpture that was not magnificent. But a former faculty member's nine-dash line had shackled it to the original, faux-classical building. And once he dedicated the entire plat to the National Registry, the law school was powerless to move the dean and his student to its new location across the campus. Years later, the plinth still waited for them. In its own way the Tai Chi was perfect. Powerful, carefully-executed, and balanced, it was just right for the law. But it was not the French.

Very nearly oblivious to the students thronging around them at what was now noon, Geoff and Andrew cut across the intersection toward the new Slawson Hall, named for a Wichita alum who had created the state's largest independent oil and gas company at a time when there was real money in having one. Donald "Don" Slawson was tall, he was handsome, he was smart, and he was busy. His stenographer would accompany him when he got his hair cut on the ground floor of The Slawson Building at Broadway and Douglas, making sure those thirty minutes weren't wasted. But he was also kind; he had a smile for everyone, and he loved his Jayhawks. For those who grew up with him in Wichita, it was fitting Slawson Hall was joined to another new building—Ritchie

Hall—to form the university's new Earth Energy and Environment Center. The Ritchies had made their fortune in asphalt paving and highway construction. They also hailed from Wichita, and Proctor Ritchie and Don Slawson had been friends. That their buildings were joined to the engineering complex across the street by a spare but strong sky walk seemed just right to every petroleum engineer and wellsite geologist who had ever gone to class at KU.

Geoff and Andrew had made their way up the hill and past the Chi Omega fountain and onto the broad sidewalk that accompanied Jayhawk Boulevard on its south side, barely identifying a topic before their enthusiasm for the next one left the old one behind. But they got stuck on grade creep. Andrew, a traditionalist, thought it appalling how "anyone" could simply take a law school exam these days and expect to get a "C." But what really infuriated him was the privileged attitude of the good student who, on the strength of his merely studying for the exam, was insistent he get an "A." "Those kids really PISS ME OFF!!!" he thundered in the general direction of Wescoe Hall, startling the trio of oncoming coeds not five feet in front of them. The young women scattered like flushed quail, leaving Andrew mildly embarrassed at the fuss he had caused and Geoff nearly doubled over in laughter.

A few steps later they were perfectly abreast of the building named for the same W. Clarke Wescoe who had donated the Tai Chi to the law school. That the man who had been a gifted physician, a superb Chancellor, a successful chief executive of the pharmaceutical company that hired him away from KU, a generous donor, and a keen judge of art would be remembered by such an execrable structure was beyond irony. A generation older than Andrew, Geoff knew the story and had told it to his friend many years before.

Designed by the state's architect, the original building was intended to be "the tallest building between St. Louis and Denver." At twenty-five stories, it was an abomination even in concept. When the state's accountants wearily reported there was no way the state could afford to build anything that tall, the state didn't; but the extra classrooms and office space were still critically needed. The solution?

In a decision that would have made Sockless Jerry Simpson proud, the state decided to build only the first four stories—the parking garage. Set on the southern slope of the closed end of the U-shaped hill that was Mount Oread, its first two floors were invisible to Jayhawk Boulevard. The third floor—now the main floor—had been pierced by an occasional window and door in grudging acknowledgment there would be people occupying the squat structure, not automobiles. The top floor, just beneath its flat roof, was faced with rectangular, pre-cast, concrete panels that would have gone unclaimed at any construction-site flea market. Someone on the staff of the state architect, a high school intern most likely, decided awkward, half-oval flutes should flank the too-small windows at the center of the panels. The result was a dull-gray layer cake of concrete that looked more like a 1960s jail than its beautiful neighbors.

Only one feature of the building was a success—"Wescoe Beach." At its far west end, the building's top-most floor was held up by naked pillars resting on the concrete pad of the ground floor beneath. Late spring and fall would find the spaces around the pillars crowded with sun-seeking undergraduates and with teachers whose windowless offices were less appealing for lunch than this broad porch that overlooked the elegance of Anschutz Library, and far to the south, the trees of the Wakarusa River Valley. Although early January it was warm, and Wescoe Beach was crowded.

Geoff and Andrew crossed Jayhawk Boulevard at the intersection just past Bailey Hall and continued east. In the spring their approach to the original law building, now named "Lippincott Hall," would have been heralded by rows of iris planted just north of the sidewalk in the sloping triangle of green space. They passed by the Daniel Chester French, passed the Natural History Museum, and reached the Union. It was good they had called ahead for a reservation as the few tables at Impromptu would otherwise have been snapped up by other faculty, visiting parents, and the occasional student who wanted more to eat than pizza.

Back from the Holidays
Quantrill's Raid on Lawrence

MONDAY

Richie had been in Lawrence since the end of first-semester finals. No trip to Cancun; no short seminar to Costa Rica. He had stayed at his mom's new house during the four-day run-up to Christmas and the next day. But they had a game on the 28th—Harvard—and he had returned to McCarthy on the 27th. They dispatched Harvard without any trouble and had made a terrific start on the Big 12 Conference schedule, winning at home against TCU and on the road against both of the Oklahoma schools. They had returned from the game at Norman last night, Sunday. Coach Bennett gave them the day off, so Richie slept in.

Twice Monday morning he awoke from a dream and briefly opened his eyes; twice he rolled over and went back to sleep. When it was just past 11:00 he awoke for real to the feeling he needed to see two people—Geoffrey Pfeifer, his Honors 190 instructor from last semester, and Farieh. At the end of his Freshman Honors Seminar in December, Professor Pfeifer had given the ten students his cell number and had told them they could call him at any time. Much earlier, he had given everyone permission to call him “Geoff.” Richie dialed Geoff’s number, caught him at home, and had the presence of mind to ask about Geoff’s family and their holidays. Then he asked if he could see him the next morning at 10:30. Richie had a team meeting at 9:00. As Geoff had his own meeting at 10:00, they settled on 7:30 a.m. Richie was looking out on a January day that had already topped fifty-eight degrees. Not one to frequent the weather app on his phone, he did not know about the front pushing in from Colorado and the forecast for a dramatic overnight drop in temperature.

Farieh was more of a challenge. He had seen her only across the bread counter at WheatFields. And while Richie had returned four times between Thanksgiving and Christmas to order the same rustic Italian loaf so he could again look into the haunting eyes of the girl with the yellow head scarf, and while she had told him her name, he did not have her cell number and did not know where she lived. He knew she worked at WheatFields. That was it.

He rolled out of bed and looked for his roommate. The Kansas point guard was in the living room reading the latest ESPN Magazine. “Can I borrow the Camaro for an hour?” asked Richie.

“More bread?” Billy had replied with a smirk on his face. “Sure,” he continued, leaning across the low table to snag the keys. In a continuous motion he rolled back and threw a strike to Richie, who was moving to the bathroom. “Knock yourself out.”

TUESDAY

Unlike his roommate, who had to be jackhammered out of bed if it was early, Richie had no trouble waking up at dawn. He showered, dressed, stole out the door of their room so as not to wake his softly-snoring roommate, took the stairs to the main floor, glanced through McCarthy’s tall windows, and caught a glimpse of a day that was just beginning to brighten over the top of the student rec center to the east.

Out the door. OMG! The six degrees were hard enough. The south wind pushing through the construction materials at Oliver Hall and blowing north against the entrance door of McCarthy almost drove Richie back to his room. Wishing he had worn the wool-lined mittens his mom had given him for Christmas and not his beat-up gloves, he pulled up the hood of his parka, pulled down his ball cap, and leaned into the sidewalk that ran to the DeBruce Center and breakfast.

Waffles, extra sausage, orange juice, hash browns, milk. He would wait to get his coffee. He picked up an extra pat of butter for the waffles, added an extra ramekin of syrup, checked out—a nod of the head from the KU athletes worked at this point in the year—and headed for a seat. There were two other students in the entire place at 6:45 that morning. Richie knew one of them: a swimmer. But she and her friend were in an energetic conversation, so he walked a couple levels up and sat by himself. He checked his messages, scrolled through the entries on the Jayhawk app, and thought some more about the Missouri game, now two weeks away. Finished, he stacked his plates on his tray and walked down the same levels he had walked up in order to put the tray on the belt on the ground floor. Then he did a 180 for the coffee bar, which was up the back stairs just inside the north entrance.

Richie liked the coffee bar's donuts and cinnamon rolls. The coffee bar also had scones, a "pastry" he had tried once in Salina. He thought they were perfect for someone who liked carbs and sawdust. After that the coffee bar had granola and an excellent brand of chocolate-driven energy bars. But Richie had just eaten. What he had waited for was a vanilla latte. It was a frou-frou coffee drink, for sure. But he liked them, and the one the baristas made at the DeBruce Center was amazing. Rationalizing it would help him make it up the hill to Nunemaker, he ordered a *Grande*, paid (even athletes had to pay for drinks from the coffee bar), and walked through the north door. The thermometer had made it all the way to eight. But Salina taught you some things, and one of them was how to handle a hard day in January. Again pulling up his parka and pulling down his ball cap, he let the flat light of the January morning walk him behind the law school to Bob Billings and then up the hill to the Honors building.

Richie decided Nunemaker was no prettier in January than it had been in August, when he had first seen it. It was still squat, still featureless, still without color . . . , and now it was cold. But it was handy. Had he not pledged KU Basketball, his status as an Honors freshman would have gotten him a room in Templin Hall, which was only a narrow parking lot west of Nunemaker. Richie approached the battered screen door that stood a ridiculously-effective sentinel to the Honors Program because it was always stuck. It would stick in any weather; eight degrees guaranteed more than a tussle to get past it. Richie planted his feet and heaved at the aluminum relic from the previous century, and it yielded.

Geoff Pfeifer was by now emeritus, one of three Honors faculty entitled to an office at Nunemaker. His room was straight ahead to the railing that saved distracted visitors from falling into the atrium, then hard right to the first space past the Honors office. Thanks to his grandfather, Richie knew the only thing that differentiated the motor oil served with Army "mid rats" from the gag-inducing stuff at Nunemaker was the chevron on the mug. That was the biggest reason he had brought his own coffee.

Richie looked through the door opening at Professor Pfeifer, knocked expectantly on the door frame, and let himself in just as his teacher welcomed him: "Richie, how good to see you this bright January morning. How *are* you?!"

"I'm good," said Richie. As he walked to the chair across from Professor Pfeifer he was struck once again by the juxtaposition of the flat-glazed, pre-Columbian figures and the gleaming Biedermeier desk. "I'll bet you miss Mexico on mornings like this."

"I do," said Geoff. "It can get this cold in the Sierra Madre, but I have always had the good fortune not to be there in the winter. Did you get some coffee?"

"Yes, for sure," said Richie, his voice careful not to diss the home brew just as his biodegradable "DeBruce Center" coffee cup gave him away.

"To what do we owe the great pleasure of your visit this bracing January morning," inquired Geoff broadly. "Do you have a girlfriend I need to know about?!"

Richie did not have a girlfriend. Richie wasn't even dating. But his attraction to Farieh was powerful and vexing, and he blushed at the question—so brightly that even Geoff, whose bantering had been built entirely on rumor, was himself embarrassed. "I apologize, Richie. That's none of my business. What *is* on our agenda?"

"It's the Missouri game, Professor Pfeifer."

"That's still several weeks away, am I correct?" asked his mentor.

"Yes, right," said Richie. "But what I will call 'the build-up' has already started, and it's pretty intense. I wanted to talk with you about why."

Geoff knew Richie was poised to go on, but he interrupted anyway in order to clarify what Richie wanted to talk about. "What is it you find 'intense,' Richie?"

"I guess all of it. Missouri is three games away and we already seem to be obsessing over it. The coaches are taking players aside to make sure we all get it. Yesterday, we listened to the recorded pre-game pep talk by an old KU football coach, somebody named 'Fambrough.' Did somebody from Missouri carjack his mother? People in Lawrence obviously hate Missouri. But why? We don't even play them anymore in football, and Missouri isn't competitive even in the SEC in basketball. So why all the hype?"

"I know this term doesn't advance our discussion, Richie, but Missouri is 'complicated.' Today, apart from the relentlessly reactionary politics of its rural majority, Missouri is a fairly successful state. She has two cities vastly larger than anything we have in Kansas. She has physical beauty—have you ever been to The Lake of the Ozarks?"

Richie had not.

"Her finances are sound. And she has good people. One of the recent faculty additions at The University of Missouri, for example, is a Marshall Scholar and Oxford Fellow who got his undergraduate degree from KU. He was one of my students—one of my best students ever. I would trust him with . . . well, with *your* life.

But Missouri was a different place during The Civil War. She was committed to slavery and equally committed to making Kansas a slave state, and the hope for that end unleashed extraordinary means. What they call 'The Border War' was a bitter struggle that went on between here—Lawrence—and the band of Missouri counties that border Kansas on the east. Pick whichever evil you want—burglary, armed robbery, burning, looting, petty crimes, kidnaping, right up to murder—and you would have found it on the agenda of the Missouri bushwhackers. These people were nineteenth-century terrorists. This is not to say the people from Kansas were blameless; they weren't, not by a long shot. The revered James Lane, protector of President Lincoln in the opening moments of The Civil War and a United States Senator from Kansas, was a savage when leading his own gang against innocent Missourians. But few people here think Kansas didn't get the worst of it.

It was a brutal period in Kansas history, and many people—myself included—believe what happened then was so horrible that it infects the relationship between the two states even today."

"But Germany and the United States had The Holocaust," Richie answered. "That wasn't half as long ago as The Civil War. And today, Germany is one of our most important allies."

"Yes," sighed Geoff. "The Holocaust. One wonders whether anything could ever be as horrible as that. The Border War wasn't The Holocaust. But Americans never lived The Holocaust. For the people who did live in Lawrence during the Civil War and who lived here in August of 1863, in particular, The Border War was the worst kind of hell they could imagine.

You know," Geoff paused, "I've got something that might help. I am a member of a town-and-gown club that meets during the school year; it's called 'Fortnightly.' Several years ago, one of our members presented a paper on what is called 'Quantrill's Raid.' It's a good introduction to the most dramatic moment of the period and to two of the key figures on the Missouri side; you might find it helpful to your question. Let me find it on my computer, then I'll pull it up and print it for you. You could read it online, I suppose. But I have always felt you get more out of it reading something serious on paper."

Geoff turned his back on Richie, coaxed his computer to where he wanted it to go, and hit "print." Then he stood up and left the room. The printer was down the hall and tucked into the corner of the south conference room. He was back in a moment.

"Here you go." Geoff handed the pages to Richie.

Richie took the thirty-odd loose pages, stared at them for a moment, and looked up. "Do you have a stapler?"

"Of course! Pardon my bad manners. Let me have those back from you." Geoff took the pages, turned around, and walked out his office door for a second time. "Be right back," he said over his shoulder.

This time Geoff turned left to the Honors office, used its three-hole punch on the loose pages, snapped them into a binder, and returned to hand it over to Richie. "Sorry. I should have thought of this the first time. This will make it easier to carry it back to the dorm." Geoff loved KU basketball. But he had a hard time with the delirious construction expense of McCarthy Hall, and his understated personal protest was never to call it by name. He referred to it as "the dorm."

Richie got up from his chair and held out his hand to his Honors teacher. "Thanks very much, Professor Pfeifer," he said. "This is terrific." Nunemaker's screen door stuck just as hard on Richie's way out. But he shouldered through it and was out into the arctic morning in plenty of time for the team meeting.

The Fortnightly paper was longer than Richie had anticipated. He had time to read it, but not until later that afternoon. He went to the team meeting back at Allen Fieldhouse, walked from there to calculus, then walked back for his weekly session with the team trainer. He finished his workout, showered back in his room, checked for mail—none, as usual—then met Billy for a late lunch at the McLain's just west of the Chi O fountain. The McLain's latte was not as good as the one at the DeBruce Center, but their hot ham and cheese sandwich was the best he had had anywhere. After the late lunch Richie headed across campus to his favorite study spot—the reading room at the Anschutz Science Library. He would finish his Honors English assignment there, then tackle the Quantrill paper.

Tucked between Hoch Auditoria and the ROTC building, the science library gifted by Phil Anschutz in honor of his parents was almost unknown to the university's liberal arts community. Early in his first semester Richie had taken what he had assumed was a short cut from Wescoe to Allen Fieldhouse that ran behind Hoch, and as he walked past the locked back entrance of the lecture halls he encountered the open front door of the elegant science building. He decided to look inside.

Watson, the university's main library, was also faced with cut stone, but any favorable comparison with Anschutz ended there. Watson had been magnificent in its day. Now it was old and worn on the inside—oversized oak trim battered by decades of wheeled carts and careless passersby, oak tables the same, stair treads chipped and discolored, chalkboards cracked, and message boards so overwhelmed one could as easily find news of last year's Maroon Five concert as the one next month with Chris Stapleton. Watson was also the noisiest library Richie had ever been in, its high-energy student patrons oblivious to its posted expectations of quiet.

Anschutz gleamed white in contrast. On the inside it was sandstone floors and sharp-edged counters and polished glass and stainless steel in every direction. And it was quiet. When Richie had first seen the main reading room in the fall, a room whose shelves of scholarly journals were as often titled in German as in English, there were two people there—the librarian and a young woman sitting across the room by the window. Richie had been back at least a dozen times since. He had never encountered more than three people; he had likewise never encountered anyone speaking—except for the red-haired student whose chair scraped when he got up to leave, prompting him to turn a brighter red and to apologize repeatedly to Richie and the librarian.

Richie took off his jacket as he walked in and placed his backpack gently, quietly, on the empty table. He pulled out the binder Professor Wilkins had given him that morning and set it to the side, then pulled out the English assignment—another hundred pages, give or take, of *The Great Gatsby*. Richie hadn't jumped into the characters yet; but the writing was outstanding, and he completed the assignment in under two hours. After returning the book to the backpack he stood up, stretched, made his way to the men's room, then came back to the table for a drink of water from his water bottle. He began to sit down, reaching for the binder as he got closer to the seat of the chair, but he stopped and stood up again. He did not know why he was restless, but he was, so he once again walked away and made the entire circle of the reading room before returning to the table, and the binder. He sat down, pulled the binder in front of him, and opened it. As he turned past the title page, he wondered who William T. Anderson was and why the paper was about him as well as Quantrill.

William T. Anderson, William C. Quantrill, and the Raid on Lawrence: August 21, 1863

Presented to Fortnightly June 16, 2019

By F. W. Blackmar

William T. Anderson—Bill, to those who knew him—came to the frontier in the spring of l857 as a teenager. He had been born in Kentucky and had seen little of his father growing up. But he traveled west that spring in the company of his father, William Anderson Senior, his mother, Martha, his three sisters, and his two brothers. His father, having returned from his most recent failed employment in the gold fields of California, had staked his Kansas claim on the bank of Bluff Creek, thirteen miles east of Council Grove and hard by the Santa Fe Trail. By 1860, Anderson Senior was involved with freighting, and he ran a store that sold groceries to the people in the passing wagon trains. But his bad luck continued, and his wife died in the latter part of that year—struck by lightning while out gathering wood chips. She was thirty-six, and she left her husband and six children.

Bill Junior developed a solid reputation early on. By age twenty-one, he had filed his own claim to the Kansas prairie and soon became "second boss" of one of the wagon trains that rolled past his family's home. But he and the "top boss" returned to Council Grove soon after they had left, telling the town folk the horses and mules had "strayed." That they had sold the animals and pocketed the money was confirmed to the satisfaction of many as Bill began leading ponies into Missouri, then returning with horses, which he sold. His trips, which coincided with the disappearance of ponies from ranchers around Council Grove, were profitable; his younger brother, Jim, soon joined the business.

Also from the Council Grove area was Arthur Inghram Baker, the most prominent resident of Agnes City, Kansas. Baker owned another provisions store at the Rock Creek crossing of the Santa Fe Trail, a few miles west of the Anderson place, along with "one of the best corn fields in Kansas." But the Kansas drought of 1860 and '61 wrecked his fields, the accompanying depression ruined his newly-acquired hotel in Council Grove, and then his wife died—leaving him a widower with a young daughter. By late 1861, financially and emotionally despondent, Baker decided to try his hand at jayhawking, joining other men who were "stealing themselves rich in the name of liberty." Along for the ride on an early raid into Missouri were Bill and Jim Anderson. That raid was upended by a patrol of Union cavalry, which mistook the Kansans for bushwackers—the term applied to proslavery men from Missouri who preyed upon the free-staters on the west side of the border. Baker was captured and sent to the military prison at Fort Scott, but later released at the direction of James H. Lane, widely known as "King of the Jayhawkers."

At this point, even though from Kentucky, Bill Anderson's motives for his raids into Missouri were financial, not political. As he told one neighbor, "I don't care anymore than you for the South, Strieby, but there is a lot of money in this [bushwacking] business."

What Baker needed most upon his release from Fort Scott was a wife, and he began to call on Bill's younger sister,

Mary Ellen, who was then fifteen. The calls became frequent and likely intimate. Mary Ellen's father, William Anderson, Senior, assumed they would soon be married and made no objection to the "warmth" of the attachment. But when Baker proposed, instead, to a seventeen-year-old schoolteacher, the senior Anderson went crazy with rage, as did the brothers. All believed Baker had dishonored Mary. And when Baker formed a posse, chased one of the Anderson boys' cousins—a participant in their pony business who had just stolen two horses from the schoolteacher's father, and obtained a warrant for the cousin's arrest, the Anderson men lost it. They rode to Baker's house and threatened to kill him unless he withdrew the warrant. Baker refused.

The wedding was the next day. That very morning, William Anderson Senior showed up at Baker's house with a double-barreled shotgun, drunkenly demanding that Baker come out and face him. Baker, who was upstairs dressing for the ceremony, did not hear the challenge. Anderson Senior dismounted, burst through the door, and started to climb the stairs, still shouting. Now well-aware of the situation, Baker grabbed his own shotgun, stepped suddenly onto the landing, and let loose with both barrels, hurling the mortally wounded Anderson backwards down the stairs.

Not long after, Baker obtained a warrant for Bill's arrest, also on charges of horse stealing. When the justice of the peace unexpectedly released him on bond, Bill and Jim headed straight for Missouri. They sent for their sisters soon after.

On the night of July 3, 1862, a stranger knocked on the door of the Baker house. When Baker answered, the stranger told him he was the boss of a wagon train and wanted to buy whiskey for his teamsters for the next day's celebration.

Baker said he would go to the store and get some. But the bottle in the store was empty, so Baker took the oil lamp and went down into the cellar to refill the bottle from the barrel. When he turned around to hand it to the trail boss, he was face to face with Bill and Jim Anderson. Baker had worn his own pistols, and he was able to draw one and wound Jim, but Bill downed Baker before he could fire again.

Upstairs was Mrs. Baker's brother, a sixteen-year-old boy. Bill shot him, too, and dumped his body down the stairs. Then he closed the trap door, covered it with boxes and barrels, and set fire to everything. Once confident Baker and the boy were dead, the Anderson brothers joined their friend the "trail boss," set fire to the barn for good measure, and headed for Missouri. They stopped at each stage station for fresh horses and tipped their hats to the rising sun as they crossed the border.

Neither Bill Anderson nor the fire had killed Baker. Not wanting to be burned alive, he had shot himself in the head.

The boy, hideously burned as well as gunshot, escaped the cellar by squeezing through a small window, then crawled to the creek bank and slumped into the water. The neighbors found him there that morning almost lifeless. With the few breaths left to him, he told them about Bill Anderson.

Back in Jackson County, Bill and Jim Anderson turned to full-time bushwacking. Operating south and east of Kansas City, but robbing Unionist and pro-Southern alike, they soon attracted the attention of William Clarke Quantrill, head of the largest pro-Confederacy outfit in Western Missouri. Quantrill sent a detachment to apprehend them, take their horses, and warn them they would be killed if they were not more selective. Jim and Bill moved east and set up shop between Lexington and Warrensberg. On February 7, 1863, the editor of the *Lexington Weekly Union* noted: "[T]here is no act of villainy or cold-blooded murder, where a dollar could be made, which they will not do."

By July of 1863, the brothers had formed their own band of forty bushwackers. They attacked a German settlement in Lafayette County early that month. Then, on July 31, they crossed the border into Kansas, destroyed a wagon train headed for New Mexico, and attacked the houses at the "Junction"—a well-known intersection that included the road between what is now Kansas City, Kansas, and Shawnee Mission—murdering a Wyandotte County commissioner in the process.

The month before, the former Chief Justice of the Kansas Supreme Court, who was also William Tecumseh Sherman's brother-in-law, assumed command of the District of the Border, comprising most of Kansas and the western tier of Missouri. Quantrill celebrated Brigadier General Thomas Ewing, Jr.'s swearing-in ceremony by ambushing and killing fourteen Union soldiers in Westport that very afternoon.

Ewing's ability to deal with the bushwackers was handicapped in many ways. His troops were inexperienced, and they were poorly equipped. When they had a firearm at all, it was likely a musket—a poor answer to any question posed by a bushwacker packing four Colt revolvers. And nearly half of his troops had been transferred to General Grant's Vicksburg campaign, leaving him outnumbered, as well.

But all of these were details. Ewing's biggest problem with Quantrill and the others like him was he could not find them. There is a hill on Interstate 70 between St. Louis and Columbia. Cresting it in August, the westbound driver sees a ribbon of highway bordered by belts of ash and sweet gum and hackberry and elm whose canopies are as wide as the trees are tall and so thick no daylight strays there. Oak and sycamore join them, jostling for space. When I first saw it, I was reminded of the tale of the colonial squirrel that traveled from Philadelphia to the Mississippi River without touching the ground. During the civil war, the same trees covered bushwacker country. Missouri's great forests neither fed nor clothed these men; they had friends and family for that. But her towering trees and dense, summer thickets hid them, and that was enough.

Determined to harass the bushwackers from every direction, Ewing ordered the arrest of Missouri women suspected of spying for or aiding and abetting the Southern partisans. Nine were rounded up in early August and taken to the Thomas Building in Kansas City, a three-story brick structure at 15th and Grand. Solidly built in 1859, the building had only recently been the residence of its owner, George Caleb Bingham, the celebrated painter, who had added the third story for his studio. Among the women arrested were two of Bill Anderson's sisters. Mary Ellen was now sixteen; her younger sister, Josephine, was fourteen. Janie Anderson, the youngest of the Anderson girls at ten years, was not arrested. But as she had nowhere else to go, she accompanied her sisters. The nine Southern sympathizers were housed on the second floor.

The Cockerel House, which shared a common wall with the Thomas Building, had earlier been taken by General Ewing as a guardhouse for Union prisoners. The guards discovered that other women—women "of bad character and diseased"—were imprisoned in the cellar of the Thomas House, and it took them little time to cut large holes in the common cellar wall so they could get to them. Cut away with the plaster and rubble were the center-posts, leaving no support for the girders and floor joists of the Cockerel House. While the below-ground house of prostitution flourished, the stability of the adjoining structures declined.

It was August 10 when Quantrill called his own lieutenants and the leaders of the allied bushwacker bands to a council at his camp near Blue Springs. Bill Anderson was there; so was George Todd. Frank James—Jesse's older brother—and Cole Younger would arrive later. Over the next twenty-four hours, as Quantrill presented his ideas for an attack on Lawrence, Kansas, many of the men raised objections. Those opposed did not like the distance they would have to travel to get there, and they were convinced they would have to fight their way all the way back to Missouri.

But Quantrill was a teacher, and a planner. He had sent Fletch Taylor to Lawrence to spy on the town, and Taylor's report—offered the afternoon of August 11—was enticing. The Union troops under Lt. Hadley, posted in Lawrence to quiet rumors of a bushwacker attack, had been withdrawn when the attack never happened. Only two small military contingents were actually in the town—one white and one black. They were raw recruits, and neither group was armed, in deference to the municipal ordinance that prohibited firearms in the city! Taylor said the citizens were complacent. Finally, he said, the streets were wide and "ideal for charging horses!"

Quantrill had William Gregg speak next. Gregg remembered the Jennison raid of January 1862. He had arrived just as the redlegs had left, leaving thirteen burning houses. A year later, again winter and with snow on the ground, a different Kansas bunch had swept in on the Sanders place. They forced old Mrs. Sanders to cook them supper, burned her house down, then shot her husband. They rode to the Crawford place next, killing Uncle Jephthah. With the house burning down in front of his widow, they snatched the lace cap from her head and tossed it into the fire.

"How many of us," Gregg asked, "have been burned out and murdered by Lane and the others?" He went on: "Age makes no difference. Do you remember Henry Morris and how they killed him? Do you remember how old he was? Eleven!"

It was time to decide. Quantrill got up, walked deliberately to the front, then turned and looked at the men who sat and stood in small groups beneath the branches and leaves that were as important to them as their pistols.

"Lawrence is the great hotbed of abolitionism in Kansas," he said. "All the plunder stolen from Missouri—or at least the bulk of it—will be found stored away in Lawrence. And we can get more revenge . . . and more money . . . there than anywhere else."

They voted. It was unanimous. They would ride on Lawrence!

Two days later, perhaps pushed over by a steady wind, perhaps driven down by what we would now call a "microburst," the Cockerel House collapsed. As it sheared away from its neighbor, the Thomas Building, too, began to shake, its walls splitting one from another as window frames cracked and glass shattered. One guard scooped up two of the girls and carried them outside; another girl jumped out a window; another girl, thirteen years old, who had annoyed the guards earlier that morning and had been shackled to a twelve-pound ball to keep her still, went down with the wreckage.

Dust lifted even higher by the heat of the August day obscured everything. Some of the girls who had been buried near the surface and who had managed to work themselves free stood up and cursed their captors. Then the bystanders heard fifteen-year-old Josephine Anderson—buried, unseen, but screaming—begging for someone to take the bricks off her head. She begged again and fell silent.

Josephine, along with three others, died. Mary Ellen, the oldest of the Anderson girls, was crippled and disfigured for life. Janie, only ten, was lifted out of the rubble with two broken legs . . . and a lacerated face.

Major Plumb, Ewing's Chief of Staff, arriving to find a crowd on the verge of riot, ordered his headquarter guard to fix bayonets.

The buildings' collapse was pivotal to historian Richard S. Brownlee. In his *Gray Ghosts of the Confederacy,* he notes the event cast a "shadow over the rest of the Civil War on the border" and fired the already-"ferocious hatred of the guerillas for the Union forces." Brownlee believes the deaths and injuries of these young girls—none older than twenty—"tore the last thin covering of mercy from the hearts of Quantrill's boys."

For Bill Anderson, Brownlee goes even further. He says:

> [F]rom this moment on, Bill Anderson . . . became insane . . . .
>
> —
>
> [B]ecause of the injury to his sisters, his attitude toward all men who supported or served the Union was that of a homicidal maniac.

Not even a week later, General Ewing issued Order No. 10. Its essential sentence read:

> The wives and children of known guerillas, and also women who are heads of families and are willfully engaged in aiding guerillas, will . . . remove out of this district and out of the State of Missouri forthwith.

Those who failed to remove “promptly” were to be sent “under escort” to Kansas City “for shipment south,” along with such clothes and necessary household furniture and provisions “as may be worth saving.”

One of the thousands of people forced to vacate their homes because of Order No. 10 and its companion, Order No. 11, was an eleven-year-old girl who later gave birth to the 33rd President of the United States, Harry S. Truman.

Quantrill did not attack Lawrence because of the August 13 building collapse, or because Order No. 10 was issued five days later. But these two events erased any doubt about the raid that may have lingered in the hearts and minds of the leaders. When they broke from their several camps the evening of August 18 and rode to the rendezvous on the Blackwater River, they were ready. Quantrill led 150 men; Bill Anderson brought his forty; Andy Blunt led one hundred more.

With sun-up on the 19th, what had become a column of horsemen four-abreast and nearly three football fields long swung west toward Lone Jack. The need to send scouts out in all directions slowed their pace, and they made only ten miles that day. But they arrived at the Potter place with plenty of light in the sky, and Quantrill told them to stand down, feed their horses, have supper, and wait for darkness. Once it came, he gathered the entire group. For the first time, he shared their destination with everyone: they were going to Lawrence.

"Boys," he said, "this is a hazardous ride." He told them there was a chance some of them would not make it back. "Hell," he said, "we could all be annihilated!" He gave everyone the chance to stay behind: "Any one of you has the right to stay here; no one will call you a coward." By ones and twos, a few men left. But when the column rode out into the night air, it was essentially intact.

Bushwacking demanded its own discipline, and the men and their horses moved smoothly and quietly out of Jackson County and south into Cass County. A number of men tied themselves to their saddles to make sure they did not fall off if they fell asleep. At dawn on the 20th, at the headwaters of the Grand River, just four miles from the Kansas border, they dismounted into the heavy timber and rested until afternoon.

When they moved out again at 3:30 p.m., they were almost immediately joined by Confederate Colonel John Holt and a hundred new recruits from northern Missouri. Quantrill had invited Holt to join him and "christen" his troops, and Holt was there to accept the invitation. Soon after that, another fifty or so farmers and townspeople from Bates and Cass Counties brought the total to 450 mounted men, the largest partisan force ever assembled under one command during the Civil War.

Even more alert now as it crossed the Kansas line, the column eased into Squiresville, then a rest stop on the road from Olathe to Kansas City, arriving near sundown. As the horses were fed, Quantrill pulled out and consulted his "death list," meticulously compiled from his own experiences and the input of various spies and informants. After dark, they moved again—following the Santa Fe Trail west to Spring Hill and then to Gardner. It was at Gardner that they left the broad, dirt roadway and urged their horses northwest onto much narrower paths toward Lawrence. Even Quantrill, who had once lived in Lawrence, was unsure of the way on the moonless night. And when the trail wound into the woods, it was pitch black. They therefore commandeered assistance from the Kansas settlers in their path. Several horsemen would surround the house and call for the owner. When he came out, they would insist that he guide them until the next house came into view. Then they would shoot him. They killed eight men in ten miles. Now close to Lawrence, they came upon Joseph Stone, who had had George Todd arrested in Kansas City at the beginning of the war. Not wanting to shoot him and risk a neighbor's racing to Lawrence with a warning, Todd beat him to death with his Sharp's carbine.

As Stone lived on the Little Wakarusa River, Quantrill became more comfortable with where he was. But it was still dark, so he seized a boy who lived on the Stone place and made him lead the column to Franklin, a small, pro-slavery community just four miles southeast of their target. The men walked their horses through the town. Then, with the sun backlighting the sky to the east, they saddled up and broke into a gallop that carried them to a ridge overlooking the abolitionist capital. Again, Quantrill sent out scouts. As he awaited their return, a few of the men became anxious, concerned they had lost the advantage of darkness and would be easy targets for 2,000 awakened citizens. Quantrill had not come this far to give up. Wheeling his horse to face the men muttering behind him, he stood in the stirrups and shouted, "You all can do as you please. As for me, I am going to Lawrence!" When he turned again and spurred his horse down the ridge, they followed him to a man.

The Wakarusa River crossing is said to have been a narrow, wooden bridge laid across limestone columns. Today, Fred Six will point it out to you, as the remains of it lie on his place. Once across the river, Quantrill continued along what is now Haskell Avenue, then swung northwest on a diagonal toward the town. The vengeance preceded the looting. The Reverend S. S. Snyder was sitting on a stool milking a cow at his farm east of town. Two riders peeled away from the column, rode through his gate, and shot him dead.

They would not catch up to the main body, as Quantrill had begun to divide it into smaller groups in keeping with the military organization of his attack. Holt rushed his pickets to the east while Blunt galloped west. Eleven men rode to the top of Mount Oread, where they could look north across the Kansas River for the approach of Union cavalry from Ft. Leavenworth.

They were now on 11th Street, just north of South Park. With his pickets in place, Quantrill divided them into four companies, one each for Vermont, Massachusetts, New Hampshire, and Rhode Island Streets. That was the last bit of order imposed on the men that morning, for their blood was up and their horses were rearing.

Gregg knew the location of the white recruits. It was barely daybreak, and they were still asleep just north of Tenth Street between Massachusetts and New Hampshire. Nearly a hundred bushwackers road over and through the tents, trampling the young men who did not move, shooting those who did. Seventeen of the twenty-two were killed; all of the rest were wounded.

The next target was the nearby 2nd Colored Regiment. But these recruits had heard the noise of the other attack and fled.

Quantrill had once lived in Lawrence, and he chose Massachusetts Street for himself. Fletch Taylor had been right–it was ideal. If there were a moment in time when these killers looked their best, it was while galloping their excellent horses. One Lawrence resident remembered them as she might have remembered a Remington painting:

"The horsemanship of the guerillas was perfect. They rode with that ease and abandon which are acquired only by a life spent in the saddle amid desperate scenes. Their horses scarcely seemed to touch the ground, and the riders sat upon them with bodies erect and arms perfectly free with revolvers on full cock, shooting at every house and man they passed, and yelling like demons at every bound."

The mayhem of the morning was interrupted only a moment later, when Quantrill reached the Eldridge House. What stopped the riders was the hotel's wildly-ringing gong. The Eldridge was a tall, brick building affording excellent firing ports for pistols and long guns. Not yet drunk enough to be careless, the Missourians reined their horses . . . and waited.

Captain Alexander Banks, the provost marshal of Kansas, was a guest in the hotel that morning. Immediately aware of what was happening, he pulled the sheet off his bed and waved it out the window, calling for Quantrill. Quantrill obliged. Riding forward on the gelding surrendered to him by the Union commander after the Battle of Independence, he was the picture book bushwacker—brown woolen shirt with needlework provided by a lady admirer, pants pushed into his boots, a soft hat, and four Colt revolvers stuck in his belt. His only distinctions were the gold cord he wore in place of a hat band and the fact that his boots were of the knee-high, belting-leather variety favored by cavalry officers.

Banks had reached the front door, and he called his question down to the street as though he did not know the answer:

"What is your object in coming to Lawrence?"

"Plunder," Quantrill answered.

"We are defenseless and at your mercy," Banks continued. "The house is surrendered, but we demand protection for the inmates."

Though Quantrill agreed to the terms, he had not come just for plunder; he had a different fate in mind for the other men of Lawrence. As he spun his horse to face his riders he shouted:

"Kill! Kill and you will make no mistake! Lawrence should be thoroughly cleansed, and the only way to cleanse it is to kill! Kill!"

Many businesses were blazing as the last of the Eldridge "inmates" moved outside. The hated Lawrence newspapers—the *Republican* and the *Kansas Tribune*—had been marked early. The saloons were also marked and broken into. One of the early drunks was Larkin Skaggs, a Baptist preacher-turned bushwacker. The Reverend Skaggs cut down a large American flag, tied it to the tail of his horse, and raced up and down Massachusetts—turning and jumping the animal so that the red, white, and blue cut furrows in the deep dust of the street.

Quantrill's order that women and children were to be spared required the clearing of many homes before they could be burned. Dr. Jerome Griswold, a newlywed, ran a boardinghouse. His renters included the Honorable S.M. Thorpe, a Kansas State Senator, and two other newly-married couples, Mr. and Mrs. Trask and Mr. and Mrs. Baker. Baker was a grocer; Trask was the editor of another Lawrence paper, the *State Journal.* Stepping onto the porch to investigate the noise, Trask saw five bushwackers ride through the gate, level their pistols, and demand the house be surrendered. Trask agreed to do that so long as the women and children would not be harmed. One of the riders replied:

"They will not be. We have come to burn Lawrence. If we can help it, we don't want to harm any of you. If the citizens make us no trouble, they will receive no harm."

He went on:

"You and the other men will be moved from here to join the others, until we do what we came for. Then you can all go free."

Trask went inside and brought everyone out with him. The men were immediately robbed, then marched single file toward Massachusetts Street. Riders joined each one, cursing them for moving so slowly, and when the pace of the prisoners did not change, they shot them. Like the others, Trask's warder carried two braces of pistols. When he cocked one and pulled the trigger, the misfire allowed the newspaperman to run. But he rode Trask down in a moment and shot him with a different Colt, touching his left ear before blowing the right side of his head off.

The wives who had watched all of this from the porch and had tried to go to their dead and dying husbands were driven back with threats and obscenities, then robbed. Mrs. Trask, married only a few months, pleaded to keep her wedding band. But that conversation was not pleasing to the rebel leader, who reached out from his saddle, grabbed her hand, slammed it to the porch post, and yanked the gold ring free.

Quantrill's men made a good effort at burning everything. They burned the county courthouse and all of its records. They burned the Simpson Brothers' bank and the Johnson House Hotel. Colonel Eldridge, who gave his name to his own hotel, also owned a clothing store. Wanting access to the store's imposing safe, the raiders directed one of the two young clerks to get the key from Eldridge's partner, which he did. The bushwackers emptied the safe, forced the clerks to fit them with new clothes, then killed them both before setting the store ablaze.

John Speer, the publisher of the *Kansas Tribune*, was a name on Quantrill's death list. When the bushwackers came for him at his home well east of town he was hidden in the undergrowth with his younger children, and he survived. But his three sons had worked at the paper so late the evening of the 20th that they bunked with friends and apprentices in town rather than walk home.

"Billy" Speer, fifteen, had stayed in the liquor store with his friend, Charles Prentice. They hid in the back of the store when they heard the gunfire, and that worked for a moment. When they heard the bushwackers trying to batter down the front door, they went out the back and crawled beneath the building. While the raiders inventoried the booze, the boys lay motionless beneath the floorboards. When the drinking was finished and the building was set on fire, the two boys crawled up into the street. Billy was accosted as soon as he stood up, the man demanding his name. "William . . . Smith" he replied. As there was no "William Smith" on the death list, he was released to take care of the horses. Billy's agreeing to hold the bushwackers' mounts while they looted the town almost certainly saved his life.

But Billy used up all the luck there was for the Speer boys that morning. Robert, seventeen, and his friend had spent the night at the *Republican* offices. The two did not escape their building, and the fire that roared through foolscap and ink burned so hot no human remains were ever found. Still, no remains allowed a desperate hope for Robert's mother, who set a place for him at dinner every day until she died.

At thirteen, John was the youngest of the Speer boys. He had spent the night at the *Tribune* with Mr. Murdock, the printer. When they heard the alarm, Murdock climbed down into a well and survived. John set off for home to protect his family. He had barely crossed the street when Larkin Skaggs, the same Baptist preacher who had dragged the flag down Massachusetts, pulled his horse up in front of him. Less gay now, but more drunk, Skaggs demanded John's money. John gave him what he had. It wasn't enough for Skaggs, so he shot him in the back of the neck and rode away.

John Speer did not die from that gunshot wound. With the synapses that controlled his arms and legs firing for the last time, he stumbled to one of the hundred houses ignited by the raiders and collapsed, paralyzed. The bushwacker who had set fire to the house and who was now staring at young John Speer was Bill Anderson. With nothing better to do right then, Anderson was quietly calculating how long it would take the flames to reach the boy. John begged him: "Move me, please! I will die anyway, but I don't want to be burned alive!" Anderson thought about that for a moment, then reached out his boot and rolled the boy toward the house. But John's screams finally became annoying, so Anderson put his pistol to the back of the boy's head and quieted them.

Atop Quantrill's death list was "James Henry Lane"—U.S. Senator, protector of Abraham Lincoln in the opening weeks of the war, and head jayhawker. Quantrill, who considered Lane a murderer and a thief, intended to capture him, haul him back to Independence, Missouri, and hang him in the courthouse square.

At the first note of early-morning gunfire, Lane raced out of bed to the front of his house, where he wrenched the nameplate off the door. Barefoot and wearing only a nightshirt, he reversed course and ran through the back door and out into a cornfield, then west through more fields until he came to a ravine in what is now Old West Lawrence. He hid there for a while, then headed farther west to a farmhouse, where he borrowed clothes. Walking still farther west, he reached another farm, borrowed a plow horse, and rode off bareback to warn the rural residents and organize a posse. Lane did form a posse, and he did ride back into town, but the bushwackers were long gone.

While Mr. Lane was making his escape to the west, his beautiful wife was left to entertain the visitors in their new home. In the parlor was her piano. Her husband had stolen it in Missouri, along with the wagon he used to haul it back to Kansas. Despite its provenance, she was fond of it. In deference to her charms and her cordial conversation, the bushwackers had saved other prized possessions from the fire they had set to the house, and they tried mightily to save the piano. But they were too drunk, and the ivory keys went up with the draperies.

Quantrill had witnessed much of the goings on at the Lane home. At the end, he extended his courtesies to Mrs. Lane and to her husband, although not without a wisp of sarcasm: “Give Mr. Lane my compliments,” he said. “Please say I would be glad to meet him.”

Mrs. Lane replied in kind: "Mr. Lane would be glad to meet you, as well, but under more favorable circumstances."

Shortly after 9:00 a.m., Quantrill's Mt. Oread pickets reported they had seen the dust of a mounted force in the distance, north of the river. Knowing that had to be Union cavalry, Quantrill sent word the men should form up at the south end of town. But Larkin Skaggs, still drunk and determined to finish some of his own business downtown, rode the other direction. The alcohol had overtaken him when he was overtaken by a party chasing Quantrill, which drove him southeast toward Eudora. He was finally blocked, knocked from his horse, disarmed, and herded back toward Lawrence. Skaggs was near the Speer house when he broke free and ran toward the young man sitting on the porch. Vengeance, as it turned out, was not reserved that morning for the bushwackers. Billy Speer had made it home and was sitting on his porch with a musket in his lap. When Skaggs was ten feet away, Billy put its stock to his cheek and dropped him.

There were others racing to catch Quantrill who came upon Skaggs at that moment. White Turkey, a Delaware, drew his bow, shot Skaggs in the chest with an arrow, then scalped him. Others hung him from a tree in front of a growing band of Kansans who threw stones and fired bullets until their arms were tired.

Next morning, Skaggs' body was cut down by recruits from the colored regiment and dragged behind a horse, just as Skaggs had dragged the Union's colors behind his. And when his clothes and his skin had been worn away, Larkin Skaggs was thrown into a ravine and set on fire, his bones left for the feral pigs and the coyotes.

Bill Anderson had been busy that August morning. When the Missourians vied with each other over who had killed the most men in Lawrence, Anderson won—with fourteen. Wanting to keep a record of that, he found a silk cord and tied fourteen knots in it, then joined the ends and wore it around his neck. Anderson liked the cord, and the number would grow—to fifty-three. Along the way to that number was not just killing. Added, but without knots of their own, were robbery and rape and the mutilation of his victims.

"Earn it!" is a common watchword for sports teams, professional organizations, and individuals. Some deeds will earn the individual a nickname, even one for posterity. During this same war, Thomas Jackson became "Stonewall."

At Centralia, Missouri, on September 27, 1864, Bill Anderson earned his nickname. After blocking a train and murdering the Union troops it carried, Anderson ambushed and massacred the three companies of the 39th Missouri Infantry who had come to relieve the train. When Anderson and his men rode away that afternoon, the soldiers of the 39th lay naked, staked to the ground with their own bayonets. Some of the bodies had been scalped and had no hair; some had no eyes, or ears, or noses. The heads that had not been pounded into mush had been cut off altogether, then placed like Halloween jack-o'-lanterns on fence posts and tree stumps. If the head on the body were intact, it most likely belonged to someone else.

Counting those taken from the train, Anderson and his men killed 146 soldiers and three civilians in Centralia—a tally only just shy of what he and Quantrill had run up in Lawrence the year before. William Clarke Quantrill was seldom called anything other than "Quantrill" or "chief." But after that September day in Centralia, Anderson was "Bloody Bill."

According to the list published each year by the *Lawrence Journal World* in its Memorial Day edition, the August 21, 1863 raid killed 161 men and boys: seventeen recruits from the 14th Kansas Cavalry and 144 civilians. We'll call it 162, as the *Journal World* 's list does not include young Robert Speer, whose remains were never found.

END

The winter sun had fallen behind clouds newly arrived over Allen Fieldhouse and the campus lights had just come on when Richie turned the last page and closed the binder. That there was no one to talk to was just as well; he had nothing to say. He stood up from the table and walked to the west windows and looked out at the clouds and at the sunset just ducking out from beneath them. People had recovered from Quantrill, and from Bill Anderson; the entire country had made it past the Civil War. Richie felt terrible, nearly sick. But he was unwilling to resign himself to those feelings when he knew the families who had lost their husbands and their sons had survived that time more than 150 years ago. He stood at the window for another few minutes, watching the sun flash orange and then red and then disappear. Then he walked back to the table and placed the binder in his backpack as though it were the host remaining after a Sunday-morning mass. As he walked out into the cold January night and as the entrance door closed behind him, he thanked Mr. Anschutz for his library, for its quiet, and for the white-washed purity of its space.

“Pillow Talk”: Utah

H*ey, Richie. You OK?*

The question came from Richie’s roommate Billy Nixon. It wasn’t all that late really—not even midnight. The Utah game had finished at 9:00 and they had come back to the hotel in downtown Salt Lake City, had the team meeting, showered, and eaten something light before Richie had peeled off to start on the last of his homework. He had finished that and was just walking into their hotel room when the light came on; Billy was already in bed.

“I think so,” began the freshman. “Yeah. Yeah—I’m OK. I’ll be fine.”

Richie closed the door behind him and made his way to the desk, where he placed his backpack next to his water bottle and cell phone. Missing the soft sound of a head falling back against a pillow as he moved to the bathroom, Richie continued to talk from there.

“I know Coach is a defense-first guy, and I know I missed that first read, and I know I was late to help right after that. And I can get coming out. But coming out for the whole game?!” Richie was now brushing his teeth—but still talking.

"And I could have helped the second half. We were only down a couple at three minutes, and nobody was making anything, and Utah's guards were both 6'1", and if I had made a three then we would have been ahead. But no! I was stuck near the end of the bench and all I got to do was watch us lose to a team we should have handled easily. What's the point of that?!"

Richie rinsed the toothpaste out of his mouth, turned off the bathroom light, and came back into the still-lighted bedroom. His roommate, who had taken the bed next to the window, had his back to Richie and was sound asleep.

When he sat down on his own bed Richie was facing the bathroom, so he had to pivot and lean across the bed in order to turn off the lamp. Billy was snoring now. Unable to keep from smiling, Richie shook his head. "Night, Billy," he said to himself. "See you tomorrow."

Missouri

The Jayhawks' basketball rivalry with Missouri had been one of the most ferocious in college basketball. But when Mizzou bolted for the SEC, that was too much for the KU faithful. Some—the extreme partisans—were content never to say the word "Missouri" again, much less play them. Gene Bennett was close to that camp: he could not have cared less whether his ball club played the Tigers and he was open about it to the media and to anyone else who cared to listen. But the media has its own dollar-driven agenda, and years of pressure finally forced a format Bennett felt he had to say "yes" to. They would play on a neutral court, the T-Mobile Arena in Kansas City; and they would play for charity. They would also play for a nationwide television audience.

The Mizzou backers said they wanted the game, and maybe they did. But just as it had been years since Missouri had played Kansas, so had it been years since Missouri's basketball team had played competitively against anyone. Even in its early years in the SEC, when "Power Five" applied only to football and not to a basketball conference that might have been called "Kentucky, Florida, and the Dozen Dwarfs," Missouri was only average. Then, as schools like South Carolina and Tennessee and Arkansas and Alabama hired new coaches and developed strong programs, and as Auburn came out of nowhere to become a national power, Missouri failed to keep pace. That was the Mizzou squad that would play the Jayhawks in Kansas City.

Kansas was as amped up to start the game as Coach Bennett could have hoped and as Coach Fambrough might have wished. The scoring opened quickly at 3-0 when the Jayhawks controlled the tip and Billy Nixon found Richie Armstrong—a surprise starter—alone in the corner. Bam! From there it was 10-2, 18-5, 27-10, and 35-15—the last eight points coming from two more threes from Armstrong and the dunk born out of the slick, behind-the-back pass from Nixon to Thomas Williams. But the Hawks weren't done yet, and neither was Armstrong. Feeling the hot hand, Richie took three more passes from his roommate and made three more from deep. When Kansas ran to their locker room it was 50-22.

The second half wasn't much better for the Tigers, and Gene Bennett had his non-scholarship players on the floor with six minutes to go. Having sat him for nearly ten minutes, the coach put Richie back in only because one of the assistants told him one more three–pointer would give his freshman sharpshooter a personal high for the season. He already had twenty-three points, and he had had twenty-five against K-State in Manhattan. Coach Bennett waived his point guard over and told him to give Richie the next shot.

The time remaining had just rolled past the two-minute mark, the Jayhawks were up 40 at 97-57, and Richie knew they were nearing the time when his coach would not want anybody to shoot, personal best or not. He grabbed the rebound off a long Missouri miss and underhanded the ball to his point guard as he sprinted up the court to a spot on the far side of the Kansas bench, just even with the free-throw line. Missouri had covered him casually all game long and nothing changed on this possession; the only people paying attention to him were the Kansas fans in the front row and the Rock Chalk Dancers under the basket. The Kansas point guard had been taking his time, but as the shot clock passed ten seconds he got the ball to Richie and set a screen against the possibility that anyone from Mizzou would care. Richie faked the base line, dribbled left, and went up.

Good shooters will tell you they know whether a shot is true when it leaves their hand. Ritchie had two thoughts—images, really. The first, a number, was immediate: "26." He was about to get a new personal best. The second pushed its way in as the ball reached the top of its arc and fell across the lower-level suites toward the north basket. The backboard became a dining room table in an old home in Lawrence and the basket became a chair—one that had been empty for a long, long time. Richie was glad to fill it.

Walking Farieh Home

Just shy of 7:00 on a cold Friday evening in January, Richie stood directly across the street from WheatFields and just in front of the two drive-through lanes of the bank. He was wearing his new Adidas basketball shoes, his new jeans, his new dayglow yellow North Face parka, and his KU ball cap—also new. Only Massachusetts was more brightly lighted than Ninth and Vermont on a weekend night in Lawrence, and Richie was as inconspicuous as a young giraffe might have been at Broadway and 42nd Street in New York City.

The people who ate their evening meal at WheatFields came early, and by 6:30 the tables in the back had started to clear. Farieh was expecting Richie. But she had made it clear she did want him waiting for her inside the bakery. "No matter how cold it is," she might have said. There was a reason for that. Richie did more than fidget or shift his weight as he tried to stand still. And as Richie could not stand still as he waited for Farieh, he paced.

The first time he came to pick her up at the end of the evening he came inside. He was twenty minutes early! So, he paced. He transited the now-empty glass display cases in three paces; four more steps returned him south to the cash register by the bread counter; five more in the opposite direction carried him past the main register to the soft drink dispenser on the far side of it. The pacing might not have distracted the remaining customers, who were seated farther away from the registers at the tables toward Ninth Street. But Richie also got bored. And when he had exhausted the retail front of the bakery he took off for the tables. His quizzical approach might have worked once or twice: tall, handsome, young man; almost certainly a student; most likely a KU basketball player; probably looking for the person he came to join for dinner. But the person Richie had come to join was still working—putting the paddles away and sorting the silverware for the next morning. So when Richie circled the center column past the bathrooms, moved past and between the tables, and smiled a goofy, self-conscious smile while saying nothing, then did it over and over . . . , people became uncomfortable. Farieh's friend Kaz was still working the main register; she saw the customers' discomfort, and she alerted Farieh she needed to talk with him.

Farieh saw Richie as soon as she reached the back of the bread rack. Even with her smaller steps, she covered the distance between the retail counters and the tables more quickly than he had. He was making perhaps his sixth trip around the center column when he looked up and saw Farieh right in front of him. For the first time in their relationship, Farieh reached out and touched him. But the touch was quick—to the sleeve of his parka, and it was anything but affectionate. With a barely muffled, "What on earth are you DOING?!" she pulled him away from the tables to the front of the bakery and out the door until they were standing on the sidewalk. "I will be done in five minutes, Richie," she said, hoping the irritation she felt would burn through the nearly sixteen inches of night air that separated her mouth from his ears. "Please wait for me outside the bakery!" Her dish towel had been in her other hand the entire time. She threw it over her shoulder, pushed open the glass door, and stormed back inside. That was the last time Richie had set foot inside WheatFields.

But this was a new night. Richie was again early, although only five minutes this time. And as he was as incapable of standing still while waiting for Farieh outside the bakery as he had been on the inside, he paced north to the 9th Street intersection, then south almost to the Congregational Church, then back to the bank; then he started over. Farieh left the bakery through the back door and had made it through the corner of the parking lot and nearly across Vermont before Richie saw her. When he did, he ran into the street to meet her, forcing her to grab his parka and use his momentum to pull him out of the path of the black-on-black GMC Yukon that had turned south off of Ninth and was coming right at him. Farieh had seen the big SUV; Richie had seen only Farieh.

Richie still seemed unaware of the Yukon when, with one breath, he managed: "How are you? How was work? How did your week go? Did you remember we play West Virginia tomorrow? Do you think you'll ever want to go to a game? I can get you tickets. I can get you two tickets if you want to bring someone. It's cold tonight. What do you want to do?"

Farieh heard her laughter before she felt it, and when she realized she was still holding Richie's parka she released the yellow fabric. She felt like a big sister, wondering whether her adorable, impetuous brother would ever grow up. She felt like an older woman, trying to make sense of this handsome, tall, impossibly-young man who so plainly adored her.

They left WheatFields and walked slowly west on 9th Street, past the bank and the hair salon. In short order they were nearly to the new pizza place that had replaced the laundromat at 9th and Mississippi. It was cold, and a surprising fog was settling down around them. Neither had said anything, and Farieh's imp—the one that lived not very deep within her—saw an opportunity.

"Are you this quiet with all the girls you go out with? I'm asking because we just walked past my street."

Richie's mind had been racing from one lame conversation candidate to another, discarding each as quickly as he came up with it. He was horrified at the reminder he had said nothing so far, and at the thought he might be turning a weekend outing with the most enchanting person he had ever met into a disaster of self-consciousness and stage fright. He became so focused on his dejectedness he kept walking rather than turning around, as he should have done. That too dawned on him too late, creating even more discouragement.

"I am so sorry!" burst out of him as he finally stopped. But he managed to lift his head enough to catch Farieh's as he turned back to the east, and her bemused smile and bright eyes restored him. Richie laughed at himself, Farieh laughed with him, and Richie so forgot himself he gushed, "You are so beautiful!" Then he apologized a second time, his crimson face the exclamation point.

They stood a moment just looking at one another before Farieh responded to him. Although her eyes were never anything less than green, they changed from a deep cold emerald sparkling in the light from the corner restaurant to something softer. "Richie, you are a charming young man. I am enjoying myself being with you, even if you are so quiet! But let me ask you to tell me about something you know about. Then you can talk about it as we walk up the hill.

"Do you like sports? You are tall. Do you play basketball?"

That silence had once again fallen into step beside her surprised Farieh, as she thought she had asked a perfect question for a young American male who was having trouble talking with a person of the opposite sex. For Richie, Farieh could as easily have asked whether he liked breathing. He could answer the questions; but tonight, they were as confounding to him as she was.

"Yes." He began as they transitioned from the flat of 9th Street to the hill that would lead them up to the campus and across it to Farieh's scholarship hall. "I like sports. I like all sports. But like most kids in Kansas, I narrowed the list as I got older, finally deciding on track and basketball because I could do them at different times during the school year. I guess I liked basketball more, and I started playing on an AAU team…"

Farieh interrupted. "What is 'an AAU team'?"

"It's a team that plays mostly in the summer when school isn't happening. They are privately funded, and the coaches select the players from a fairly wide area, often one that surrounds a large city. The team I played for, for example, was made up mostly of kids from Kansas City. Because an AAU team isn't limited to the kids from a single high school, or even the same city, they tend to be very good."

"But you lived in Salina," Farieh said. "How did you participate on a team from Kansas City? Did you drive all that way yourself?"

"Mostly it was my grandfather. He loved basketball. He loved watching me play and he didn't mind the driving so he took me to the practices and the games."

"I interrupted you," she said. "Please go back to liking basketball more."

"In a way track is a team sport, and in a way it isn't. My events were what they called 'sprint' events—the 100- and 200-meter dash. When I competed in them, especially in large meets, I was the only person from my school who was running; the other kids were from different schools. So even though I was part of a track *team*, and even though everyone's score in all of the events would be added up at the end of the meet to make a *team* score, the actual competition was individual. I was running alone against kids from other schools who were also running alone."

"Were you . . . what is the word for 'speed' in track? Were you 'fast'?"

"Yes," he said, "I was. I set the school records for both the 100 and 200 when I was a junior, and I had the fastest 200 in the state that spring."

"But you chose basketball." Farieh was clearly puzzled. "Why—when you were so successful with being fast?"

"I liked it better. Basketball is a team sport. There are always five players on the court for each team. And while a really good player can take over a game, that doesn't happen very often. It's the school that has the best team—whose players know each other the best and play together the best—that usually wins. Teams practice together. They study and learn plays together. They usually hang out together. When a teammate is having a bad game, the others can help out. And when you win, there is somebody right there to celebrate with. It's completely different than track."

"Oh," said Farieh. They had crested the hill and were walking past The Oread Hotel, whose street-level, stone-bordered terrace was barely visible in the dark of the January night. "Are you being successful in basketball, too?"

Except on game days, when it was hard to avoid, Richie did not measure himself according to his three-point percentage. He was proud to be a part of the KU team and he loved being a part of the KU basketball family—his mom had been right about that. But he was a freshman. While he hadn't been asked to red-shirt, neither was he playing thirty-eight minutes a game like his roommate. He had played in every game so far, he had made one big shot to win the game against Kentucky, and he hoped he would make the eight-man rotation that coach would choose for crunch time in the conference race. But he was unable to look far enough past his own situation to gauge his progress against the thousands of freshmen playing for schools that weren't ranked number three in the country. And for Farieh, whose general knowledge of sports and whose specific knowledge of KU basketball were no clearer than the fog-wrapped student union straight down the sidewalk, he was unable to translate "red-shirt" and "eight-man rotation" and "Kentucky game" into terms that either did or did not stand for "success."

"I think so," he answered. "I hope so, anyway."

Farieh's desire to be supportive made her overlook the ambiguity that was there in Richie's answer, so she said, "That's wonderful!"

They were quiet again as they passed Dyche Hall.

"Do you like Danforth?" Farieh asked the question as they stepped down from the curb and moved across Jayhawk Boulevard toward the brown-stone Gothic chapel with its three arched windows that stood right in front of them.

Welcoming the soft-ball question, Richie said "Yes" quickly. Then, more comfortable than he had been since they had starting walking, he allowed himself to slip into an old habit and said the first thing that came to his mind: "I understand it's a terrific place for weddings."

Had there been a hole big enough he would have jumped into it in a Jayhawk minute. But there wasn't, so he walked the block that remained to Miller in silence. Farieh had to summon all of her core strength to suppress the giggles prompted by the flummoxed young man with his head down who was walking beside her.

Miller Hall's porch is protected from the night by a high chandelier. When they walked up the steps and got to the door and Farieh turned to face Richie, whatever illumination was provided by the light over their heads was an afterthought beside her smile. "Thank you for walking me home," she said. "If you would be willing to walk me home again sometime, Richie, I would like that very much." Then she turned and opened the door and let herself in.

The thirty-second clock had expired twice before Richie turned his face away. Beaming, he bounced down the steps and back toward Danforth Chapel.

Julius Nelson

Tom Erickson walked into the Philosophy Department office like he was walking back in time. Julius Nelson, the current department chair, loved the plaster-of-Paris copies of the busts of the ancient philosophers that had been purchased a century ago by what was then the "Classics" department; he had saved them when Philosophy moved from its old spaces in Lippincott Hall to the ones it currently occupied in Wescoe.

Lippincott was the most formal of the classroom buildings on Jayhawk Boulevard, its four large columns supporting four elaborate, Corinthian capitals that in turn supported the pediment. In Lippincott, the ancients had peered out from right-sized alcoves created for their comfort on all three floors of the building. But they felt especially at home in the high-ceilinged library that was straight up the double stairs. In Wescoe, a child of the '70s, they were strewn about a small entry space that had to accommodate a receptionist, mailboxes for the faculty and staff, a Danish-modern sofa, not-quite-matching chairs, and a tile-topped coffee table whose mosaics may have been fired at the time of Cicero.

"Is Professor Nelson in?"

Tom knew Julie, the receptionist; he was a philosophy major, after all, and had been here many times. He was at ease, his tone was friendly, his manner off-hand.

But Julie was ever-professional, ever-crisp. "Is he expecting you?"

"I hope so," said Tom. "It's his invitation."

"I will inquire," said Julie, removing her glasses. She placed them in the center of her desk, stood up, brushed between the desk and Tom—nearly toppling Socrates—and disappeared behind the stack of boxes at the corner. She was back in a moment.

"He will see you," she said.

Still standing, Tom turned slightly, thanked her, and moved into to the narrow hallway that Julie had just emerged from.

Professor Nelson was a different kind of crisp. And, in a way few receptionists could ever be, he was formidable. But unlike his receptionist he could also be charming. He heard Tom's approach and boomed a "Tom, come in!" before Tom had even appeared outside the doorway. Tom had barely crossed the threshold when Nelson boomed again: "Sit! Sit! How good to see you, Tom."

There were two large, tufted leather chairs directly in front of the massive partner's desk, and Tom chose the closer one.

Nelson was up on his feet almost immediately, moving to the door Tom had just walked through. "Mind if I give us some privacy?" It was not a question. Professor Nelson closed the door firmly but quietly, then returned to his own chair behind the desk.

"You were good to come, Tom. I have two matters for you, one dependent upon the other, as it were."

As Tom had no idea why he was summoned to meet with Nelson, he said nothing—only smiled and nodded slightly.

"Do you recognize this?" Nelson asked as he reached a small, stiff piece of paper across the broad desk. Tom took it and looked at it intently, as though it were a business card handed to him by a visiting professor from Japan. It looked like a business card because it was a business card—Tom's business card. It was blank on the back. On the front was the image of an old-fashioned quill pen resting in an ink bottle. Surrounding the image, in gleaming black letters, were these words:

Tom willed himself to stay still and to show only a moderate level of interest. In fact, he was on high alert.

Before he could make his own response, Professor Nelson helped him. "I found it attached to the mid-term paper of a student in my 230 class. I'm sure you remember it—Philosophy: The Greeks. You took it last spring. You were always prepared, brilliant in the discussions, and both your mid-term and your final were the top papers in the class." Nelson reached behind him, pulled a container of Sail tobacco off the lower shelf of the bookcase, and set it on the narrow ledge behind the desk. As he was looking down, prying open the top and making ready to push his briar pipe into it—only for the aromas of course and never to smoke it—he said as though to the person conning the sailboat across the front of the tin, "Do you like Richard Boone?" Then, the bowl of his pipe broadcasting one of the smells he liked best in the world, Nelson turned to Tom, put the stem of the pipe between his teeth, and smiled. For that moment, he looked like a campaign poster for Theodore Roosevelt. It was clear Nelson knew.

Tom Erickson was smart, he was articulate, and he could really write. While classmates who needed money worked behind the counter at Office Depot or, best case, hired on as research assistants, Tom made himself available to create lights-out papers for students too lazy or too busy or too dumb to write them themselves. He had done this a couple of times his freshman year for desperate friends at no cost. When he discovered there was a ready, rich market for his services, the gratis work ended and the marketing began.

It was Tom's uncle who had introduced him to a sophisticated western series about a lone-wolf gunman for hire that was produced at an unsophisticated time in American television. "Paladin," the main character played by Richard Boone, was best-in-class at everything he did. Whether it was poker at the back table of the saloon, a fist fight in the lobby of the hotel, or a shoot-out on Main Street, Paladin won—usually without breaking a sweat. He was tall, he had a full head of curly, black hair and a smart mustache, and he was athletic; he dressed in black with a black cowboy hat; he was debonair—living in San Francisco when he wasn't on the road; and he was a loner. But he was entirely comfortable being a loner. Tom could not get enough of the show and its lead.

Like everyone else who watched it, Tom was fascinated by Paladin's business card. In the upper center was the image of the knight from a chess set. Four words flanked the horse. Beneath that text and the image of the knight was additional language—name and location. Altogether, it looked like this:

Professor Nelson broke the short silence. "You are still a scholarship student, aren't you, Tom? The Summerfield, as I remember it." He put the pipe back in his mouth.

The Summerfield Scholarship was KU's top academic award, renewable for four years. It paid Tom's entire tuition, his books, and even a small stipend toward living expenses. Without it, Tom would not be at KU, sitting across this walnut desk from the chair of his own department, talking with the faculty member appointed just last week to be his major advisor.

All of this—the card his brain-dead client had forgotten to remove from the term paper when she turned it in, this eerily-cordial confab with Nelson, that proving Tom's academic code violation would be a lay-down, and the threat drawn back at his Summerfield Scholarship like an arrow drawn back from a compound bow—all of these pieces were related. But like the teeth of only one gear, they needed to be mated with the teeth of the other before work could be done. The pieces Nelson was holding fit against something, that was clear. But what?

"You know Professor Matthews, don't you Tom?"

Of course Tom knew Matthews. Every KU student knew Jacob Matthews. He was the Jerry Seinfeld of the lecture stage, the Beyoncé of the chalkboard. He was as handsome as he was geeky-smart, and he could be serious when he wasn't cracking everyone up with his crazy comparisons between today's rock stars and those of a different age. In his field, at least, and for the three hours each week he held court from his televised throne room at 205 Wescoe Hall, he was the mascot and the chancellor and the cheer squad and the men's basketball coach all rolled up into one.

But Professor Matthews was also the guy who gave him an "F" on a take-home mid-term for plagiarizing an obscure text on Sartre, resulting in his only "C" in a major course. Tom had found the article in the stacks behind the main reading room at Watson, the University's main library. Although nearly seventy years old, the article was insightful, and funny as hell. Tom liked philosophy;

he actually studied for his major courses. He was familiar with many of the reviews and other scholarly publications in the field, and he had never heard of this journal from a publishing house in Terre Haute. Maybe because he had had to blow the dust off of it before he could read it, Tom decided he was safe borrowing a paragraph or two, and so he did. Ultimately, Tom wove nearly three pages into his own mid-term. Confident it would be the top paper for the class, and maybe for the department that year (there was a prize for that), Tom turned it in and waited for the applause.

Tom still did not know how Matthews found out the paragraphs were stolen. But he remembered how Matthews had wordlessly presented him with his paper and the journal article—placing them oh-so-carefully on the table in the department's one conference room, side-by-side, like he was the head archivist at The Spencer Library and was allowing him the privilege of comparing two of its sacred texts. Matthews never said a word, and Tom finally left. That was a Tuesday.

He got the formal charge that he had violated the Honor Code on Wednesday. Anxious days had stretched into weeks, and he remembered the dread that had beaten back the pickets of his self-confidence. He remembered prostrating himself before the Director of the Honors Program, begging—yes, really begging—not to be dismissed from school and sent home. And he remembered being alone in his dorm room when he received the decision. He would be allowed to remain at KU—although on a tedious academic probation. When he got to the end of the letter and read he would be allowed to keep his Summerfield, he curled up on his bed and wept. Yes, he knew Matthews.

But Nelson had to be fully aware of the plagiarism episode. It happened to an Honors student in Nelson's own department, a student Nelson knew well from having him in his own classes. So, what was up with the phony naiveté about Matthews?

"I believe Professor Matthews' notoriety—his 'fame,' if you will—has become detrimental to our department. Highly detrimental." Nelson turned away for more tobacco, turned back to Tom, and continued. "I have talked with Professor Matthews about this, encouraging him to present lectures that are more scholarly and less . . . exciting." He paused. "Professor Matthews does not believe that is necessary."

"So, he said no?"

"Yes." Nelson was serious now, the twinkle faded from his brown eyes. "He did."

"What does this have to do with me?" Tom asked.

"You, Mr. Erickson, are the perfect instrument by which to bring Professor Matthews' feet back to terra firma. I have a plan in mind for that. If you are willing to join me in that plan, I will forget that Richard Boone has a twenty-first century acolyte here at KU."

They had finished their conversation soon after, Erickson had left his office, and Nelson watched him walk down the north-side steps of Wescoe Hall. As a department head he could do that—he had one of the few offices in the building that had a window looking out over the main entrance.

The main entrance had been uninspiring when first completed decades ago. But its struggles against weather and time and budgets had made it shabby, not just boring. The spalling concrete on the steps was spreading and Erickson had to jump a step to avoid what was becoming a pothole. Compromised building, compromised student, compromised teacher. Sun-bright visual images of the first two joined an image of the third that was steadily pushing out from the backrooms of Nelson's consciousness.

Julius Nelson looked like someone on a day trip from a nursing home. He was thin, he was balding, he was experimenting with a comb-over, and he had crescent moons of folded flesh beneath his eyes. But he was smart. Degrees from Williams College, where he studied classics, from the University of Pittsburgh, where he was introduced to philosophy, and from the

University of Michigan, where he received his Ph.D. in philosophy, spoke to that. He had made his way to Kansas years ago. Once at KU, he let seniority take him to department chair; once in charge, he had taken a slumbering philosophy department and kept it sleeping.

He was good with that. He had heard from a classmate at Pitt years ago that there were three stages to an academic's relationship with his college:

First stage: you are exhausted. There is endless hard work as you try to keep slightly ahead of your students. You have six to nine hours a week of class and you have the many hours of preparation that go with each hour at the blackboard.

Second stage: you are competing. You have a handle on the classes—they are the same as last year and the preparation for them requires less effort. You spend more time on your publications and your presentations to your academic conferences and less on your office hours as you push your way to tenure.

Third stage: you are stealing. You have tenure. As you are teaching the same classes from the same syllabuses, they no longer require any effort. You decreased your office hours even further. You are paid to host or co-host conferences, not to do the research and make the presentations.

When he first heard this, Julius Nelson laughed. Now he lived it.

Julius met his friends at the Union for coffee at 10:00 and for lunch from noon until 2:00. He was home by 4:30, where for the remainder of the day he had four tasks: (1) avoid "the wife," because she bored him and because she always wanted his help with something; (2) walk his Labrador retriever, "Moose," the best way to accomplish #1; (3) endure dinner with the same wife; and (4) retreat to his library. In the library, the door closed behind him, Nelson could spend the evening as he wished. Not with Aristotle or Aquinas or Kant or Hume, or even Marcuse or Sartre or Russell, whose volumes one encountered first upon entering—first three shelves on the right, shoulder height, directly in front of a curious visitor—but with Vidal and Nabokov and Updike and others whose language skills he appreciated and whose dalliances he appreciated even more. He was in bed each evening by 10:30, asleep three minutes later.

Once he became department chair, the fact that his classes did not fill quickly and sometimes did not fill at all did not bother him . . . until the arrival of Jacob Matthews. Recently, on those few occasions when Nelson heard himself speaking Matthews' name out loud, he would append "boy wonder" under his breath. Matthews was not only younger and irrefutably handsome, he was articulate and charismatic. When he came to Kansas, he almost immediately needed a larger space for his classes because the fire marshal would not accept students standing against the side and back walls. They moved him first from a tidy, thirty-seat classroom in "new" Fraser Hall. More than fifty years old at that point, it was still referred to that way in deference to its splendid predecessor.

The original Fraser Hall had been designed by John Haskell, a Brown University-trained architect who had worked in Boston before coming to Lawrence to join his father, one of the earliest members of the Emigrant Aid Society that had founded the town. Stone-clad and sited on the crest of the hill, "Old" Fraser had a length and breadth that would have been noteworthy without the twin towers that rose powerfully from its roofline. Red-roofed and supporting twin flag poles that extended their height even more dramatically, the large stone towers with their Victorian caps were an instant landmark, and soon after the very symbol of early KU. "Old" Fraser stood until the 1960s, when inattentive students—and even attentive ones—began to trip and fall trying to make their way along its oak floors, which had warped into waves the Navy ROTC cadets referred to as "Force 1." It was razed then, but it was never forgotten.

Matthews taught next in the auditorium at Dyche, a slope-floored gem of a space in another splendid old building, this one still housing the Natural History Museum built by the building's namesake a century ago. Matthews' seating capacity had increased six-fold; he lasted two semesters.

By then, Hoch Auditorium had been struck by lightning. The entire interior of the Gothic masterpiece that housed the university's main stage and the court where Clyde Lovellette had played basketball for the Jayhawks had burned in the fire that followed. But the limestone walls withstood the fire; and with unanticipated creativity, the university's architects placed three glorious teaching auditoria within them. Two seated 500; the largest 1,000. Asked which he wanted, Matthews took the largest—and filled it his first time out.

He did not keep it for long. Hoch was as expensive as it was magnificent, and the Provost insisted that departments teaching there pay the invoices for the lights and the heating, which he gladly forwarded. Philosophy, whose budget was nearly invisible in comparison with, say, electrical engineering, took the hint and moved Matthews to his current 200-seat classroom in Wescoe Hall. But he was allowed to film his classes for anyone who wanted to watch them in real time; and with the video feed, his audience raced past 1,000 to multiples of that.

Somewhere along the way, Nelson's resentment of the department's juvenile supernova overtook him. Most likely it was that moment at the beginning of last summer when Matthews was sitting in Nelson's office, meeting with his department chair over his teaching schedule for the coming academic year. Four times over the course of those thirty minutes, Julie Richterhoff, Nelson's AA, received "urgent" phone calls on the department's land line. Because each call was from a KU administrator whose seniority exceeded Nelson's, Julie was forced to interrupt the meeting each time. Every call was for Matthews.

Nelson brought himself back to the present. The foolishness of Erickson's client was heaven-sent; Tom Erickson would be the perfect foil for Matthews. Though younger, he was also articulate and charismatic. He loved debate. What it dealt with, what he was so good at, was advancing and contesting topics created for that moment. Nelson would make sure Erickson's topic and his preparation were up to the occasion. Though he projected a convincing, devil-may-care persona, Erickson was serious about one thing at least: he had something important to lose. Yes, this was the right time . . . , and Erickson was the right instrument.

K-State

ALLEN FIELDHOUSE FROM THE EAST

By: Sean Grogan
Lawrence, KS (AP)

I hadn't looked at the statue of Phog Allen that stands at the east entrance to Allen Fieldhouse for a while, so I walked that way first and then into the building and through the Hall of Fame. The video monitors were playing parts of Kansas' last conference game against Missouri, so I stopped and watched Thomas Robinson take a pass on the low block, move relentlessly around his man, and dunk the ball so quickly you nearly forgot how powerful he was. "We just don't have anybody like that this year," I said to myself as I moved past the I950s-era red jump circle from Hoch Auditorium and into the concession areas.

The video that is played before the Kansas players are announced is a moving part of the home game experience for me. Everyone sees Thomas Robinson, of course. But this time he's executing the greatest block in the history of AFH, then glowering at the camera as though he were tearing his shirt in two. It's a primal moment that reveals a determined young warrior. Watching the video, I had the same thought I had moments earlier in the Hall of Fame: "Where are we going to get that from this team?!"

K-State isn't Missouri. Kansas fans have never really hated the Wildcats like they hate the Tigers. But the in-state rivalry has had its moments, and we had some tonight.

FIRST HALF

This was the game the Hawks needed. They needed to play defense, they needed to stay with K-State on the glass, and they did both. Frank Agbani held the very dangerous Rodney Cooper to three points the first half. Kansas was aggressive throughout the first 20 minutes; the Wildcats' 29 points and their 18-point deficit were eloquent testimony to that. With three minutes to go, K-State was shooting 32% and had eight boards to the Jayhawks' 15. [The rebound margin would be 41-23 by game's end.]

The other thing KU needed Monday night was to make baskets. Kansas did that, too. Gene Bennett had inserted Richie Armstrong early, the freshman was soon on his way to 17 first-half points, and the KU break was working like everyone remembered it. Jeff closed the half with a slick drive down the lane and a left-handed give to Tommy Barnett, who rolled it in at the buzzer.

SECOND HALF

Gene Bennett opened the second half with an intriguing five—Thomas Williams, Luke Simpson, Richie Armstrong, Billy Nixon, and Jeff Hanson: both centers, both point guards, and the sharpshooter from Free State. KU took the ball to the north end and got it to Simpson, who was under the basket and had picked up a double-team. *Williams should be open,* I thought to myself, and he was—unaccompanied and moving down the lane. Luke got him the ball and Thomas flushed it, but not without major contact from Henry and Russell. The only person in the vicinity not to foul him was Staples, who had obliged every other time Williams had been open beneath the basket. When Thomas came down he had "that look" on his face, and all of a sudden he was doing the Thomas Robinson gesture—pretending to tear his jersey in half. Thomas Williams is not Thomas Robinson: he is not as powerful, he is not as fast, and he doesn't have Robinson's repertoire of moves to the hole. But when he gets pissed off as he did the second half—when K-State was mugging him beneath the basket on every KU possession—Thomas Williams can be a force to be reckoned with. Monday night he was wonderful, collecting a double-double [17 and 10] to go with his five blocks.

We were only a few minutes into the second period when the Wildcats served notice they had not yet left the building. Gene Bennett had put Armstrong on Will Staples, who had shot it well in the opening moments of the first half. Armstrong controlled Staples, but K-State's other guards went on a tear. McPherson, he of one-two-three points the first half, had nine more in the first four minutes of the second, 15 second-half points at the eight-minute mark, and would finish with 23 for the game. But KU withstood the K-State run by hustling and making their own shots. And KU won both halves, finishing at 83-62.

How did Kansas manage all of this in the wake of two tough losses, one the lamentable outing against TCU in Fort Worth? Allen Fieldhouse helped. The noise level hit 120 decibels just before the tip and the crowd kicked it higher than that in the second half. The Rock Chalk chant, which began right on cue with 1:30 left on the clock, rocked the rafters. We had much better guard play. Kansas, which had 11 assists in the game against Oklahoma, had 10 in the first half against K-State. A slumping Billy Nixon missed most of his shots. But he hustled and earned major style points chasing—and recovering—a loose ball in the second half. There was nobody more jacked at the end of the game than Billy. Frank Agbani plays big-time defense and is a wonderful athlete. He made a terrific put-back layup and, when he was not in foul trouble, neutered the guy in the purple jersey who had the bad luck to draw him. Williams got the KU all-time block record, was back in business prowling the paint, and made free throws. So did everyone else: the team finished 19 of 22! Tommy Barnett was full of energy and the beneficiary of several inside passes that resulted in layups or dunks. Collectively, Williams and Barnett and Agbani went for 40 points, 23 boards, and 6 blocks.

Jeff Hanson looked every bit the point guard of the very near future. He can get the ball across the timeline, he can shoot it, he can drive the lane, he can dish inside, and he can find the open guy on the wing and whip the ball out there. Jeff did all of that on his way to eight assists against one turnover, seven points, and two boards.

KU was tough under the basket, the Hawks hustled all night long, they made plays, and they played solid defense, especially that first half.

Did I mention that the Pop-Up Video featured young Mr. Armstrong? Who knew "Stretch" was his nickname and that Monday was his birthday? With a nudge from the pep band the crowd sang the birthday song to Richie, who liked it well enough to shoot 5-for-10 from behind the arc in the first half. His ability to make anything was remarkable, given the first-half clocking he took at the hands of Jordan Henry as he was just about to dunk the ball off a break. The refs finally reached consensus it was a Flagrant-1; the real issue was whether Richie would get up off the deck. But he did, he made both free throws, and he went 7-for-7 from the stripe for the evening. He has a very pretty stroke.

As the game was winding down and "R-o-c-k C-h-a-l-k, J-a-y H-a-w-k, K-U" was wafting up from the student section, Richie blew out the candles with his seventh three-pointer. That gave him 30 points for a game he didn't even start. Happy Birthday . . . , Stretch!

J'Accuse!

The student in the first row did not raise his hand but stood up instead. And as the quiet he had counted on spread around him, with even the students who had been taking notes on their laptops lowering their hands to their laps and raising their heads, he cleared his throat, jumped up on the stage to gain the same level as the teacher, lifted both arms to shoulder height, and fairly shouted.

"Grant! Grant! Grant! Why are we spending so much time on an out-of-date warmonger who sits on metal horses all over the country?"

Jake Matthews had anticipated a moment like this for more than a year, ever since the Chancellor had been shouted down at the Student Union as she tried to facilitate a discussion about the murder of the protester at the white supremacist rally in Charlottesville. He lowered his head, removed his glasses, looked up again, and asked, "Do you want to talk about monuments, or people?"

The student was Tom Erickson. Watching him enter and leave the classroom that semester, Jake had pegged him as a wise-cracking fraternity guy; he never imagined this kind of confrontation coming from this kid.

For his part, Erickson was certain he could feel a tremor in the room as he prepared to speak again. It was like a rift in the Force in a Star Wars movie—a subtle shift in power from one combatant to another. He couldn't help smiling. But he remembered to harden his face before it folded into a smirk and continued.

"Monuments. People. Both. Your hero Grant, who rides these horses, was a racist! We ought to tear them all down, just like we ought to tear down all of the monuments to Washington."

Jake knew the student's name, just as he knew the names of all his students. He answered, "Mr. Erickson, I am still uncertain where you are headed. Do you want me to respond to whether Grant was a racist, or to your comments about monuments?"

Erickson answered, "Let's start with the monuments, Professor Matthews."

"Professor" was delivered in distinct segments—one, two, three. "Matthews," enunciated as though it had a hyphen in the middle, made four, then five.

"Whose," Jake wanted to know, "Grant's or Washington's?"

"Let's take them in order. Let's start with Washington."

"OK," Jake responded. "Why should we tear down the Washington Monument?"

"Because Washington was a racist."

Jake countered quickly: "Why do you say that?"

Erickson feigned exasperation. "He was a slave owner, for God's sake! Surely even you know that. And so was your buddy Grant!"

But Erickson wasn't only talking. He had backed toward the chalkboard that dominated the stage. Glancing over his shoulder, he located the chalk, turned and picked it up, and then turned back to Matthews.

"But it isn't Grant's racism that infects this miserable classroom, Professor Matthews, or Washington's. It's Twain's."

With that, he turned back to the board and wrote out the N-word. He used the barrel of the chalk for depth, and he made the letters two feet high.

He stepped back to admire his workmanship, tossed the chalk toward the tray—it hit and stayed, of course, not bouncing to the floor, then executed a smart about-face and snarled a question:

"Do you know you are the only teacher at KU who assigns work that includes the N-word?!" He said the word next, out loud, and slowly. Then he added, "The only one?"

Huckleberry Finn had not been assigned. Nor *Tom Sawyer*. Had Erickson ever read the syllabus, he might have remembered that. In their place were the speeches and the essays and selected other writings. No one had been asked to read the N-word; no trigger warning had been necessary. The syllabus directed the students to the antics and the sarcasm and the hilarity, to be sure, but also to comments like this one from a letter Clemens had written to the dean of the Yale Law School, explaining his decision to pay the tuition for one of its first Black students:

> We have ground the manhood out of them, & the shame is ours, not theirs, & we should pay for it.

And this, from his posthumously-published, anti-war piece, "The War Prayer," written and titled in sarcasm:

> O Lord our God, help us to tear their soldiers to bloody shreds with our shells . . . to lay waste their humble homes with a hurricane of fire; help us to wring the hearts of their unoffending widows with unavailing grief; help us to turn them out rootless with little children to wander unfriended the wastes of their desolated land in rags and hunger and thirst . . . .

Only a few minutes had passed, but time enough for Jake's roll-over accident of two years ago to flash past, including the moment when his SUV had refused to steady itself and, at eighty miles per hour, had yielded to the downslope on the right. Flashing past as well was the crazy thought that had come to him as his left wheels lifted off the pavement: *This is not going to be good.*

Jake had that same thought now, and he was just as powerless to stop what came next. His blood was up; he knew he ought to be careful. But he could not take his eyes off the chalkboard, where some primitive creature dedicated to the death of scholarship and fair discourse had smeared hatred across the slate like it was the blood of Socrates.

Matthews shifted his gaze to his student.

"Have you ever written a book about race?" The question needed no answer, and Jake did not pause for one. Neither did he pause after any of the next questions, fired in a slow staccato like rifle shots at a military funeral:

- Have you favorably portrayed a slave in a novel—for the first time in American literature?
- Have you gone city to city, speaking at least occasionally about racism, either mocking it or condemning it directly?
- Have you published articles decrying war and the impact it has on people?
- Have you ever helped anyone who was dying, or his family, or his children? Whether or not he was a hero who, with Lincoln, had saved our nation?
- Any of these things?

It was fluorescent light that marked the stage. In that moment all of it seemed to draw into Jake's frame, pooling at the back of his head before it burst from his eyes upon his student. There was no sound. A BIC pen rolling off a desk would have been like an anvil let go from the ceiling.

"I'll take that as a 'No' . . . , MISTER Erickson."

The percussion came this time from Matthews' side of the stage. Jake enunciated each syllable of the student's name as though spitting out pieces of a spoiled stew.

"So, tell us," he said to the student, "**WHO** the **FUCK** are **YOU?!!!**"

Professor Matthews closed his notebook. "Class dismissed," he said, and left the stage.

Homa's Fountain

Farieh parked her sky-blue BMW convertible in Homa's driveway and sat for a moment, taking in the neighborhood. Two-story frame houses whose lawns bordered concrete driveways and their obligatory basketball goals ran east and west along the sidewalks. And while it was not yet 3:00 in the afternoon, Farieh could picture the same houses and driveways filled with noisy children once school was out. She unbuckled her seat belt, reached for her bag, and walked to the front of the house at 917 Legends Drive. Homa opened the front door before Farieh could knock.

"Farieh—how lovely to see you again. Please come in." Homa did not wear a head covering in her home, or anywhere else, and her shoulder-length auburn waves complemented Farieh's, whose equally-thick brown hair lay beneath her yellow head scarf.

Farieh stepped into the living room and immediately took in a low table covered with teacups and saucers, a teapot, glasses of water, and plates of dates and pistachios and cucumbers and yogurt and what looked exactly like gigantic chocolate-chip cookies. When the sweep of Farieh's gaze stopped on the cookies, Homa smiled. "Oh, yes, the cookies. My daughter's. When she left for college last fall I insisted she leave me the recipe. I can serve anything to our guests, it seems, and what they want to know about is the cookies!"

Homa sat down, gesturing that Farieh should do so as well. When Farieh had taken her seat, Homa continued. "How is school? I heard you were successful in completing your math degree by examination. Congratulations! And when we first talked last year, you had become excited about history, and English literature. How are those classes coming?"

Farieh had been taken with Homa's warmth last fall at a meeting of the KU Persian Student Association; now she was taken with her memory. That was six months ago. Farieh had been as lonely then as any of the other freshmen foreign students; she missed Iran, and she went to the meeting because she felt she was supposed to check in there. But Farieh had quickly become enthralled with the Honors Program, the Honors Program had as quickly become enthralled with her, and she had not been back. She remembered Homa, though. One of the Association's advisors, Homa had hosted the meeting, and Farieh felt like she had been reunited with an aunt who had moved to the United States years before. This semester, when it became apparent her relationship with Richie was moving past the very casual toward something more than that, Farieh felt the need to talk with a mature woman of her own culture and get some guidance. She still had Homa's card. Homa seemed perfect, and she had called her.

She and Homa talked about Professor Helen Lochlear, and how the excitement Farieh had experienced in her Honors Seminar had expanded this semester in her literature classes. They talked about French revolutionary history and how exciting it was for Farieh to speak French with the professor and several of the other students in the class. And then they seemed to bog down. Homa had picked up the plate of the cookies, and when she offered them to her guest she asked, "Why don't you pick the one you like, and then we can go out into the garden? It's winter now, but it has its own charm in winter."

Homa led her across the driveway to the far edge of the garage and the crushed-stone walkway edged with sandstone that carried them around the corner. The walkway bordered the windowless east wall of the garage and, in the spring, disappeared into a wall of ebullient forsythia. Now, the branches bare, the forsythian wall was easily seen as the right-angled entrance to the garden that lay behind the house and took up the entire back yard.

There was no high wall around Homa's garden as there was around the garden Farieh knew so well in Iran; Homa's husband Amir had not built one. Even in high summer, the many shrubs and decorative trees Amir had planted around the perimeter were not quite mature enough to shield the interior from the neighbors, as they would be later. But the openness did not make Homa's garden any less lovely.

Farieh remembered the fountain in the center: cut stone, laid up by a fine stone mason, and large. The center tower was eight feet tall and the rim of the circular basin, fifteen feet in diameter and fully three feet high, was faced with panels of cut stone and bronze. A thin sheet of ice at the bottom of the basin was shining back against the winter sun. The narrow ring of sandstone that circled the basin was in turn encircled by the crushed stone walkway that had brought them into the garden. Now six feet wide, it branched off into narrower pathways that took visitors out into the garden's many plantings. Remembering her visit in the fall, Farieh had unconsciously separated herself from Homa as she approached the fountain in order to return to the garden's southwest corner, which Amir had filled with maples—both the Japanese maple and the "October Glory" and "Red Sunset" varieties of the American tree. Red oaks and crab apples, whose red berries had glowed like holiday lights in the glare of that afternoon sun, and grape vines whose dusty orange leaves guarded the fruit Amir was saving for ice wine had filled out the space. Farieh remembered how she had gotten lost in thoughts of her family's own compound in Tehran and the garden it too concealed from the street in front, and how she might have wandered the autumn walkways until dark had Homa not called for her to return to the meeting. Homa was calling again now, this time her gentle intrusion reminding it was cold and that neither of them had thought to bring a jacket.

Inside, Homa allowed Farieh to settle into her chair before continuing their conversation. "My husband and I have lived in the United States for a long time, and we are citizens here. When he asked whether we might add a garden to our backyard, I responded like my American friends would have responded, wondering whether we would plant sweet corn as well as tomatoes! Even when he showed me the plans, I confess I was so busy with my teaching it did not register what he had in mind. But he has a beautiful soul, and he misses Iran as much as I do, and he has created something that brings me joy every time I walk into it."

"But," Homa paused only a moment to refill their cups. "You did not come here to see my garden or to eat my daughter's cookies. What is on your mind?"

Farieh took a long sip of the tea, staring into the cup as she did so, then looked up. "It's a boy. His name is Richie Armstrong, and he's a basketball player. He is very tall—much taller than me. And he appears to be very successful even though he's only a freshman member of the team. He has brown hair and brown eyes, he is very handsome, and he is smart—he's in the Honors Program. He follows me around like a new puppy! And even though he can be—What is the American expression?—goofy when he wants to say something sweet or act affectionately, he is still so very cute when he does that.

He came into WheatFields the day before Thanksgiving to pick up bread for his mother. After that, he came in time after time to buy the same bread—I have no idea what he did with all of it! And then he asked my name, and whether he could walk me home after work. I have said 'Yes' to the walks, and they have been fun for me, even when he goes off into his goofiness.

I know he is working himself up to asking me on a real date. I don't know that a real date is a good idea for me, but I do enjoy being with him. A real date for him will involve pizza or tacos, which everybody likes but me, and a crowd of young people who are drinking beer and fighting for his attention. And I know it's selfish of me not to want that, but I don't want that. I would like to go on a date with him and I want him to be just for me. Is that horrible?" Farieh looked down into her tea again and waited for Homa's rescue.

Homa was flattered this capable young woman would consider coming to her with these questions. She was even more impressed that she had done so. Seeking out the counsel of an older person in matters as important as these is what Homa and Amir had taught their own daughter to do. And on occasion, she had done it! She put her teacup on the table and reached across it to take Farieh's hand.

"You are a lovely, confident young woman who has managed an unusual relationship very skillfully, I think." She allowed Farieh's hand to fall back onto her blue jeans, looked at her softly, then went on. "And now you are on the verge of a change. Have you talked with your mother about Richie?" The question did not surprise Farieh—only confirmed that her choice of Homa had been the right one.

Farieh had tried to talk with her mother about Richie after he had first walked her home from WheatFields. Her mother was an intelligent and loving person who kept up with the times: her computer skills were excellent, she spoke several languages including English, and she was an active participant in social media. She knew current events as well as she knew mathematics, and she knew young women—having raised three of them. But she was also conservative. When Farieh mentioned Richie, she said nothing to signal he was a believer in Islam, because he was not. As a result, Richie never blipped her mother's radar screen, and she continued their conversation as though she had never heard his name. Farieh did her best to explain all of that to Homa.

Homa responded. “Dating is a challenge for an Iranian student, even in a place like Lawrence. The restraints that would be so clear in Iran are less visible here, but they are still present. You said you did not want to go on a date for pizza—that you wanted Richie just for you. What do you mean by that?”

“I mean a nice restaurant—a place that serves real food and does so well. A place where Richie and I can sit at a table and have a conversation that involves just the two of us and not everyone else who might recognize him.”

“Do you have such a place in mind?”

“Yes,” said Farieh. “It’s downtown, it’s called ‘715.’ I’ve been there before and I really liked it. I think Richie would like it, too.”

Homa thought for a moment, then reacted to her young friend. “I know 715. And I agree it would be a good place for you. How are you going to get Richie to ask you to go there? Do you have a mutual friend who could suggest it to him?”

Happy with Homa’s positive response, Farieh fairly pounced on the question: “No. I thought I would ask *him* out! That would solve my problem and prevent any ambiguity on his part.”

Homa could not help laughing. “OK, then!” she said, her voice bright with affection. “I think you have a plan.”

It was Farieh’s turn to reach across the table, and she took both of Homa’s hands in hers. “You have been so wonderful to listen to me! May I call and tell you how our dinner went?” The latter was as much a segue as a question, for Farieh had stayed far longer than she had anticipated; she was nearly late for her afternoon class at The Hall Center, and she had to leave. Still holding Homa’s hands as she stood up, Farieh hugged her, then stepped alongside as Homa walked her toward the front door. Homa picked up a napkin as she approached her daughter’s cookies. “Here,” she said, folding two cookies into the napkin and the napkin into Farieh's over-the-shoulder bag, "these will get you through your class!"

Farieh was through the door and quickly into her car, but not so quickly she did not see Homa waving from the front step. She could hear her as well: "Goodbye, Farieh. Good luck!"

Alex Cartwright

He was the junior lawyer at KU—not even an "assistant" General Counsel. He had spent his undergraduate years at Vanderbilt, in the town where his mother's sister Abby lived. Abby, or "Abigail" in what she still referred to as "polite company," loved Nashville. It was as country as the day is long yet irrepressibly contemporary, as country was now very cool. But it was also Southern, and traditional. Abby lived in a large house with white columns in front, built on the grounds of what had once been an actual plantation just south of the university. Alex was there a lot. He wasn't into studying all that much, and Abby and her family were always glad to see him and feed him.

When he graduated, he learned a "B" even from a place like Vanderbilt didn't count for much. And studying for the LSAT at Louise's, his favorite Mass Street bar back in Lawrence, hadn't helped. But he got into law school at Tulsa, he studied harder when he was there than he had ever studied at Vandy, and he graduated in the top ten percent of his class. Along the way he decided against private practice. When the KU job was posted online, he applied. His parents had both gone to KU, and their contacts helped him get hired. He had been with the KU General Counsel's Office not even a year when he was asked to review the YouTube video of the eruption in Philosophy 275 and draft a notice of faculty code violations.

Alex watched the video; then he watched it again. He had no idea how this confrontation between a student who was obviously gunning for the teacher and a professor who had done all anyone could expect to maintain his composure—until the student went to the chalkboard and pushed the thing way over the top—could possibly make out a violation of anything. When he went to his supervisor, Julie Samford, and said exactly that, the supervisor said nothing. Instead, she got up, walked past Alex, and closed the door. Then she sat down in the side chair next to the university's newest lawyer.

She opened with, "I can safely assume you have read the Faculty Code of Conduct, right?"

Alex said he had.

"Did you read the part about maintaining control of the classroom?"

Alex said he had. But he didn't like her tone of voice, and he fought back. "Come on. This kid might just as well have thrown a hand grenade against the back wall. When Professor Matthews walked out there was nothing left to control. The kid had taken the classroom and blown it up. He's lucky Matthews didn't throw his ass off the stage.

"I'm sorry," Alex added immediately. "I shouldn't have said 'ass.' But you know what I mean."

Julie Samford did not know what Alex meant. "Let's start with this," she began. "The obligation to maintain control of the classroom continues until the class period is over. If the professor feels they are losing control, they can ask for help. They can ask for help from their TAs. They can also call the campus police, if it comes to that, and ask them to come.

The student—Erickson, I think is his name—challenged Matthews about racism. He was entitled to do that. This university empowers its students to engage in free-ranging discussions with our professors. Erickson just happened to do it in a dramatic way—putting on the chalkboard what everyone who had read *Huckleberry Finn* had already seen. Matthews' responsibility at that point was not to yell at him and walk out, but to engage him in an intellectual conversation. He might have used the moment to explain why assigning a novel that used the most hateful word in the English language was acceptable!"

Alex decided this was not the moment to correct his supervisor—to remind her the novel had never been assigned and was not a part of the syllabus.

"And, when he was finished, his obligation was to go to the chalkboard and get an eraser and **ERASE THAT WORD!!!** He did none of that. He just threw a fit, cursed at his student—**CURSED** at him—and **LEFT!**"

She waited until she felt the heat fading from her face, then looked down and smoothed her gabardine skirt. When she raised her head and reengaged Alex over her glasses she was all business. "***I*** think Matthews is a racist pig. But my personal opinion has nothing to do with your assignment." Even spoken quietly, the *nothing* hit like a hammer. "What you are supposed to do is write up the violation."

The pause in the conversation lasted maybe five seconds, and she stared at him the entire time.

"You got that?" she asked.

The menace in her voice had taken shape, crawling over her lower lip and jumping down onto the small table between them.

"Yes, ma'am," Alex replied.

Open Table

715 was Lawrence's most popular downtown restaurant, named for its location at 715 Massachusetts. While it was a serious restaurant, a far better choice for Farieh than one of the local pizza shops, or the sports bars with their numbing variety of chicken wings—all with the same five sauces, 715 was also noisy. Its stone walls dated to the nineteenth century; its bar was kept lively by skilled and occasionally wise-ass bartenders; and its patrons—Lawrence regulars of all ages, though mostly younger, and foodies from all over the region, though mostly from Kansas City—filled it night after night. Having decided that was where she wanted to go, Farieh asked Richie to dinner. Caught entirely off guard, Richie stammered through an enthusiastic acceptance. Farieh knew the team's upcoming schedule: game this Saturday at noon; Big Monday game up next, but away. They agreed on Saturday night.

When Farieh checked Open Table for a Saturday evening reservation, she saw the next one available was in three weeks! Her disappointment must have raced across her face, for as she slowly put her phone down the person working next to her—Elizabeth Perry, her boss at WheatFields—had noticed. "What's wrong, Farieh?" Farieh had shared the plans she was making for her first date with Richie, and Elizabeth had enthusiastically confirmed her choice of 715. When Elizabeth heard about the jam on Open Table she offered to help. Her head drooping now with both the disappointment and her gratitude, Farieh answered softly, "That would be wonderful."

Elizabeth asked, "What time?"

"I know 7:00 is their most crowded time," replied Farieh as she looked up, "but that would be perfect. Richie has to leave early the next morning with the team."

There was no breakroom in WheatFields; there was no real privacy of any kind. Employees went out the back door to make their personal calls from the stoop or from the parking lot. But Elizabeth was a manager, the second most important person in the bakery. Not moving, she reached beneath her apron to fish out her iPhone and dialed the number from memory. "Mark," she said, "this is Elizabeth."

Mark Donohue was 715's current manager. He was also its original manager, and he had guided the restaurant from a subdued opening ten years ago to its wildly-successful current level of operations. He had managed a different downtown restaurant before 715, and his success with it—and especially with the kitchen and the wait staff—had attracted everyone's notice and respect. He knew culinary talent, he embraced diversity, and he would allow his rainbow collection of chefs to wear pretty much what they wanted so long as they showed up sober and on time, wore their caps, and served great food.

He supported his servers by listening to them and by working alongside them when someone got sick. He knew their significant others and he knew their kids. He knew who was having a good month financially and who was struggling, and he had a way of helping the people in the latter category without making the others angry. He also kept the longest hours—he was visible with a capital "V." The 715 investor group bought the iconic storefront just south of the Eldridge Hotel from Lawrence's best-loved jewelry maker and his wife on the eve of their retirement. After they had all signed the papers, the investors' first call was to Mark.

Elizabeth had been the pastry chef at WheatFields throughout all of this. She had gotten to know Mark at his first restaurant. They had never dated, but they had become good friends when Mark opened 715 and they had remained good friends, regularly sharing their successes and their disappointments over a familiar pinot noir or a bright new zinfandel until they knew each other better than any of their siblings and cared about each other more as well.

It was 6:00 in the evening and the din was already building behind Mark as he pressed his cell phone to his ear and made for the back of the restaurant, where it was at least a little quieter. "Elizabeth! What's up?"

"I need a favor . . . "

"Done!" interrupted Mark. "What is it?"

"I know you're mobbed this Saturday after the game. But I've got a special friend who wants to have her first date with her guy at your place. He's a KU basketball player, and this Saturday is the day he's available; the team flies out early Sunday morning for the Big Monday game at Lubbock. She . . . I . . . was hoping you could take the two of them at 7:00. Any chance?"

Any other person in Lawrence would have asked who the player was. Mark did not; he jumped in with something else: "What part of 'Done!' didn't you get?! We'd love to have them at 7:00. The only table I can't offer them is Table 1 [Table 1 was right in front, looking out a large window onto the sidewalk and Massachusetts Street.]—it's been reserved for a month. But anywhere else is good. Where would she like to sit?"

Elizabeth turned to Farieh. "7:00 is OK. Which table would you like?"

Farieh knew the restaurant well enough to answer. "The one farthest in back, in the corner, just south of the back door."

Elizabeth repeated the request to Mark. “Got it!” he said. “The table will be ready. What’s her name?”

“Farieh,” she said. “Her name is Farieh.” She added, “Thank you, Mark!” She did not add, *This is really important to them.* She and Mark were professionals; beyond that, they knew Lawrence. It was a college town. First dates were important. They knew that.

She had barely ended the call before Farieh hugged her and whispered her own thank you.

Geoff Pfeifer

Richie had again taken advantage of his Honors advisor's invitation to call him. But this time the subject was not basketball. This time the problem was a girl. Farieh had asked Richie to dinner, and they were going, and Richie had no idea what to talk about once they got there.

He and Geoff had again made an early appointment. Now February and a little warmer, it was also calm. The sudden gusts that could scramble a coed's hairstyle without conscience would not appear until March. It was also quiet—a perfect moment for a young man to think through some things. But Richie's thoughts were one moment scattered like bunny rabbits and the next jumbled like the 8:00 a.m. lab sequences in organic chemistry when he'd gotten no sleep flying back from a Big Monday game in Morgantown. Richie was glad to get to Nunemaker, balky front door or not.

His teacher had his back to his office door and was looking out the window, his ceramic mug of coffee sitting like a poor relative on the gleaming surface of the Biedermeier. Richie said, "Good morning!" as he walked through the open doorway and carefully set his backpack on the Bakhtiari carpet.

Smiling, Geoff spun around. "Well, good morning, Richie. I can see you have no coffee this time. Can I get you some?" Richie forced up his own smile and said, "Sure, Professor Pfeifer, that would be great."

"Cream? Sugar?" The questions were automatic for Geoff. "Yes, plenty of both. Thanks," replied the young student, remembering what "Honors coffee" tasted like.

"Please have a seat," said Geoff as he stood up from his desk chair. "I'll be back in a moment." And he was.

Geoff handed Richie a look-alike KU mug and a coaster, then circled the big desk and sat down. Sensing the tension in his student, it was Geoff who spoke first. "The team is playing well." Unable to catch himself, Geoff immediately grinned at Richie and continued, "And the Quantrill paper must have hit the right note, because your three-pointer at the end of the Missouri game was not only deep, but beautiful. Well done!"

Geoff spoke again: "It seems you've got something on your mind, Richie." Now wanting to hear from his student, Geoff simply looked across the desk. It was more than a few moments before Richie did anything. At first it was only an exaggerated change of position in the side chair. But then he took a breath and cleared his throat.

"I've met a girl, Professor Pfiefer. She's beautiful. And she's tall. And she moves like a dancer. And she's really smart. And she's from Iran. And she has these green eyes. And when she looks at me my mind just goes . . . I just seem to freeze up. Half the time I can't even respond to her and she has to say something again to snap me out of it. And I've tried to see her, but all I've been able to do is walk her to her scholarship hall or around campus . . . and I usually make a mess out of that. And I was trying to figure out how to ask her out on a real date and then she asked *me* out. And I said, 'Yes,' of course. And we're going out to dinner, and she picked the place and I've never been there before, and I have no idea what to wear or what to eat or what to say, and it's already

Wednesday and we're going out Saturday—just before the team leaves for the Texas Tech game early Sunday, so I can't even stay out very late . . . . It's just a mess!"

In a different setting Geoff might have smiled at the tumult of run-on sentences, but he was careful not to do so this time. It was his turn to pause. When he spoke again he was quieter. "Where are you going to dinner?"

"715."

"That's a wonderful restaurant," said Geoff. "They have a straightforward menu, and they have excellent servers who can help you with it. I'm sure you will have no trouble with that. They also have relaxed expectations about what people wear; you can wear jeans and a sweatshirt or anything up from that. So, let's talk about what to say. What would you like to say?"

"That's the biggest problem, Professor Pfeifer. Every time I try to say something to her I either screw it up—I'm sorry, I get it wrong—or I get tongue-tied and give up altogether."

Geoff was listening intently. He was also reacting slowly, concerned not to be abrupt in his responses. But Richie plainly needed help, so Geoff tried a different approach. "What if you focused on having her..." Geoff had realized he did not know the young woman's name. "Who has asked you on this date, Richie?"

"I'm so sorry, Professor Pfeifer. Her name is Farieh. She's from Tehran."

"All right, Farieh. What if you focused on having her talk to you? Unless they become self-conscious about it, most people like to talk about themselves. Have you had the chance to learn much about her? Where she's from? Who her parents are? Whether she has siblings? What her goals are after college? Those things?"

Richie conceded he had not. They had had only a few walks, he said. From Richie's perspective, most of them had involved long periods of quiet interrupted by one gaffe or another on his part, often met by Farieh's bemused smile or even her outright but always-polite laughter.

"Well, then," said Geoff, "we have lots to work with."

"But how am I going to keep a conversation going during an entire dinner when I can't even walk from Danforth to Miller without saying something stupid?"

"We can give you a script," replied Geoff, now seeing a light at the end of this tunnel.

"But if I am too nervous to carry on my own side of the conversation, how am I going to remember a script?"

Geoff had been thinking about that very problem, and he had an answer: "Do you know the term 'acronym'?"

"Sure," said Richie. "It's a collection of letters where each one stands for something. Like 'NASA' stands for National Aeronautics and Space Administration."

"Just right," said Geoff. "What if we create an acronym made up of the topics you want Farieh to talk about? That way all you have to do is keep the letters in mind. You could even write them on a small piece of paper and put it in your shirt pocket. But if we can settle on a small enough number of letters, I'm sure you will be able to remember them.

Let's start with 'Family.' Did you say you really haven't talked with her about her family?"

"Correct. I don't know about her parents, or whether she has siblings, or any of that. That's my fault, I know, but…"

"Don't be concerned with whose fault it is, Richie. It's a perfect subject to start with when you get to the restaurant. So 'F.' What else don't you know about?"

Richie had brightened a little and he responded quickly. "I don't know anything about her when she was younger, when she was growing up in Iran."

"OK," said Geoff. "Growing up—'G.' What else?"

"She's studying English literature and history now, but only because she's so smart she tested out of her entire math major first semester! We've never talked about what she wants to do when she graduates."

"We could use another 'G' for graduation, but that would give us two 'G's in a row, which ordinarily doesn't work very well. Maybe a 'V' for 'vocation'?"

"Sure!" said Richie. "That sounds good."

"What else?" asked Geoff.

Richie thought for a moment. He lowered his head, but only because he was concentrating; he no longer seemed discouraged. Then he looked up past his mentor and out the window. Distracted by the day as it brightened around the dormitories to the immediate west of Nunemaker, the soft light had also reassured him. When he spoke again both the student and his mood had changed. Richie was "back," thought Geoff, and he had something important in mind.

"I told you Farieh is beautiful, Professor Pfeifer. She is. She is the most beautiful woman I have ever seen—in person, in a magazine, in a movie, anywhere. But I don't know what *she* thinks is beautiful. I would like to know that."

"'Beauty,' then." And as Geoff wrote the word, he imagined how such an insightful inquiry might prompt dozens of reactions—even tender ones—in the mind of what had to be a remarkable young woman. "Let's see what that gives us." Geoff looked down at the notes he had been making. "We have 'F' for Family, 'G' for growing up, 'V' for vocation, and 'B' for beauty. FGVB. Not exactly memorable, I'm afraid!"

"No," agreed Richie. "I could remember 'KGB,' but that doesn't seem right for a dinner with Farieh!" They both laughed.

"Give me just a minute," said Geoff, returning his eyes to his notes. When he looked up again he had a new set of letters.

"What if we switch 'adolescence' for 'growing up'? That will give us 'F – A – V – B'."

"Better," agreed Richie, "but still not very memorable."

"I agree," nodded Geoff. "What can we substitute for 'Beauty'?"

"I don't know," said Richie. "But 'F – A – V – E' is something I think I can remember. Can we do something with 'E'?"

There was another pause before Geoff responded. "This is a bit of a reach, but what about 'esthetic'? It derives from the Greek word that means to perceive. If you can remember you are asking Farieh what *she* perceives to be 'beautiful,' then we have 'F – A – V – E.'"

"Great! I can work with that!" Richie added "Thank you!" as he reached across the desk to shake Geoff's hand. Then his eyes scanned the clock Geoff kept on the table behind his desk. It wasn't striking midnight for Cinderella, but it had the same effect: he was late. "I'm so sorry, Professor Pfeifer!" Richie's exclamation was as abrupt as his standing up out of his chair. "We have a team meeting in ten minutes. You've been fabulous—thanks so much!" And with that he had grabbed his backpack and was running down the hall to the front door. Geoff cringed in anticipation of the next sound. Nunemaker's reluctant front door swung outward. Never patient enough to work with it, Richie always hit it like a running back hits an undersized safety. But he got through it without breaking it, and once again Geoff smiled as he shook his head at his young friend from the dorm.

Helen Lochlear

Helen Lochlear was born to be a don at Oxford or Cambridge—except for the fact she was born across the Atlantic Ocean in a small, county-seat town in southeast Kansas. She had cats and gigantic dogs, she read widely, she lectured insightfully and without notes, and she could write. Uncommon for a faculty member at a modern American university, where she taught, she could also listen.

Aware of her ability to listen (Helen had a special sensitivity to others, especially younger others) and of a kindness that drew students to her like a stray cat is drawn to a bowl of milk on a well-lighted porch, Helen's department head gave her their largest Wescoe office, the only one assigned to the Department of English Literature that had two windows. Helen made good use of it. She moved her desk into the corner. The rest of the space became a kind of salon. The combination of a large couch and a side chair tucked between large, overstuffed chairs would accommodate six. The last seat on the couch and the overstuffed chair on the left as you walked into the office faced each other obliquely. Separated by a Duncan Phyfe table, these last two seats made a cozy corner for the two-person conversations she was famous for. Helen always took the chair, having learned over the years that her students, and especially the young women, might soon want to arrange themselves in ways that only the couch could handle.

The table supported bright porcelain teacups and saucers, heavier coffee mugs in earth tones, napkins, a plate of today's pastries that were usually gone by noon, and a large Waterford bowl of candy. What was in the bowl depended on Helen's mood and whether she had recently made it to The Merc, Lawrence's original natural-foods cooperative. M&Ms were the stand-by, but a given Monday might find Halloween-size Snickers bars or Gummy Bears or Hershey's Kisses. Helen had learned that nearly all of the students who came by to talk would decline the food, and especially the candy, when she first offered it . . . then help themselves as the conversation went forward.

It was Farieh who sat in what the students called "the poets' corner" this morning. She had been Helen's Honors 190 student in the fall, and it was Mary's curtain-pulling introduction to English literature that prompted Farieh to get her math major out of the way—so she would have the time for Shakespeare and Gibbon and Byron and Keats and Orwell and Woolf and Churchill, but especially for Austen and Bronte and Shelley and Eliot, and for J.K. Rowling. Farieh had always credited Harry Potter for keeping her awake in statistics.

Farieh had not slowed as she walked in, tapping the door frame out of habit and not for the notice as she had called ahead. Farieh was a tea drinker; Helen knew that and had a pot done and two cups poured. As it was only 10:00 o'clock, there were two small peach scones on the plate between the teacups, each atop a crimson-and-blue Jayhawk napkin. Helen was a fan. Already seated in the corner, Helen rose to greet her with the abbreviated yet affectionate hug she shared with her women students, then sat down as Farieh made her way around the larger table and back again to Helen. They picked up teacups at the same time and drank at the same time. Farieh put hers down, reached for a scone and a napkin, and said, "I have a problem."

Helen, who was still holding her tea, said nothing.

"It's Richie." Helen knew Farieh to be direct, but she was getting right into it this morning. "I have a date with him Saturday night and I'm not sure how it will go. I have really planned this—probably too much. I want this to be fun, and I want us to talk. I want to talk about important stuff—not all basketball—and I want the evening to help me sort out how I feel about him. But mostly I'm nervous about it."

"What kind of planning have you done?" Though the question was spoken quietly, Helen was looking straight across her teacup and directly into Farieh's green eyes.

"I chose the restaurant, for starters," continued Farieh. "I did not want pizza or enchiladas or street tacos or ribs or any of that. I wanted a place where we could talk and the really good food that goes with a really good conversation. Thanks to Elizabeth, I was able to get into 715." Helen knew Elizabeth. From Elizabeth, Helen learned Farieh had taken the job at WheatFields only hours after Elizabeth had offered it to her.

"715 sounds just right," said Helen. "But it can be a little loud."

"I know!" said Farieh. "I've been there a couple of times before. But the food's great, and Elizabeth got me just the table I wanted—in the back corner, where we are not so likely to be interrupted by every KU fan who walks by and recognizes Richie."

"Sounds like good planning to me," Helen responded, putting her cup down. "Why are you concerned about it?"

"Because it was peremptory on my part. I knew Richie was working himself up to asking me out for a first real date—something different than the walks we have been taking. And I was afraid if I waited for him to ask me, he'd pick a place I didn't like that had boring food and that was full of young KU students who would ignore the fact he was with me and just barge in and talk with him. I've seen that all over Lawrence with other KU players. I just didn't want that to be our first date. So I asked him. And now

I'm self-conscious that I did." Farieh had finished the scone and threw herself back into the couch with more drama than Helen was used to.

"I assume he said yes. Did he?"

"Oh, sure. He was cute, actually; he fell all over himself saying yes."

Helen just looked at Farieh for another moment. "So you were observant, and you were decisive, and you were direct. Isn't that who you are?"

"I suppose so," said Farieh.

"Don't you suppose Richie knows that?"

"Sure. Well, I guess so anyway."

"Trust me," Helen went on. "He knows that." She took another sip of tea, put the cup down again, and continued. "You are as capable a student as we have here at KU, Farieh. No matter how good Richie is at basketball, you are as good academically. I think Richie knows that. But beyond any intellectual appreciation he may have for you, he's crazy about you. You may want to be at least a little sensitive to him at dinner—he will not have had the experience with a restaurant like 715 that you have had. And you may have to work a little harder than usual finding things for the two of you to talk about. But I think Richie is looking forward to this very much, and I don't think he cares a whit it was your idea."

It was Farieh who was quiet this time. As she looked across at her mentor, her face began to relax; Helen Lochlear had that effect on her students. Then Farieh remembered she had class in ten minutes. "Thank you!" she said. "This is just what I needed." She put her napkin back on the plate, stood up, and left.

Notice of Departure

The stiffly-titled "Notice of Departure from Faculty Code" had arrived that morning. Jacob Matthews opened the envelope, scanned its contents, and called Andrew Stevenson at the law school.

"Andrew?"

"Jake!"

"I'd like to hire you."

"For what? Do you need a Vanna White for your Rockstar class? Someone svelte of form, like me, to keep everyone's attention?!"

"Will you be serious for once? I need a lawyer and I want to hire you."

Andrew did calm down. There was actually a pause in his repartee, an historic moment; but he recovered quickly.

"Good lord, man, what did you do . . . shoot the student in the third row who keeps looking at her phone?!"

"No," said Matthews. "I've been accused of violating the Faculty Code of Conduct."

Stevenson came back immediately: "Surely, you're not talking about that kid who blew up your class? They can't be serious!"

“Apparently they are,” said Jake. “He filed a formal complaint; the Provost turned it into a ‘Notice of Departure’; I have a week to make a written response to it. If that’s all I do, the Provost will review both submissions and what he gets from the Office of the General Counsel and forward it to the Chancellor with his recommendation. Or, I can forego the written response and ask for a hearing in front of a faculty panel. The panel hears the case and makes a decision, a kind of verdict, I guess. But the Provost appoints the panel.”

“That’s what we’ve got to protect us!” said Stevenson. “The Provost couldn’t select a fair-minded panel for a dog fight. He’s got one goal in life—saving money, and faculty reduction is his favorite tool. If he picks the panel, there will be one token member who doesn’t hate your guts, and the rest will.”

“That may be,” said Jake. “But even if he appoints the members, a panel is the only option I can see where’s there’s any hope.”

“OK,” said Andrew. “You’ve got yourself a lawyer. Can you come over after dinner? We can ask for the panel today. But this is obviously burning a hole in somebody’s pocket; I suspect we’ll see the panel and get a hearing date inside of two weeks. We’ve got a lot of work to do.

By the way,” he continued, “what’s the charge? What part of the Faculty Code are you supposed to have violated?”

Jake answered: “Losing control of my classroom. Oh, and demeaning a student.”

“What absolute horseshit!” said Andrew. “See you in my office this evening. Let’s make it a little later—say, 9:00.”

715

They met on the sidewalk just outside the restaurant. Richie was once again early, once again pacing, heading north away from 715 as Farieh walked past the entrance to the Mass Street Fish House two doors to the south. When he turned and spotted a crimson head scarf framing green eyes, his face lit up and he ran to meet her. But he remembered he was not to hug her, just in time, as his wrists had already begun to pull his hands up in the direction of her shoulders. He stopped abruptly. Farieh smiled her appreciation that he had remembered this important boundary of their relationship, and they turned up the steps and into the restaurant.

The interior glowed. Having caught the welcoming light from hundreds of skillfully-placed ceiling bulbs and nearly as many surrounding the bar, the honeyed stone walls draped it around Farieh as she followed the hostess toward her table in the back of the restaurant. But Farieh was focused on the seating, not the ambience, and she asked the hostess if she could sit with her back to the wall and with Richie facing her. The placement was conventional: a woman should be seated so she could see the people who approached her table; the hostess would probably have seated her there without the reminder. But it was also studied, and it was critical to the evening. Farieh did not want Richie's increasingly-familiar face looking back at every Tom, Dick, and Harry who made their way to the restroom, for the resulting string of interruptions from his growing list of well-wishers would have wrecked their dinner. Especially tonight, as Richie had played twenty minutes that afternoon, had scored fifteen points on three-for-four shooting from behind the three-point line, had a break-away dunk after a steal, had made four free throws, and had collected five rebounds. All of this had been highlighted in Coach Bennett's post-game radio interview, which would have been available to anyone eating at 715 this evening who had not actually gone to the game.

Elizabeth was not above calling Mark and asking for a table as a favor, but she did it rarely, maybe a handful of times since Mark had opened. As Farieh was plainly important to Elizabeth, Mark had selected his assistant manager, Maggie Campbell, to work with her. Maggie was as lovely, as tall, and as graceful as the KU student who awaited her in the back of the restaurant, and she knew how to handle young people out on a first date. "There you are," said Maggie as she arrived at their table, head high and smiling. "Welcome to 715."

"Thank you," said Farieh. "Please tell Mark how much we appreciate his help this evening."

"I will," smiled Maggie. "But he'll come by. He wants to meet you, and he wants to be sure you're having a good time."

Maggie waited until Richie had found his napkin, then continued. "I will bring some water for both of you; would either of you like anything else?"

Farieh did not drink alcohol and she told Maggie the water would be nice. Richie, barely nineteen, added, "I'd like a Diet Coke, please." Maggie nodded and turned back toward the bar.

Able to take in the restaurant from her corner seat, Farieh realized Richie blocked her view of the entire seating area in front of the grill. There was so much new to her about being with a broad-shouldered athlete who was 6’6”. She grinned at the thought, then asked, “Have you been here before?”

Richie took most of his meals at the DeBruce Center, the modern glass building on the north side of Allen Fieldhouse. The DeBruce Center kitchen served a multi-tiered training table for all of KU’s athletes. Beyond that, Richie had been out for pizza and barbecue and burgers, but nothing like this. “No,” he said, “we can’t.” His face broke into a devilish grin Farieh had never seen. “Coach Bennett says it’s too noisy!” Farieh almost spit out her water at the joke—so right for the cacophony of the restaurant and so unexpected from Richie. Delighted with himself, Richie continued. “That’s really not true. The coaches come here a lot, after games and after practices. Coach Bennett caught me after the game today and asked where I was headed tonight. When I told him I was having dinner at 715 he smiled. He likes it here.”

Farieh kept her next thought to herself: *That’s two great recommendations for the place, one from Elizabeth and one from Richie’s coach; maybe we can come back here.*

She wiped the water from her lips and asked, “Do you like the restaurant so far?”

“I love it,” said her date. “It’s loud, sure. But the people have been so friendly, and everybody seems to be having a great time.” His voice slowed and his grin receded. “I like the company, too. Thanks for bringing us here, Farieh.”

“What shall we eat?” She was trying to bring him back, her voice energetic.

“I don’t have any idea,” Richie answered. “Guess I should look at the menu.”

Maggie had returned. “Did you find tonight’s features? They’re on the right side, at the top.”

Farieh had found them, and she had a question. “How many pieces are there in the crab ravioli? Elizabeth told me it’s wonderful.”

"Usually seven or eight," Maggie replied, pulling a ballpoint pen out of her apron. "It's one of our most popular entrees."

"I'll have that," said Farieh. "And a salad. You have three or four salads; do you have one you like the best?"

"I like the Caesar," said Maggie. "It's simple. It's just the right size. And it's delicious. It would be a fun counterpoint to the taste of the ravioli."

"Then that's what I'll have," said Farieh.

"What about you," Maggie asked in Richie's direction. "Have you decided?"

Richie had not decided. Part of the problem was the number of choices—there were too many. The other part was his unfamiliarity with the choices that were listed. He had heard of many of them, but he had tasted almost none. Only the steaks were familiar. Maggie read his expression and moved a small step in his direction. "We have more features than usual tonight," she said empathetically, "maybe I could tell you about them?"

Richie was eager for the help, and he and Maggie soon settled on the lamb ragout and another Caesar salad. Richie had asked first about the filet, something he knew about. But Maggie had nudged him past it. "Our steaks are good," she said. "But will you let me tell you about a few more items?" When she had finished describing the lamb ragout, she could have sold it to him three times over.

Richie's eyes followed Maggie as she moved toward the kitchen, then returned to Farieh. "She's really nice." Farieh had of course watched the entire interaction between her callow friend and their skilled server. Maggie's sensitivity to Richie about the menu and the patient way she led him through the options to an entrée Richie was pleased with—you could read that in his smile, which had trailed Maggie's departure—had smoothed over a potential rough spot. Farieh couldn't wait to meet Mark so she could thank him.

They had just started their salads when a man in a plaid shirt moved toward them. His brown hair looked like he had brushed it once that morning then used his fingers in repeated failed efforts to put it back in place. His face had not caught up with the rest of him, for he was still talking with the server off his left shoulder as he came to a stop behind Richie. Finishing that conversation, he squared his shoulders and turned to Farieh. “Hi,” he said. “I’m Mark.” Soft brown eyes took in their entire corner of the restaurant. Farieh liked him instantly. And when he smiled and said, “I’m really pleased you’re here tonight,” Farieh believed it the way she believed the sun would come up in the east the next morning. “What did you order?” Mark directed the question to both of them.

Richie jumped in first to tell Mark about the lamb ragout and the Caesar salad. “Great,” said Mark. “You’ll like that.” He looked across to Farieh and smiled. “You’re Farieh, correct? Elizabeth’s friend. Do you work with her?”

“Yes,” Farieh said, smiling back. “Elizabeth is wonderful. And I ordered the crab ravioli. I’m excited about it.”

“That’s our most popular entrée,” said Mark. “We’re excited to be able to serve it to you.” He turned his head to his left again as yet another server vied for his attention. He began to move away, then stopped and turned his head back to them for a moment longer. “Looks like I’ve got someone else who needs to talk with me. Please enjoy your dinner. I’ll check back with you before you leave.”

There’s that smile again, thought Farieh. Then he was gone, just as Farieh remembered she had not thanked him for Maggie.

Maggie brought their entrees a moment later. Farieh had her fork poised over her first bite when Richie asked, “What do your parents do?”

“Just a second,” she said. Farieh speared the first bite, inhaled it, put her fork down, then looked back at Richie as she wiped the butter sauce from her lips. *He's serious*, she thought. *He really wants to know*.

"My mother and father both studied mathematics as undergraduates. Mother had just found her desk in the physics lab at the University of Tehran when my father walked in and introduced himself as her lab partner. Mother told me he was the most handsome man she had ever seen. A week later, she decided he was also the smartest. They married a year later. They both graduated with honors and stayed in Tehran—my mother as a graduate student in mathematics at the university and my father as a banker. My mother finished her Ph.D. and taught at the University of Tehran for several years. She stopped working when my oldest sister was born and never went back. My father continued with his career and is now a senior officer in Bank Melli, the National Bank of Iran. They are busy with two things—our family and my father's work. They have done well financially. My two sisters and I are doing well—my sisters far better than me—and my parents remain crazy about each other."

"That's outstanding," said Richie. "I assume you grew up in Tehran. What was it like?"

Farieh had managed barely a second bite of the ravioli; she was as surprised by the second question as she had been by the first. Again she put her fork down and wiped her lips. "It was magical," she began, then paused, wondering just how much to say—no matter how lovely the evening was turning out. But the evening *was* lovely, and she continued. "My parents loved each other, they loved all three of us, and my sisters loved me. I may have grown up in a cocoon, but it was truly made of silk. There wasn't a day I wanted for anything or was afraid of anyone. We had a beautiful home in Tehran and skilled people to help my mother with it. We had a home in the mountains outside the city. In the summer, when Tehran was as hot as your Salina, we would go to the mountains for two months and play in the trees and swim in the lakes and go to bed when the sun set and get up again when it peeked over the crests to the east. We made snow angels in the winter until we were old enough to ski. When we were older, we made them after we finished our last run.

For families in the United States, college seems to be hard on the parents. My roommate's mother drove her oldest son to Madison for his freshman year at Wisconsin and cried the whole way back to Kansas City. But when I left Tehran to come to school at Kansas, I was the one who cried—for 13 hours—until the plane landed at JFK. I was the only person in business class under the age of thirty, and I was a mess. I think of my parents every day."

"Wow," said Richie. He had stolen bites enough to finish his salad and half of his ragout while Farieh was talking. "Were you political when you were in high school?"

"No," she said. This time she put her fork down without eating anything and sat up straighter. Holding Richie with her green eyes, she responded in an entirely different tone: "I was not political. My father does not work for the government, but his position is still sensitive. My sisters and I knew that, and political involvement was not something we went looking for." She held his eyes a second longer, then reached for her fork and the next bite of the ravioli.

"OK," said Richie. He had finished the ragout and the Diet Coke, and he moved quickly to the next item on his list to get past the discomfort of the last one. "I get that. What are you thinking about for after you graduate?"

The staccato of the pre-planned Q&A might have been evident to an onlooker, but not to Farieh. She was in a noisy and friendly place, she was eating the best food she had tasted since she had come to Lawrence, and she was sitting across the table from the tallest and most attractive man in the room. The question was again comfortable, and she answered it.

"I'm thinking about graduate school, probably economics or business. What I haven't quite worked out is what my undergraduate majors will be here at KU. I came here to study mathematics and petroleum engineering. I have already completed my mathematics degree. But I love English literature and history, and I can't figure out how to take all the courses I want and still complete the oil and gas courses I need. I'm sure it will work out."

Richie's next question was the one he had been the most intrigued with when he and Professor Pfeifer had discussed it. They had needed an "E" to make the acronym work; it was Geoff Pfeifer who had suggested "esthetics." He saw Maggie walking in their direction, turned toward her, held up his empty glass to signal he wanted another Diet Coke, then looked back at Farieh. "What do you think is beautiful?"

Farieh had finished the last of her ravioli and was far more prepared for dessert than she was for this question. Her first response, "No one has ever asked me that," was honest, but it was only a place-holder. Recognizing she could go a hundred different directions, she chose the one in front of her and spoke to it.

"I think this evening is beautiful, Richie."

She dropped her eyes to her lap, lifted her napkin and reflexively brushed it across her lips, put it back in her lap, and lifted her head to continue. "I asked you to dinner because I did not want you to ask me. I selected the place because I did not want you to pick it. And I selected the table because it is the only one here that would force you to talk with me and not with all the KU fans who crave familiarity with the basketball program and the players. I'm sorry for that; that wasn't very generous of me. But it's true. You were about to ask me out, and we were going to have a real date, and I didn't trust you to make it special.

But you did make it special. More than special, you made it beautiful. Instead of talking with everyone else, you have spent the entire evening listening—listening only to me. I love talking about my home, and my parents, and my sisters, and my school, and what my plans might be. Nobody asks me about these things. But you asked, and I have loved giving the answers to you."

The second beautiful thing in front of her was the young man across the table. Farieh was debating whether to say something that forward, no matter how honest, when Maggie appeared again at Richie's shoulder.

"Matt told me you needed to leave at 10:00. I know you haven't had dessert yet, but it's ten minutes before ten o'clock, and I thought I should at least remind you of the time before taking a dessert order we couldn't make good on."

Though they had been there a full three hours, Farieh was startled by the news their dinner might be over. She asked Richie whether the team curfew had changed from 10:30. When he confirmed it hadn't, Farieh told Maggie they would have to have a check instead and Maggie left to get it.

In a tone as earnest as he had used all evening, Richie said, "I know you set up the whole dinner tonight, Farieh, but I'd still like to pay for it. It's supposed to be a date after all."

Farieh had planned for this, too, and had been poised to insist they share the bill. But she had lost that poise. She was still sailing on Richie's last question . . . and on the beauty of their evening . . . and on the recognition it was Richie who had made it beautiful. "OK" was her only response.

Mark appeared again as Richie was signing the credit card invoice. "You'll have to come back when you have more time," he said with a grin. "Or at least when you have time for dessert. When you do, dessert will be on us—our pleasure. It was really nice to meet you both." Had Farieh not been looking right at it, she would have missed the light squeeze Mark gave Richie's shoulder as he walked away from their table.

They stood together, put their napkins down next to their water glasses, and made their way past the bar where the regulars were still packed shoulder-to-shoulder. Outside on the sidewalk, Richie offered to drive her home. Besides being late, it was too cold for Farieh to walk and they both knew that. But they also knew Farieh would decline the offer, and she did. "I can get an

Uber, Richie, but thank you. Thank you so much, much more for this evening. It was perfect."

Richie would wonder as he drove home alone whether looking at Farieh's eyes as she said "perfect" was as good as a goodnight kiss. As Farieh rode the Uber back to campus, her thoughts of Richie were different. They were positive—her thoughts were all positive, and there were feelings stirring beneath them.

The Uber dropped her off in front of her scholarship hall and Farieh was quickly through the door and up the stairs and into her room.

"You're early! How was it?!" Her roommate Jamie was sitting cross-legged in the middle of her bed, and she was excited to know. But Jamie had her own impish sense of humor, and she answered the question before Farieh could take off her parka "I know, it was 'tolerable,' your favorite word lately. And Richie was 'cute,' but still 'impossibly young'—your favorite way to describe him. And all he could think of to talk about was the basketball team and the trip to Lubbock tomorrow morning and growing up in Salina. And that led to gross stories about The Cozy Inn. Am I close?!"

"What is 'The Cozy Inn'?" asked Farieh.

"It's an amazingly-small, amazingly-popular hamburger joint in downtown Salina. They serve tiny burgers made with hamburger meat and grilled onions that they cook on a hundred-year-old grill and serve on tiny buns. They tried a new grill once; but the customers hated it so much they had to go to the dump and get the old one back. You can't go into the place unless you want to smell like fried onions for the rest of the day, so you use the take-out window. I heard about it for years before I was finally in Salina long enough one weekend to try it. The hamburgers *are* small. But, you know, they're fantastic. I ended up eating six."

"Six!" exclaimed Farieh. "Good grief, girl!"

"Sounds like he didn't talk about The Cozy Inn. What did he talk about?"

Farieh thought about the question for a long time, at last realizing Richie had hardly talked at all. He had only asked questions, allowing Farieh to talk about herself. And she did. And it was the most wonderful evening she had spent since she had arrived at KU.

"Do you have an answer to that question, Farieh darling?" Farieh became "Farieh darling" whenever she drifted off in the middle of their conversations, usually to Iran and her family. Jamie had been teasing with her voice, but her eyes were serious; they were looking for the clues to her roommate's evening. As Farieh took longer than usual to drift back and as her face settled into a reverie Jamie had seen before, but never on Farieh, it was clear the connection between her roommate and the impossibly-young basketball player had changed tonight. Jamie lifted her eyes to the ceiling of their small room, nodding to herself as she did so.

Lubbock in the Rear View Mirror

By Sean Grogan
Lawrence, KS (AP)

EARLY SUNDAY MORNING: TOPEKA

I got the invitation to accompany the team to the Texas Tech game by phone last Friday. It took me two seconds to say "Yes!" because I had to sneeze first.

The chartered MD-80 boarded the team and its travel party at Forbes Field in Topeka. Once we're on board, five empty rows separate the team and the coaches from the guests—a half dozen Williams Fund stalwarts, one Williams Fund staffer for each couple, and me. There's a choice of soft drinks, and the PB&J sandwiches come creamy or crunchy.

Gene Bennett moves easily down the aisle to greet everyone. Big man; big smile! The senior cabin attendant has worked the Jayhawk charter before and has seen how even the folks at Million Air, the Topeka Fixed Base Operator, light up when Gene comes by. Coach Bennett talks to them too. Part of it is the Kansas coach's recognizing that ALL of these people can help his program. But a big part of it is simply Gene Bennett, who loves people and has never met a stranger.

The plane eases away from a terminal that serves only a handful of commercial flights per day. But there is a real Air Guard base here and a real 10,000-foot runway—so long the crown of it becomes the horizon as we begin our take-off roll to the west.

75 minutes to Lubbock. Thomas Williams is sitting somewhere forward, ear buds in place, looking like all the other royal-blue-clad Jayhawks with their heads down and their thoughts in their play lists. Thomas got dinged two games ago and did not dress last time out; he practiced full-speed yesterday and that means he'll play tomorrow night and that means there is less chance of an upset. Tomorrow night, for the first time this season, the United Event Center may be full, and that would mean 15,000 screaming Red Raiders. Kansas always draws like that. And Gene Bennett knows there is always a chance for an upset. That's what keeps him up nights; that's why, when he walks out onto the court just before each game, he blows into his hands. His hands aren't cold, and he's the best there is at this business of coaching college hoops. But he also knows there are no guarantees. Not cold; just nervous.

30,000 feet. Cumulus clouds just off our wing tips; Oklahoma's panhandle below. Long columns of hills stand at attention in their winter brown guarding thousands of water courses no longer than the street in front of your house. My fascination with the geological diversity of even the most barren reaches of the Sooner State is interrupted by the invitation to try the freshly-baked chocolate-chip cookies. Impressive—just like the tall glasses of cold milk they serve next.

The Williams Fund guys talk quietly with folks they already know well. This is the quintessential soft sell—moving donors who already love everything crimson and blue just a little further along.

The pilot has swung the stretch MD-80 a few degrees to the south and the sun, now fully awake, can light our path all the way to Texas. It's been fun already. From this guest's perspective, a guy who loves chocolate-chip cookies and milk, Kansas has thought of everything.

LUBBOCK

Brown dirt; irrigation circles; flat. Really flat. Like flying into Colby . . . but without the hills. [As I would often have to explain to my editor in Boston, "That was a joke."]

I look out the window and see the roller bags and the boxes bumping down the conveyor belt and realize the team brings its own Gatorade! Cases of it. I also spot the garment bags for the players: each is new; each is embroidered with a big bright-red "KANSAS."

We board the bus and head south and pick up a skyline that makes even Topeka look good.

MONDAY MORNING

I finish breakfast and step into the elevator and there's Lou Heinz, the former Illinois Coach who retired there and turned over the keys to Gene Bennett. Lou is in town with his son-in-law, a New Mexico State grad according to his golf shirt [it's WARM in Lubbock!], to visit with Coach Bennett and to speak to the Jayhawks at their coach's invitation. Coach Heinz is probably every day of 80. I suspect he now lives in New Mexico as he coached at New Mexico State before he went to Illinois. He was energized Monday morning, still beaming after having had the chance to meet this year's Kansas squad. That Gene Bennett anticipates these opportunities, plans for them, and carries them off with such affection for the people who have helped him along the way tells you a lot about the Kansas coach.

MONDAY NIGHT

United Spirit Center. Like the Red Raiders' impressive football stadium, the mass of their basketball arena is on the other side of a Spanish Renaissance façade that is splendidly executed in brown brick and stone accents. We approach the arena at 6:15 and are glad to see more than a few blue-clad fans walking toward the game. One in particular caught my eye—an old guy with boots and a Stetson to accompany his KU shirt who looked like he'd been saying "Rock Chalk, Jayhawk" for a while.

At 6:30 we're inside and seated. It's nowhere nearly full yet, but the students are already here and there's plenty of buzz in the air that will become a roar when the Red Raider takes the court in her mask and flying cape and the lights go off. When the players are introduced, their names are accented by gouts of flame from the large portable flame throwers wheeled out for the occasion. I'm fifty yards away and I can feel the heat; OSHA must have closed its Lubbock office.

The lights come up and Bobby Smith, Tech's coach, is handsome in his suit and tattersall shirt and tie—looking as much like the president of this university as its basketball coach. His eyes scan for Gene Bennett, and when they find each other Gene gives him a big smile. Gene likes Bobby; Bobby is a real coach and has built a team that can really play.

FIRST HALF

Kansas comes out with energy. There's some good defense and Percy Jackson is taking it to the hole from the get-go. A deep 3 from Billy, another from Percy, and it's 17-7 Hawks.

But Percy is missing his free throws. And when he misses his defensive assignment a second time and gets dunked on, the students pick it up several notches and Gene Bennett calls time out. Percy and Richie Armstrong, who is also having trouble keeping up on the defensive end, come out in favor of Luke Simpson and Paul Preston. Tommy Barnett joins them, spelling Williams.

Preston misfires from three but Simpson stuffs it back through the net for two. Then Tommy Barnett works hard for a rebound and takes it right back for two more. Kansas is doing well.

Frank Agbani jacks up another 3-ball that misses. No problem with Gene Bennet there: Agbani is a shooter with an attitude and Gene can handle the quick trigger finger. But when Frank loses his man on two consecutive defensive plays—once for a layup and once for a trip to the line after Frank fouled him—and personally surrenders four very quick points, he finds himself on the bench.

So often on the road a substitute guard will get hot and confound the scouting reports. This night it would be Dusty Hastings, a 6'4" sophomore from Little Rock who looks like the lead singer in a boy band but who was a heavy-metal hangover for Kansas on Monday night. When he made his second 3 of the half, it was KU up by only one and Gene Bennett called another timeout. This enabled him to sit Percy, Richie, and Billy—all with two fouls—just before the half. The incoming Jeff Hanson made his coach look good as he got fouled and made both of his free throws. But on KU's next possession Williams would get covered up and make a sharp pass . . . to where Hanson used to be, and the Hawks had turned it over again.

Kansas got the ball back but there wasn't enough time and the half ended: 30-29 Kansas.

SECOND HALF

Bobby Smith knows how to take the air out of a game, and he did that to within two seconds of perfection in this second half in Lubbock. Nearly every Red Raider possession went down to the last few moments on the shot clock; far too often the guy on Bobby's team would make it at the buzzer. The half started that way when the Tech guard nearly swallowed the clock himself before sneaking inside for a layup.

A simply terrible push-off call on Thomas Williams was followed by a legitimate charge call on Percy Jackson, giving Percy his third foul and sending him back to the bench. When Thomas was called for goaltending it was Tech in the lead, 35-32.

Bobby's combination of a zone defense at our end and his milking the shot clock at his end resulted in a nail-biter of a second half during which Kansas trailed a good bit of the time. The only consistent pleasure for the Hawks was Percy Jackson's driving on Jabari Wilson and getting fouled in the process. That worked three times in a row and allowed Percy to make six of his eight free throws for the evening over the course of 75 seconds. Even Thomas got caught up in the "let's take it to the hoop" mentality. When he drove it down the middle of the lane from the top of the key and got fouled and made both it was KU on top again, 46-45.

Kansas would exchange baskets and misses, the Hawks would turn it over some more, and they would be behind four after Truman made yet another basket at the buzzer. That's when Billy Nixon, who was hardly having a stellar night, hit the biggest shot so far—a 3-pointer that got us back to one down with just under three minutes to play. But Dusty Hastings was having too much fun, and when he missed a runner over the KU bigs, it was Dusty himself who grabbed the offensive board and put it right back in. Tech up three; two minutes left.

Kansas was finally getting it that inside was the place to be and they got it to Williams, who was immediately fouled. Williams' clutch free-throw shooting got KU to within one, and great Kansas defense at the other end resulted in a jump ball that went our way. 45 seconds left.

Everybody in the place knew Billy Nixon was going to get it and drive it, and he did. But he missed. No problem, as Thomas skied for the rebound and rammed it through the cords to give KU a one-point lead with thirty seconds to play. "Get back; get back!" screamed Gene Bennett. But Bobby Smith was calling a timeout before anybody in red and black had the chance to beat KU for a layup.

We knew Bobby could run out the clock and take the final shot; we also knew that if his guy missed that final shot the evening would end badly for the coach in the bespoke shirt and tie. Something was going to go down earlier. Sure enough, Robert Cerner beat his man off the dribble and got to the base line and Thomas had to move over to wall him off. Because the wall was still moving when Cerner ran into it, the contact sent him to the free-throw stripe, where his two made free throws put Tech back in the lead 63-62. 12.8 seconds. Timeout Kansas.

Inside! Inside! Inside! Jeff Hanson took the inbounds pass under intense pressure and had to dribble it backwards to the Tech free-throw line. But he spotted Thomas and got him the ball. Five seconds left: Kansas has it right where it wanted it. But the heavy traffic around the basket looked like a Texas feed lot at chow time, and Williams missed the shot.

Gene Bennett is fond of saying that "Big-time players make big-time plays," and Kansas got one now. Paul Preston fought off the Tech bigs and used his fabulous vertical to grab the rebound and lay it off the glass and onto the rim, where it bounced . . . and bounced . . . and bounced . . . and finally settled through the nylon. KU up one! The one-point-seven seconds left were not enough for the Red Raiders, and Kansas had escaped with a "W":

KANSAS 64 — TEXAS TECH 63

POST-GAME

Texas Tech is a proud university, and its student section stood tall after the game ended and belted out the alma mater. While Tech did not sell out the United Spirit Center, it came close, and there were more students at this game than had ever attended a basketball game in Lubbock. That was a proud thing too.

The trip home Monday night was as quiet as the trip down on Sunday morning. A brilliant moon rode shotgun out the right side of the aircraft as we made quick work of the 700 miles back to Topeka. Another tough road game; another outing where Gene Bennett and company had found a way to win it.

Snow Falls on Iowa State

By Sean Grogan
Lawrence, KS (AP)

Seems like it always snows for the game in Ames. The snow started hours before game time. By the time they let us into Hilton Coliseum the flakes were dropping down from everywhere, large, wet, and demoralizing.

Near the end of regulation, Kansas was demoralized, too. The Cyclones had made 20 of 22 free throws and 15 of 27 3-pointers. When Charlie Rabb muscled his way past Paul Preston for a layup and Kwamie Loose made yet another 3 to put the home team up seven at 72-79, the separation Kansas had been hoping for the entire game was moving in the wrong direction, and the needle at the packed Coliseum was moving well past "Rowdy." But Iowa State missed its next two offerings, the long caroms allowed two Jayhawk fast breaks, and a slick, behind-the-back move by Billy Nixon for a layup became the prelude for his second move—this time a dish to Thomas Williams. KU had closed to three. Michael James answered with a guarded, How-did-he-make-THAT? 3-pointer to get the Cyclones back to five before yet another Billy Nixon drive, this time "and one," got it back to two.

Kansas was now seriously out of time. But Kansas got a stop, and crimson and blue hearts were racing again. Next up, Billy's unforced error gives the ball back to the Cyclones at half court, we have to foul James, he makes both, and it's once again four. Frank Agbani, who played another outstanding game and would finish with 19, scrambles for a loose ball at the Kansas end and gets fouled. Frank is very good at shooting free throws in the closing minutes of a game, and he makes both to get us back to two. One minute left; here we go! Or, not. George Newman, who has been taunting Williams from the free throw line and deeper throughout the evening, launches yet another three . . . and hits it. This gives his team 17 threes for the night, an Iowa State school record, thank you very much! And with 45 seconds to go, the Hawks are again down five.

Billy gets the ball, his guy bites on the drive-fake, and Billy launches the pretty step-back three that everybody knew was coming. He makes it! We have to foul a driving James, and we do, but the refs can't see that it's Thomas who commits it and not Barnett, so they call it on Barnett. Kansas says nothing; they want Williams in the game. Iowa State says nothing! They want Barnett out because Williams can't guard the three-point line. So Tommy is banished, Williams takes his place beneath the basket, and James—who made the layup—goes to the line for the and-1. One made free throw later and we're back to a five-point margin. But now there are 12 seconds left!

The ESPN guys says Billy is "feeling it." To prove the point Billy puts up yet another 3 . . . and he makes yet another three. Lights-out stuff! Cyclones by two—89-87.

James seems to be the only guy in gold and red who has clearance to handle the ball in the last 45 seconds. He gets it again and he gets fouled again. As he goes to the line ESPN reminds everyone that Iowa State has now made 22 free throws in a row. When James misses the first one, the Kansas faithful thank the Big Monday staff for the stat line and the jinx that followed it. Not taking time to breathe, the Kansas bench watches Billy bring the ball up for KU's last possession.

When Gene Bennett needs two, he doesn't want anyone swinging for three. Sure enough, Billy drives the lane. Depending on what colors you're wearing, Newman either gets there or he doesn't, Billy runs right into him, and . . . nothing! It's a Top-Ten no-call for the month. Four seconds left; pandemonium; ball's loose on the deck. When George Newman reaches over Billy to get it, and misses, and then reaches through the Kansas point guard, the refs call it on George and the Cyclone faithful go bonkers. Billy calmly makes the first. Iowa State's coach, who was not born last night, calls a time out. But neither ice nor snow nor bedlam in the Coliseum will deter this senior this night; and when he goes back to the line, he makes the free throw that ties the game. Two seconds: Michael James misses at the buzzer. Overtime!

Anyone interested in learning about being a point guard need only watch the replay of the OT, for as Gene Bennett blurted out later, "Billy just f[ ]king took the game over!" Of the 18 overtime points scored by the guys from Lawrence, Billy got two out of three. He began with a driving layup, followed that with a runner, then followed Frank's 3-pointer with his own. Before you knew it the Hawks were up eight and everybody wearing gold and red looked sucker-punched.

But Kansas had just watched the Oscars, and this Kansas group knew the value of suspense. There were still several minutes left—still time to spice things up. Back-to-back turnovers on in-bounds plays, Thomas Williams fouls out, and two quick baskets for the Cyclones and it was once again "game on." But Billy had been watching the Oscars from the wings, he had overheard the presenters, and he knew whose name was in the envelope. He ran the clock on the next possession, then drove the lane. When he got blocked, he pitched it out to Jeff, raced to the three-point line, and signaled for the ball. Jeff got it to him with one second on the shot clock and had the front-row seat for the most remarkable basket of conference play—a high-arching beauty from at least five feet behind the line that streaked through the net and sealed the win. Sure, Hanson would get fouled and make a free throw; Percy Jackson would rip down a rebound and get fouled and make both; and Billy would throw down a dunk at the buzzer. But the game was over when Billy made the shot from the bookstore at the Cyclone student union.

You don't get 108 at Hilton without a lot of guys doing good things. The Jayhawks shot 54% from the field. Thomas Williams got another double-double with 13 and 10. Tommy Barnett wasn't far behind with 13 and nine. Jeff Hanson had nine points on some very large makes to go with three assists. If there was a disappointment it was Paul Preston, who managed to disappear in the cold and the snow swirling about the Coliseum.

In his giddy post-game remarks Gene Bennett complimented a lot of things: rebounding—KU had 47 to Iowa State's 33; "How 'bout Jackson?! Eight big points; six big rebounds"; the whole team. As his emotions again got the better of his normally-deft media presence, Coach Bennett marveled at "the balls we showed!" Then he recovered and observed, "We stepped up and played like men tonight."

But Bennett's real praise was for his point guard from Chicago who stood quietly just off his left shoulder. Coach Bennett noted that Billy "drives us all nuts; I'm not gonna lie." Then he said:

- "Tonight, he was the best guard in the country."

And,

- "I've had guys get 30 before, but never 30 in a half!"

Reflecting on an evening that would have matched the best night Garth Brooks ever gave an audience, Coach Bennett reminded the folks still listening that Billy finished this way:

- 39 points, with 30 coming in the second half and the OT;
- 6 3-pointers;
- 7-for-7 from the line, including the ones that made all the difference with two ticks left on the clock in regulation;
- 5 rebounds; and
- 7 assists.

Then he tied a ribbon around it: "That's as good as we've had any guard play here. Ever!"

Now it was Billy's turn. The announcer knew about a conversation Billy had had with his coach during the game and she asked about it. In a masterpiece of courtesy and circumspection, the Kansas point guard noted the conversation was "personal," between him and his coach. But he acknowledged it had helped get him "fired up" and focused. He reflected upon the Hawks' losing streak, how it had upset him, and how his emotional reaction—his vulnerability—had demonstrated to his team how much they meant to him. And he talked about the Big 12 race and how important this win was to that. The win here went a long way to clinching it for Kansas; a loss would have tossed Kansas into a pot with three other contenders.

As I listened to him, I had this thought: What Kansas fans want is that moment when their point guard becomes the person they're looking for. For Jacque Vaughn that moment came early: it was the shot that beat Indiana his freshman year. For Kirk Heinrich, it was when he left the court one winter night with a badly-sprained ankle and returned the second half to win the ball game. For Sherron Collins, it was the end of almost any game, when Sherron wanted the ball and the fans *knew* he would make the basket to win it. For Frank Mason, it was his fearlessly taking the shots even Sherron wouldn't try. And for Devonte Graham, it was that moment when he stopped pitching the ball into the seats and began to dazzle us with his quick-draw 3-pointers. Such moments came for Jo Jo White and Tyshawn Taylor, too, and tonight that moment came for Billy Nixon. But tonight, Billy became something more than the point guard the fans were looking for. Tonight, he became the person Billy was looking for.

Senior Night in Waco

By Sean Grogan
Lawrence, KS (AP)

One gifted player can beat you. Billy Nixon at Iowa State is proof enough of that. When there are two who go off on you on the same day you don't stand a chance. That was the story Saturday as Peter Jacobs and Kerry Jepson shot 85% from the field and combined for nearly as many points as KU's entire team [they had 53] to lead the Bears to a 81-58 stomping of the Jayhawks.

Numbers don't tell the whole story in Waco, but they are interesting. Here are a few:

- 3 field goal attempts by Thomas Williams for the game;
- 4-for-4 by Kerry Jepson from behind the arc;
- 4 turnovers by Paul Preston [when guarded by Kerry Jepson—one of Russell Pugh's several outstanding recruiting efforts; these would often lead to breakaway layups];
- 8-3 blocks [Baylor had more];
- 8-7 turnovers [KU had more];

- 17-11 assists [Baylor had more; Jacobs had 9];
- 25: distance in feet from the basket where KU was forced to run its offense;
- 42-31 rebounds [Baylor had more].

At the half, with KU down nine after an already-withering performance by Jacobs [Baylor's gifted point guard] and Jepson [its freshman power forward], I said to the colleague on my left that we would be OK unless Baylor shot lights-out the second half as well. The Bears did just that. And as made basket after made basket drove the Bears' enthusiasm and energy levels ever-higher, it became clear this one was headed even farther south than Waco. In the first half Jepson had been every bit as troublesome as Jacobs, forcing Thomas Williams away from the basket, blocking Kansas shots, and having his own dunk fest at the start of the game. At the break, I made a note to myself: "How deal with Jepson?!"

The answer of course was, "You don't—not tonight." KU tried hard at the start of the second period. Gene Bennett fronted Jepson with Richie Armstrong, and that helped for a moment. At the offensive end, Nixon drove the middle, spotted Preston in the corner, and whipped the ball to him. The result was a guarded 3 that seemed to settle through the net in slow motion, cutting the Baylor lead to five and prompting the ESPN guy to observe, "That is as pure a stroke as you will ever see." But it wasn't nearly enough. Hustling harder than Kansas did throughout, Baylor got successive fouls on Williams and Nixon; and when Jacobs got loose for another layup it was back to an 11-point spread.

Kansas rallied for the next several minutes and seemed to hang with the 3-point shooting from Jepson and the drives by Jacobs, who was simply faster than anyone else tonight. Another Paul Preston bucket—this time a nice 2-pointer off a screen—cut it back to seven points at 42-49. But Jepson answered with another deep 3, Jacobs stripped Paul and went in for a layup, and at the 10-minute mark the Bears were up 12. "There's still lots of time," I said; and I thought there was. But then Jepson got the ball again, just left of the basket, just inside the line. He spun past Percy Jackson like the Wichita freshman was bolted to the floor, lofted a 16-foot fall-away jumper over the taller Thomas Williams, and made it for his 25th point. Gaping at a move Lebron would have been pleased to post on SportsCenter, I quietly called it for the Bears.

There was some good stuff still to come from Kansas, especially from Percy Jackson, who played the best game of his freshman career on offense. It was Percy's gorgeous inside move, which this time left Jepson—his McDonald's All-American teammate—watching, that got the game back to 10 at 51-61. But there was another Peter Jacobs strip of Preston followed by his pin-point post pass to Hazlitt for a dunk, followed by two more assists by Jepson, and before you could say "full-body immersion" it was 74-57. A few minutes later it finished where it finished.

Percy Jackson looked like the player Gene Bennett had wanted so badly when he was a senior at Wichita East. He was 5-of-7 from the field against amped-up and bigger Baylor players; and he played aggressively the whole way, finishing with 15 points, two boards, and one block in 22 minutes.

And Richie Armstrong had a smooth dozen that included three-for-four from deep.

But March 2 belonged to Baylor—and to its coach, who had his Bears ready. KU's last possession of the first half, for example, succumbed to thoughtfully-timed fouls that Baylor had to give and the resulting block on the shot Jeff Hanson was forced into taking just before the buzzer. Kerry Jepson, who had looked lost at Allen Fieldhouse, knew the way home on Saturday. And Peter Jacobs looked every inch the Big-12 Player of the Year, an award he has the chance to get a second year in a row on the strength of his last home game in Waco. The ESPN commentator who said he was "doing it from everywhere" was right on the money.

FINAL NOTE:

Coach Bennett is entitled to find fault with Kansas' energy level, its defense, and its casual regard for the basketball. But it was the same Gene Bennett who picked the Bears to win the conference this year. And it was simply bad luck that Russell Pugh's guys decided to shake off their three losses in a row, foreclose on the backboards, and have their two best players have career games—all on the same senior night in Waco. Kansas caught a hot OSU in Stillwater in January, too; but Kansas manhandled the Cowboys at AFH last Monday to clinch another Big-12 Championship.

Make no mistake, this was a give-no-quarter beat-down. But Kansas will be fine.

Gene Bennett Doesn't Like to Lose

Gene Bennett hated few things. But losing a basketball game was one of them, and it was first on his list. His approach to losing was in two parts—one rigorous and intellectual, and one not-so-rigorous and emotional.

The rigorous part began with the final buzzer and extended immediately into the post-game interview with whichever broadcaster or sportscaster wanted to talk with him. He talked with all of them, drawing on his full complement of self-deprecation and personal accountability. No matter how often he might be asked about the other team they were always "well-coached" and "far smarter with the ball" and "tougher" and the like. After a close game, and especially one where the fouls called were lopsided in the opponent's favor, there would be questions that tried to elicit critical comments about something—the officials, the other team's student section, anything. Gene dodged them. If Kansas had suffered twenty turnovers, then he and his coaches "hadn't prepared our guys well enough for the pressure." If the Jayhawks shot forty-one percent from the free-throw line, then Gene and his coaches had not "gotten them ready for the distractions." "That's a loud, clever student section," he would say. Outrebounded by fifteen? "This is our third game in six days; we're just tired—we'll be fine." Gene's bonhomie was impenetrable. He might not be smiling, but he was careful, he was complimentary, and he was brief.

His post-mortem with his coaches was in two parts. The one that followed closely after the game was usually a huddle at the front of the bus as Kansas lost so seldom at home. The one that came the next day followed their review of the film. If the loss were particularly hard to take, like the Villanova game in San Antonio in 2018, Gene might skip both. He had never watched the San Antonio game, and he was only beginning to talk about it. There was nothing you could do about that many three-pointers. The six in the second half were the coup de grace; the mortal wounds came in the first half—twelve of them. The second half was the flood that washed your home away after the first-half avalanche had flattened it.

Gene expected his assistant coaches to pull no punches in the post-game review, and he got on them if he thought they were taking it easy. Gene would tell anyone listening he didn't set the bar at Kansas—it was people like Phog Allen and Clyde Lovellette and Wilt, and Danny Manning and Larry Brown and Paul Pierce and Roy Williams who had put it up that high. His job was to make sure the team playing that year could reach it. The assistants' comments made their way into the notes, and the notes made their way into the next practice. Hard losses made for hard practices, unless they came during The Tournament. A loss in The NCAA Tournament sent you home for the season.

Gene Bennett's emotional reaction was private, short-lived, and intense. Hating the thought of losing control in front of his assistants and hating even more the thought of losing control in front of his players, Gene did not lose control in public. Instead, he would wait until everyone had left the field house, often late in the evening. Then he would close the door of his office behind him and begin a slow walk down the Wagnon Center corridor to the circular stair at the north end, pausing at the top rail long enough to gather himself for the even slower walk down to the ground level, talking to himself the entire way. Sometimes the conversation was audible and sometimes not. But it was harsh, it was profane, and it had a target: Gene Bennett was mad as hell and the person he was chewing out was himself.

His big Explorer waited for him just down the sidewalk that ran east of the Wagnon Center entrance and just through the opening in the concrete wall of the parking facility. Gene took twice as long to walk the sidewalk that was half the distance of the interior corridor, and now he muttered. He knew he was outside; even if it were late at night, he did not want anyone to know he was yelling at himself, even *sotto voce*.

As he passed through the parking facility wall he would press the key fob and open the front passenger door and pitch in his bag. Then he would slam the door shut, walk behind the SUV with his head down and his eyes blazing, and rip open the driver's door to get in. Bennett was a big man, and he was angry, and when he would bark his left knee against the underside of the steering wheel—as he always did after a loss—he would curse and make a fist with his right hand and bring it down as though he were trying to break the steering wheel in two. He never did.

Whether it was the impact of the steering-wheel strike or the pain that jumped from his hand to his right shoulder, that was the moment when the anger left him. He closed his eyes, slumped forward, waited a moment, then eased his left hand out to grab the door closed so he could drive out of the parking facility and go home. Only then did he feel better. Except for his hand.

Getting Ready for Trial

There were no subpoenas available to Andrew Stevenson as he thought about how to defend his friend against the university's charges. This was an academic proceeding, not a civil court. Neither did he have an administrative judge available to meet with the lawyers and talk with them about "discovery"—documents they proposed to search for that might help their side of the case, and how the judge might help them get it. There was none of that. But that did not mean Andrew was without assets. It was March 8. The *UDK* had announced in its early-afternoon edition that he would be defending Professor Matthews, and by 5:00 p.m. Andrew had received a hundred offers to help from undergraduates throughout the university, most of them Matthews' current or former students. Andrew was also approached by law students. All of the students enrolled in his spring Trial Tactics class, for example, had volunteered, and there were others. Some knew Professor Matthews and really wanted to help him. Others were motivated by "the action." Legally, this would be the biggest thing happening on the KU campus this semester.

The letter giving Matthews notice of the charges also announced the hearing date: Monday, April 12, one week after the championship game that brought "March Madness" to a close.

Jake Matthews had called Andrew when the letter was delivered to him at his office in Wescoe Hall on the 7th. But he had not mentioned the hearing date, and Andrew did not ordinarily read the *UDK*. As a result, Andrew's first knowledge of the April 12 hearing came when his friend handed him the letter as he walked into Andrew's office the evening of the 8th. With considerable effort, Andrew managed to react with only a nod. "Sit down, Jake. I'll need to make a copy of this," he said as he excused himself to do so.

At the copy center on the empty fourth floor, the door to the narrow space carefully closed behind him and the copy machine whirring its way across the single-page document, Andrew reacted again: "God *damn* it! I get the best tickets I have ever *had* to the Final Four, the Hawks are a *lock* to make it, and I get to stay home preparing for this stupid hearing brought to us by the *morons* in Strong Hall!!!" He pulled the copy and the original out of the machine and helped himself to another cup of the coffee he had made earlier that evening. He hoped the David's Blend, from his favorite downtown breakfast place, would calm him down. Coffee mug in hand, he opened the door behind him and made his way back toward his office through the library's warren of carrels and bookshelves.

He saw Jake as soon as he cleared the end of the stacks, his friend's shoulders and the back of his head visible through the narrow glass panel just left of the office door. Andrew had never seen him slumped over before, not even slightly. There had been righteous anger in Jake's voice when he had called the day before. And the set-jawed scholar Andrew had come to value so highly was the same person who had disdained a closed door for their meeting just minutes ago. But now, sitting by himself, lit from the back by the half-light from the stacks and from the front by the small bulbs of Andrew's desk lamp, Jake's body spoke an unfamiliar language—vulnerability. Andrew knew he needed to remember this moment, and he slowed his approach to his office to be sure he got it: this was about a friend's academic future, not court-side seats. When he stepped back through the door he handed the original of the letter to Jake, walked to his desk, and sat. But on the corner of his large desktop and not in his desk chair. He was not two feet from Jake. He reached across the desk, set his coffee mug on a coaster, and looked up.

"This is chicken-shit, Jake. You know it and I know it. But we'll by-God defend it!" He paused, then went on.

"We've got a lot of work to do over the next month. Good thing is we've got help. In the last few hours I'll bet I've heard from every student who ever took your class! My inbox is full, and they blew up my phone. I had a few hours late this afternoon, I got transcripts and CVs from a friend in the Registrar's Office, and I've looked through them. I have more or less settled on four people for our trial team, and I want to talk with you about them, to make sure they're OK with you.

Two are your current students, kids who were actually there. I'd like you to approve them. The other two are law students from my Trial Tactics class. But I've had them in other classes; they're the most capable students in the school when it comes to digging up facts and litigation strategy. They're also smart: one is the number one student in the class and the other is number five. They have the time—neither is taking more than nine hours this spring. And they are nearly as offended by this as I am. Are the law students OK by you?"

Jake's "Yes" was not as enthusiastic as Andrew had hoped, but there was some energy in it at least. Whatever Andrew saw through his office window a moment ago appeared to be waning.

"OK," said Andrew. "Let's move to your two students. The first is Karen West. She's . . . "

Jake interrupted. "She's perfect! She's the star freshman on the debate team and she's terrific in class: well-prepared, asks great questions, can sustain a conversation, and is sensitive to other students who are not as capable as she is. She's been here not even two semesters and she's already being talked about for the Rhodes and the Marshall. She's great . . . really. Who else?"

"Jack Smith."

Matt cut in again, "Also perfect. Best writer in the class. His mid-term paper on Vicksburg made me feel like I was slogging through the bayous myself. Best thing I've read about the campaign since Miller's book."

"OK. Good," said Andrew, looking down at his legal pad. "Then we're set. I'll contact them tonight and we'll try to meet with them tomorrow afternoon."

Andrew took an involuntary breath as he looked up, then let it out more noisily than he wanted. "How are you doing, Jake?"

In the moment before Jake responded he just looked at Andrew: no turning away to avoid the question, no looking down to signal discouragement, just a moment—a tiny tangency on the arc of their conversation that grew into something bigger . . . fast.

"I'm pissed! I'm just as angry as I was that afternoon in February when that rodent Erickson tried to take over the class. Tried to, hell! He did take it over. That's what makes me so angry.

I could have done a dozen things, things I know how to do, to deflect it. I could have moved away from the stupid lectern. But no! I just stood there like I had a pole up my ass. I could have gotten quiet, slowed it down, turned the attack back at him. But all I did was get madder and madder and blow up! It was pathetic."

"It was human," responded Andrew. "And it was the right response. You know why I think so?"

"No," Jake said. "Why?"

"Because as you were walking up the aisle in that great Alexandrian rage of yours, oblivious to what was going on behind you, the entire class, at first one student in front and then another, then clusters of them, and finally rows of them, one after another from front to back until the whole class was on their feet, the entire class stood up and applauded you. If there was a greater moment in the recent academic history of Kansas University, I don't know what it was."

"So why this charge?" asked Jake. "*Somebody* must disagree with you."

"That's right," Andrew said, "somebody does. But our job right now is to get ready to beat the charge. We don't have to explain it." Andrew got up from the corner of the desk, pulled back his large leather desk chair, looked down briefly at the pile of paper on the desktop, then looked up.

"This has been a long two days for you. And I've got a class tomorrow at 8:30. Let's call it a night. But I'll text the four people we've agreed to add to the team, and we'll plan to get together with them tomorrow afternoon at 5:00. I've already reserved the Rice Room. Does that work for you?"

"Sure," said Jake, standing up and holding out his hand. They shook. "Thanks, Andrew," he said, locking eyes with his lawyer. "See you tomorrow."

As he turned toward the stacks, the same evening half-light that had welcomed generations of students as apprehensive as Jake put its arms around him and walked him to the stairs.

Snow Angels

Farieh had a 4:00 p.m. seminar at the Hall Center on Tuesday that always ran late, and Richie gave little thought to it until 3:00, when the snow started. The team had practiced early so he decided he would meet her after class. Maybe he would walk her back to Miller. But a different idea was taking shape that seemed more fun. He left McCarthy, jogged past the field house, turned east across the front of Robinson Natatorium, and walked the rest of the long block. The day had grown steadily colder, but without wind, so when the snow came it fell in huge discs that reminded him of the doilies his grandmother placed beneath the dessert dishes for their Easter dinner. Looking up and down the sidewalk to be sure he did not make a fool of himself, and seeing no one, Richie tilted his head back, closed his eyes, stuck out his tongue, and waited for one of the crystalline lozenges to land on it. A person could experience such frozen purity only if they anticipated it. The anticipation combined with the taste on Richie's tongue, as much imagined as real, carried him back to his winters in Salina, where he had walked home from Heusner in snowfalls just like this one.

Richie entered the Hall Center as Farieh was walking down the stairs from the second floor and pulling on her parka. She saw him as she reached the bottom and, delighted at the surprise, said "Hi!" in her brightest voice. They went straight out into the evening: down the driveway, east at the bottom of the hill to the long-abandoned traffic-control booth, then up the slope toward Flint Hall, Journalism. Farieh turned right toward her scholarship hall when they got to the intersection that joined Flint with Bailey and Watson, but the excitement in Richie's voice stopped her: "Let's go to the campanile!" Farieh understood she might miss dinner if she went with him; Miller usually served it right at 5:30. But she was beginning to understand Richie. It was unusual for him to initiate something on the spur of the moment, he must have something in mind—and she could make up a meal for herself if it came to that. "OK," she said.

They crossed Jayhawk Boulevard, walked down the hill to the traffic control booth, and headed left past the WWI Memorial toward Spencer Library. Staying on the sidewalk, they skirted the south side of Marvin Grove and arrived at the bell tower built after WWII. They walked into it, through it, and out again, crossing the small concrete plaza on the north side and walking down the steps. Richie moved them onto the slope that led to the stadium, stopping maybe twenty feet out into the grass.

"Here," he said. "This will work."

Farieh had dressed warmly against the predicted snowfall; Richie was wearing his parka as well. But they had said little to one another as they made their way across the crown of the campus to this spot, and she did not yet know why they were there.

"OK," said Richie, "just watch me!" And with that he flopped onto his back and began moving his arms and legs against the solid layer of white that had spread across Campanile Hill.

"I'm making snow angels!" Richie shouted. "We did it every time it snowed in Salina. Just like you and your sisters did in Iran!"

Losing track of time and place, Farieh flew from the small hill in Kansas to the Alborz mountains outside of Tehran, to the snow she and her sisters had played in until it was dark and they were so soaked that their darling mother had made them come in. They always made the snow angels last. And as they would finally leave them and walk toward the light of the mountain house where their mother was calling, they would argue about whether snow angels ever became real. Farieh had held out for "Yes" against her older sisters, but she had always wondered whether that was the right answer.

She must have been gone for some time when she was drawn back to Kansas by Richie's voice. He was still lying on his back, but he was no longer moving his arms and legs. He was still shouting, but it was something different. What at last broke through was a question: "Farieh! Are you OK?!"

Richie came into focus in front of her, lifting his head off the snow and preparing to get up. "No!" she said, her voice rising; "No, Richie, no! Don't move!" She looked down at the impossibly-young man whose spontaneous embrace of a Kansas snow fall had connected him with her family, with her feelings, and with her. In a single motion she knelt beside him and took the glove off her right hand and reached out to touch his cheek. Richie was so stunned by the gesture he lay as though frozen to the snow, not moving and certainly not speaking, for he had no idea what to say. Farieh spoke instead. "Since I was a little girl, Richie, I have wanted snow angels to be real. But I never dreamed I would have a real one for my own." Then she stood up, extended both of her hands to his, and pulled him to his feet.

Senior Night at Allen Fieldhouse

By Sean Grogan
Lawrence, KS (AP)

That it takes a village to raise a championship-level basketball team becomes clear to Kansas fans on Senior Night. Gene Bennett did the honors as Master of Ceremonies, and his initial observation that all 16,300 Jayhawk faithful stayed for the speeches wasn't too far off the mark. He added: "The great thing about being a fan is you have a chance to see kids grow up before your eyes." There were some of us who either had not thought of that at all or had not thought of it recently. But the changes were in fact remarkable. Thomas Williams was skinny and ineffective when he first showed up. People were jazzed with the idea of Tommy Barnett, but the strong California kid with the big hair took a while warming to the chilly Midwest. And Billy Nixon, dazzlingly fast and athletic, was not much of a factor until last year's tournament. Then this year, after a great opening against the Spartans, he was just OK until that snowy night in Ames. They were all different cats tonight.

TOMMY BARNETT: Always looking for the laugh, Coach Bennett introduced him as "The worst hairdo in college basketball!" That got things rolling. Barnett kept it rolling by deadpanning he had written a really good speech, but lost it in his 'fro! Tommy thanked God, thanked his mom and his look-alike little brother, thanked his teammates and his coaches and the fans, and was finished within the Bennett-imposed three minutes.

BILLY NIXON: Coach Bennet reminded everyone that Billy's performance against Iowa State was the best by a KU guard . . . ever. When Billy spoke he thanked God first, then his family, then Angela Hughes, the strength coach who has made such a big difference to all of these men. Like his teammate, he thanked his coaches and the fans.

THOMAS WILLIAMS: Introduced according to length of time at Kansas, Thomas was up next. Coach Bennett reminded us that in Williams' first year at Kansas he was sixth (!) in line among the KU bigs. Bennett introduced him as the most-improved Jayhawk and "the best defensive player in the United States!"

Thomas thanked God first. When he thanked his family the camera zoomed in on what had to be the proudest, giddiest, most fired-up Mom in the country. His Dad, no less proud, was simply quieter.

Two of these three seniors have already graduated. Thomas, one of the two, acknowledged the team's academic advisor, Randy Brown, who had meant so much to these three men and to countless other KU athletes. Thomas thanked Angela Hughes as well—perhaps in quiet payback for Bennett's one-liner that Hughes had been "amazingly successful with Thomas: she got him from 215 pounds to 220 in only four years."

PAUL PRESTON is not a senior; and Gene Bennett—not a fussy traditionalist but a traditionalist all the same—would not let him speak. But Paul won't be here next year, and everybody knew that, so the Jayhawk Coach had him stand up on the end line. When Coach Bennett said his name, he gave the crowd permission to give the Jayhawks' most gifted all-around player one last roar, and the 16,000 in the stands did not disappoint.

In comparison with past years—think of Wayne Simien's 25-minute sermon to the largest megachurch he is likely to preach to—this was a short evening. Billy Nixon addressed this in his remarks when he observed the team was "focused" on the "unfinished business" ahead. His coach is too.

Oh, right: there was a game tonight. When it was over TCU Coach Brad Walker would remark, "It's the most difficult situation in all of college basketball . . . to come to Kansas on Senior Night." He came by his opinion honestly as the Hawks ran over and through and around and past the visitors from Fort Worth all night long.

Paul Preston had the quietest 13 points of his career, making but one jump shot—a 2-pointer from about 10 feet. He had two 3-pointers called back because of fouls on teammates. But he just did not shoot it well, going 5-for-14 from the field with the made baskets mostly layups. His senior teammates, though, had a blast! Kansas outrebounded TCU 45-23, had 18 assists to the Horned Frogs' seven, and shot 53% from the field to the visitors' 26%. Thomas Williams took and made his first-ever 3-pointer to go with 19 other points [on eight-for-nine shooting], nine boards, and four blocks. Tommy Barnett, having more fun than a guy ought to have, scored 10 the first half, made all of his free throws, and finished with 14 points and six boards.

But this gang felt the need for speed, and the guy in the lead seat of the F-35 was Billy Nixon. Billy had nine assists in the first half. But the number doesn't begin to capture what Billy was up to. Blazing across the arc and into the lane and up and down the court, Billy lofted up six first-half alley-oops that resulted in throwdowns by his buddies. Tommy Barnett rammed home a jam so ferocious I had to look twice to make sure the rim hadn't fractured, and this one came on the heels of his reverse jam off another great Billy Nixon pass. In my favorite play of the night Billy burst into the lane, saw Williams was open behind TCU's very capable center, and somehow snaked a pass through a half-dozen hands that Thomas collected nearly three feet above the rim. What resulted rattled the entire TCU bench, whose players watched awestruck as Thomas loped back up the court.

The night was full of highlight-reel efforts. Jeff Hanson made the longest, most accurate, and most opportunistic bounce pass of the season to a streaking Billy Nixon for yet another stuff. Percy Jackson, who could not buy a basket inside, stayed aggressive the entire time, got fouled repeatedly, and scored six points at the free throw line to go with his seven rebounds and four assists. It was a glorious romp, especially for the Kansas seniors.

Because I love the line, I'm going to close with the TCU coach:

Game over; press conference.

The questions were about the runouts and the alley-oops and the dunks and how the crowd seemed to get louder with each one. Asked whether that bothered him, Coach Walker shrugged. Then he smiled and said:

> "That's what they do."

Black Lives Matter

Julius Nelson's plan included Erickson's going to Black Lives Matter and enlisting their help against Matthews. So he did. Their office was in The Sabatini Multicultural Center, next to the Union on the north side. Erickson walked up the ramp of the modern brick building with the rakish angled roof, entered through the double doors, found the right office, and walked in.

"How can I help you?" asked the young Black woman behind the desk. She was maybe twenty, thought Tom Erickson, almost certainly a student, very certainly hot.

"I'd like to talk with someone who has heard about the racist teachings of Professor Matthews and who might be interested in joining me to do something about it," he answered.

"Do you have an appointment with someone here?" she asked.

It had never occurred to Tom to call ahead and make an appointment. Why would anyone need an appointment to talk with Black students about racism? But he most surely didn't have one, so he told her, "No. I don't," then added, "I'm sorry. I should have called ahead."

"Why don't you wait here?" She got up and turned toward the back of the office. "I'll see whether someone can see you. What's your name again?"

Tom hadn't taken the time to introduce himself. "Tom," he said, "Tom Erickson."

The young woman said, "OK," and disappeared around the corner.

It was a Friday afternoon and nearly every office was empty. But Emily—the young student from the front—found Khalil Abbas with his back to his open door and his focus tight on his computer. Khalil Abbas was BLM's Director. Emily knocked lightly on the door frame and stepped in.

"Khalil, a young white man just walked in who says he's Tom Erickson and wants to talk with someone about the racism of a KU faculty member, Professor Matthews. Do you want to talk with him?"

Khalil spun slowly in his chair. He liked Emily—more than he wanted people to know—but different sensors were up. There was something "off" about this visit. He knew plenty about the confrontation between Erickson and the teacher. While he hadn't watched it, he got an earful about it from people who had. Everyone he talked with thought it was a stunt. If Samuel Clemens had been a racist, and what there was to support that thesis came from the early part of Clemens' life, Erickson's failed engagement with Matthews had set the proving of it back years. The only reason Khalil could think of to talk with Erickson was to chew him out.

He said, "Why should we engage with some jumped-up white boy who got his ass handed to him by a teacher who had actually read something? No thanks. Not interested."

Emily turned out of the office and walked back to the front. "I'm very sorry, Mr. Erickson. No one is available." Ordinarily, she would have invited the student to come back the next day. She simply smiled at him.

Erickson couldn't believe he was getting the brush-off from Black Lives Matter. But there was nothing he could do about it, so he got up out of the small sofa and left the building. It was a beautiful afternoon, the unexpected high well into the eighties and only a few clouds floating across the baby-blue canvas of the sky. The tangerine halter top on the blond walking in front of him chased all thoughts about the weather. *We don't need Black Lives Matter*, he thought to himself as he turned south to follow her to the Union.

Big 12 Tournament Semifinals: Iowa State

By Sean Grogan
Lawrence, KS (AP)

The question is not, "How did Iowa State shot 68% from the field the second half in Kansas City Friday night?" The question is, "Why?"

Standard answer: Kansas couldn't guard anybody. Couldn't get stops when it had to have them; couldn't get stops the rest of the time, either.

Better answer: Michael James.

George Newman roamed the paint the second half like Warren Buffet walks the stage at his annual shareholders meeting in Omaha—he owned it. By then Michael James, who had led the 3-point barrage early and had 20 points soon after the start of the second half, was cruising at the point; and Elgin Richardson was driving it down the lane only when Newman needed a breather. That wasn't often. Final score:

IOWA STATE: 94 KANSAS: 83

"But it wasn't that close."

What happened?

PREMONITION

An elite athlete is like a stick of dynamite. The years of workouts and skill building are compressed by a superior, competitive mindset into something that can be ignited with spectacular effect. If not channeled properly, the results can be spectacularly bad for the athlete—as witnessed by the dust-up at the end of the K-State game in Lawrence several seasons ago. But the results can be spectacularly good for the athlete as well. When someone disses someone on the other team, for example, that can excite an already dangerous opponent to performance levels you don't want them to reach. Kansas, of course, is smarter than that . . . .

Friday night at the T-Mobile Center, Michael James was the fifth Cyclone to be introduced. As he stood alone at center court waiting for Billy Nixon to join him, everyone could see what an impressive athlete he was. At 6'5" and 215 pounds, the guard whose transfer to Iowa State had transformed an already good Iowa State team into something special was handsome and relaxed. Yet this was the fifth-year senior whose time at his former school had been so unpredictable, so explosive, an assistant coach reportedly asked that he be dismissed from the team. Two years ago it was James who allegedly punched a teammate at practice for not trying hard enough. Then, last spring, he allegedly threw a bottle of Gatorade at a team manager for getting his food order wrong. At the end of that season, despite another year of eligibility in his pocket, James was told his scholarship would not be renewed. That's how Iowa State got him. Famously volatile and famously talented, James had once scored 40 in a conference tournament. But he had never gone to The

Dance. That's where Iowa State wanted him to take its team, and that's where James wanted to lead them.

James was also the young man whose father had died of a cerebral aneurism during Michael's sophomore year. His dad was only 50, and that's the number we saw on Michael's chest as he waited for the Kansas point guard. Emotional in more traditional ways as well, James says he thinks of his father at the playing of the national anthem. This was the young man who, earlier this year against Baylor, had 11 assists and eight boards and five steals to go with his 30 points—numbers, his coach told reporters, "we're not used to seeing around here."

And so he stood at center court, alone in his thoughts, waiting for Billy Nixon to bounce off one last Kansas teammate and run out and give him a fist bump. But Billy forgot about Michael James; the Jayhawk point guard allowed himself to get lost in the Kansas huddle and never made it to center court. Did anyone notice? I did. And for the next few seconds a draft of the cold, outside air seemed to settle around my laptop. The already-active Iowa State crowd noticed, too, and they gave full throat to their anger at the dismissal handed out to their star. And Michael James? The 24-year-old who had found a new home in Ames and likely a father figure in his new coach? He shrugged his shoulders, turned back toward his teammates, and went to work.

FIRST HALF

Only a superlative performance by Percy Jackson and the exhausting of the emotional reserves Kansas carried over from the day before kept the Hawks in it the first 20 minutes. After the game, Coach Bennett said, "We're not going to play another team in the Tournament who's any better than Iowa State was tonight." Kansas can only hope.

Led by Michael James, whose superior speed and strength gave him separation from anyone Kansas assigned to him, the Cyclones made six of their first nine 3s and had doubled KU's score at 18-9 by the second timeout. But Thomas Williams fought hard underneath the basket and was doing a fair job of keeping Newman out of the lane, and Billy Nixon was running the offense. Although he would make no field goals Friday night, the Kansas point had seven assists and a steal, two boards, and four free throws the first half.

As a hot-shooting team almost inevitably will do, Iowa State stopped making its 3-balls, and that enabled a Kansas recovery fueled by outstanding rebounding of the Iowa State misses and an exceptional break that fed driving layups, most often by the Wichita freshman. Everyone noticed that Frank Agbani couldn't make anything, and Coach Bennett even gave him a breather—a change of scenery in the event that might revive his jumper. It didn't. But Richie Armstrong came in and made two long 3s, and Kansas went to the locker up two.

SECOND HALF

Kansas had been told to get the ball to Thomas Williams, and get it to him they did. Twice the Kansas big guy had it underneath in the opening seconds; twice the Cyclones slapped it away. When they took it back to their end, George Newman beat Agbani on a routine drive from the top of the key that forced Frank to foul him as went by. When the Cyclones threw it back in, James drained another 3.

At the 16-minute mark Richardson scored over Williams, sending the Kansas senior to the bench with his third foul. That would make a gigantic difference, but not for a few moments as Percy Jackson took it up and was fouled and made both. Those early free throws would give Jackson 23 points; he looked fabulous on offense. But neither Percy nor anyone else could keep up with Michael James. Number 50 toyed with the Wichita East graduate until the end of the next clock, then executed a picture-perfect step-back 3 that gave him his 23rd point. We were barely six minutes into the half and the Cyclones had outscored Kansas 13-4.

Frank Agbani had pretty much given up shooting the ball from outside, but he could still drive it. When he rebounded his own layup and put it back in he cut the margin to six. But another Iowa State 3-ball from James took it right back to a nine-point lead. And when Richardson burned a just-returned Thomas Williams on a chalkboard give-and-go you could have watched develop from the top of the H & R Block building, you knew Kansas was in trouble. Either tired or confused or both, but unable to keep up with the Iowa State players driving it to the basket, Williams went back to the bench with his fourth foul and opened the door for Luke Simpson, the Hawks' freshman center.

Fired up and faster than the Jayhawks, and with Williams sitting, Iowa State was now even more aggressive under the basket. Twice Percy Jackson was grabbed and pulled to the deck, the first time so obviously and so violently it baffled everyone but the most diehard Cyclones that there was no Flagrant-1 called in response. Elgin Richardson pulled Percy down the second time. But the punking Kansas was taking on its offensive glass paled in comparison to the tutorial Newman gave Simpson at the Cyclone end of the court. Three times in succession Newman beat our young center for easy layups. With Williams forced to watch from the sideline, Iowa State played through its bigs; Simpson and Jackson were powerless to stop them. Newman was fantastic in this sequence, but so was Richardson. And not all of their shots seemed easy. Newman made a difficult runner in traffic; Richardson stripped a careless Billy Nixon, led the break, and finished with a spinning layup worthy of *Swan Lake*. When Richardson stole it next from Percy Jackson, was fouled, and made both, it was Cyclones by a dozen. Kansas had been dead on its feet the entire second half and Iowa State seemed to be making everything. It was one of those nights.

At the end, his other options defeated, Gene Bennett tried a smaller lineup. Richie Armstrong joined Nixon, Abgani, Jackson, and Paul Preston. When Armstrong boldly drove it down the middle and scooped it to Jackson, Percy took it straight up, got fouled, and made both for his game-high 29th and 30th points. But on the other side of the score card were four red- and yellow-clad guys in double figures, led by Michael James.

POST-GAME

Gracious as ever, Gene Bennett complimented Iowa State's ball club and said more than once how tough it is to guard a team whose bigs can shoot it from outside as well as its guards. He noted the Cyclones went better than 50% from beyond the arc this night, much better than their performance in Lawrence. Saying out loud what every Jayhawk fan could see, especially in the second half, Coach Bennett noted, "I think I know our guys pretty well, and we played tired."

But why did Kansas play tired? Part of it was missing shots. Making shots gives you energy; missing shots drains it. That first half, when Iowa State was hitting 3-ball after 3-ball, Kansas was making a comparative nothing from the outside. Only by fantastic hustle off the occasional Iowa State miss did Kansas stay in it the first 20 minutes. In the second half, when Thomas Williams had to sit with his third and then his fourth foul, Iowa State turned the page of its playbook and drove it down the Jayhawks' throats. Scoring on layup after layup the Cyclones would shoot a gaudy 68% from the field in those final 20 minutes.

Why else did Kansas play tired? Because Iowa State was so much more active on defense. Kansas can score with anybody, but it is still uneven on defense. And when it has to work as hard for its shots as it did that first half, Kansas can get winded. The Iowa State perimeter defense was magnificent the first 20 minutes, and more than once a series of crisp passes or the Kansas weave would end up with . . . nothing. Nothing but the ball at the top of the key and 25 seconds burned off the clock and Billy Nixon desperately seeking a shooter.

Two good basketball teams played the early game Friday night, but one was so much more into it than the other: more active, more aggressive, more “tuned up,” to borrow a Gene Bennett expression. As both played hard games the day before, what accounts for the difference?

If I had only one person to ask, I’d pick the guy wearing number 50.

Finding A Witness

"W*hat we need is a witness*—someone who was in the class; someone who will tell the panel you did not lose control of it and that you did not demean Mr. Erickson."

Andrew Stevenson sat behind his desk in his office in the law school. It was like all the other offices on the fourth floor—twelve by twelve feet with a built-in oak bookcase behind the desk. Oak louvers could be closed over the narrow, full-length, glass panel next to the door to create some privacy. As it was past 9:00 p.m. and there was not a soul in the stacks outside the office, the louvers were open; so was the door. Jake Matthews sat across from him. Both had their feet up on Andrew's desk.

"But it can't be a TA," Andrew went on.

"Why not?" Jake wasn't upset, just curious

"Bias," said Andrew. "The idea is your TAs all adore you and would say anything to help, even if it wasn't strictly true. Better to avoid that."

"OK," said Jake. "Maybe this person could help." He reached into the pocket of his leather aviator's jacket, pulled out a small cream-colored envelope that might have accompanied an expensive birthday card, and handed it across to Andrew.

"Professor Matthews" was written on the front in a flowing blue script. Andrew opened it.

Inside was a card: it had a narrow border in Persian red and an embossed monogram at the top—"FB." The monogram, in gold, employed a restrained classic font. Below the monogram was the date: the card was written the same day as the class period at issue, the message began just beneath the date. Andrew read it to both of them.

Dear Professor Matthews,

I am one of your students in Philosophy 275 and was there today when Mr. Erickson jumped onto the stage. I thought he behaved abominably.

I have enjoyed your class this semester. Your other students are not rude like Mr. Erickson.

Sincerely yours,

Farieh Bukhari

"Do you know this person?" asked Andrew, carefully returning the card to the envelope and handing the envelope back to Jake.

"She's a student in the class, but I have never really met her. I found this in my box in Wescoe the next morning. I read it, then put it in my jacket pocket and forgot it was there until tonight, when you asked about a witness. Just lucky I was wearing the same jacket."

"Farieh is a woman's name in Arabic," Andrew continued. "She's probably from Iran—the red on the card is Persian red. And she's probably Muslim. If she still wears the hijab, she would be perfect."

"That's pretty clinical, even for you," said Jake, his eyebrow raised. "Maybe we should meet her and she what she has to say rather than using her because she looks the part."

"Touché," responded Andrew. "It's 10:00, probably too late to call. Can you get her contact information from the philosophy department?"

Jake responded: "Her address is on the back of the envelope. She's at Miller Scholarship Hall. Let me try tomorrow morning. I'll let you know what I come up with."

"Deal," said Andrew. "It's not too late to get a beer. You game?"

"One," said Jake. "Tomorrow's Wednesday; I've got 275 again tomorrow morning. But I can do one."

Andrew turned the light off and they made their way to the east end of the stacks. Circling north to the stairs, they walked down to the main floor and past the courtroom and out into the cool March evening.

Cowboy Stadium

By Sean Grogan
Lawrence, KS (AP)

This was my first time in a stadium where the video board is as big as my back yard.

FIRST HALF

If the cheers during the introductions were a good indicator, Kansas fans outnumbered the folks in orange and blue by a substantial margin. Soon enough we were underway, and the Hawks got a good start. Billy Nixon got the first layup; Thomas Williams followed that quickly with a dunk; Paul Preston, on his way to a very good night, blocked a layup attempt. Then came the Flagrant-1 on Billy. No question he collided with the Auburn center as he went by him. But sorting out whether Billy's elbow hit the freshman on the shoulder—or on the back of his head—took a long time in front of the monitor. When all three refs had at last reached their consensus they shared it with the coaches, and Gene Bennett shrugged his shoulders as if to say, "OK, if that's what you saw." McGuff went to the line and missed both free throws.

Then, maybe a minute later, at 16:43, Billy got his second personal and Jeff Hanson came in. Jeff played well and Kansas appeared to have weathered this odd opening. Richie Armstrong hit a jumper off a busted play; Percy Jackson got a put-back; Hanson made two layups on two strong drives; and it was Kansas up 20-11. Luke Simpson came in and blocked a shot, and when Paul Preston made a three-pointer it was Kansas 25-17. No one expected this to be a runaway; Auburn was good and McGuff in particular was playing well the first half. Still, there was lots to be happy about, not the least of which Paul Preston, who followed up a layup with a dunk off an alley-oop and followed the dunk with a banked-in 3. When Tommy Barnett swept up Frank's miss it was 38-28 and everybody in KU blue was smiling. But Jeff stepped on the end line, Auburn got it, and McGuff—shooting from outside this time—hit again. Williams, who had run out to the shooter late and had fouled him, gave the big freshman a chance at a 4-point play, which he cashed. On Auburn's next possession it was Paul's turn to foul the 3-point shooter; and when Auburn made all three the margin was down to five: 40-35. When both teams ran poor plays at the end of the half, both teams limped off the court to the same score.

SECOND HALF

Auburn came out fired up, beating our guards off the dribble and pushing it inside for layups. Seeing the same thing from his spot on the court and spotting the cause as well—Trey Bishop, Coach Bennett switched Agbani to the Auburn All-American. The result was the best stretch of the game for Kansas with Paul hitting a three and Billy taking it coast to coast for a layup and a foul. Paul missed his next 3. But he got his own rebound, sidestepped two defenders, and laid it in left-handed for his 17th point of the game. When Paul made yet another 3 it was 61-50 Kansas.

Paul had found his shot and was playing beautifully on offense, but he is still weak defensively. When Bishop beat him at the 8:35 mark and Paul drew his fourth foul trying to catch up, Coach Bennett had to put his star wing on the bench. He would not return until the 3:14 mark—remember that time—and he would not score again in the game. Meanwhile, Auburn ran its anti-Thomas Williams offense to perfection: Bishop beats his man and gets loose in the paint; Thomas comes out to pick him up; Bishop dishes to an uncovered McGuff; McGuff flushes it. One of those should have been plenty for Kansas. But Auburn liked the play, and they ran it over and over.

3:14. That's what the clock read when Kansas called its timeout and the action stopped. When the action resumed, I thought it was a Jayhawk moment. The Hawks are really good out of timeouts: Billy one-handed a scoop to Tommy who was unexpectedly camped out at the elbow; Tommy spied Thomas Williams easing up the end line and got him the ball; Williams buried it.

But much, much more had been going on. We'll spend the rest of this talking about energy, and about Billy.

ENERGY

Kansas was up eight at the 3:14 timeout and up 10 only seconds later. But it was the Tigers who came out playing with passion. In that timeout Greg Robertson III told his teammates what Thomas Williams had said to his during last weekend's second game in Des Moines: "This is our last go-round. We might regret this the rest of our lives if we don't step up now." Excepting only the Thomas Williams dunk off the splendid passes from Billy to

Tommy and from Tommy to the Jayhawk center, what followed showed how bad things can happen to good people when you get out-hustled by gifted athletes who are desperate to win. Trey Bishop figured in more of this than his last 3-pointer. He fouled Billy Nixon at least three times those last three minutes as Billy was bringing the ball toward half court. But refs give a wide berth to All-Americans, especially in The Tournament. And instead of calling a foul on Bishop they whistled Nixon for a travel! Bishop's shooting had become unconscious in the closing minutes, and his 3-pointer over a late-arriving Thomas Williams made it 74-69 KU with 1:12 left.

The tectonic plates had just started to move at 3:14. When the ball got loose in the Auburn corner at the 1:12 mark the ground split open. This was a classic 50-50 ball. Gene Bennett would say later, "We had the [possession] arrow; all we had to do was fall on it!" But we didn't. Instead, Greg Robertson III, whom Kansas had handled to that point, pulled it out of the scrum and—from his knees—lofted a prayer of a reverse layup high off the glass . . . and made it! KU again had the ball. But the Kansas lead that had seemed so solid two minutes ago was now three, and for the first time that evening KU seemed in a position to lose not only its lead but the game itself. When Billy missed the front end of a one-and-one that possibility became palpable.

Everyone knew Trey Bishop would bring it up for the last shot in regulation; everyone knew Trey Bishop would take it. Like his friend John Calipari, Gene Bennett does not like to foul in the back court in this situation and Kansas did not foul Bishop in the back court. But neither did Kansas believe Bishop would pull up eight feet (!) behind the arc and shoot it from there. And when yet another Trey Bishop basket slipped through the net to send it to overtime, the game seemed as over as it would finally prove to be.

BILLY NIXON

The Flagrant-1 on Billy gave me concern at the time and still does. Gene Bennett was asked about the elbow to the head after the game and said, "That's not how Kansas plays." But McGuff got hit hard; the refs said he got hit in the head; and I have absolutely no doubt the big freshman played a stronger game because of it. He may have missed the two free throws they gave him then, but he made everything else. And his line for the game was a career best in a tournament game. When McGuff was questioned about it in the press conference, he told the reporters the entire Auburn team played harder after the foul.

Billy did more than fire up the Tigers on a night Kansas did not need them to find the extra energy. He took himself out of the first half. When his second whistle came almost immediately after the first his coach, concerned for the guys in the striped shirts, made a sound judgment call to pull him. When Billy went back in late in the first half, he was whistled for his third foul only moments later and had to go back to his seat. Not the first 20 minutes you want from your point guard in the Sweet 16.

Billy was a factor as well at the end of regulation: the 2008 game loomed in reverse as he missed the front end of the one-and-one that would likely have won it for Kansas. And his surprising kick-out to Jeff Hanson at the end of the overtime, elected in the middle of a driving layup he had nearly completed, was so hard and so high Jeff could barely catch it, let alone shoot it.

There are Jayhawk fans who are mad at Billy—that goes with the territory when you're the Kansas point guard and you lose in The Tournament. When you feature prominently in the loss the criticism is that much harder to shake. But Billy did not lose the game for Kansas: he had made plenty of free throws before he missed the last one in regulation; he made a three-pointer in OT without which the Hawks would have had no chance; he was the center point of the Jayhawk defense that caused the shot-clock violation at the end of the OT and gave Kansas its last possession.

When I remember Billy Nixon, it will be for other moments and for other games. I will remember his playing out of position for three years, then having to "become" the Kansas point guard his senior season. I will remember his playing hurt so much of this season and saying not a word about it. I will remember him for losing barely a handful of games his senior year but accepting responsibility for every single loss. I will remember how Kansas earned a "1" seed in the NCAA Tournament and who the point guard was when they did. And I will remember that snowy night in Ames, when he put his team on his back and saved another Big 12 regular season title for Kansas.

Billy Nixon is a Jayhawk. That's how I will remember him.

First Day of Trial

The evidence had started at 9:30 a.m. after short opening statements from both sides. Never thinking to call Matthews as his own witness, Alex Cartwright was done by 11:00.

He had called a communications tech first, had her play the videotape of the classroom encounter, then offered the tape into evidence. Stevenson made no objection. Then he called his "victim," Tom Erickson. Cartwright dealt gingerly with Erickson. He moved rapidly through Erickson's background as a KU student, his being selected for the Honors Program, and his choosing philosophy as a major. As Erickson had never mentioned the debate team to Cartwright, Cartwright never asked him about it once he took the stand. At the end of his examination, Cartwright replayed the last portion of the tape—the several lead-up questions asked by Matthews and then the last one. When he had finished, he asked Erickson to tell the panel how he had felt when Matthews had shouted that last question at him. "Humiliated," Erickson answered, "I was humiliated."

They had worked on the answer over the weekend. "Embarrassed" didn't have the impact Cartwright was looking for; "scared" didn't fit at all; options like "taken aback" were far too fussy. It was Erickson who suggested "humiliated," and that's what they went with. Erickson had addressed his last answer to the panel, just as the university's lawyer had told him to do. Cartwright thought the direct had gone well—very well. "Thank you, Mr. Erickson," he said, "I'm sure that was difficult for you." He had almost sat down when he remembered he had to say something to Andrew Stevenson: "Your witness."

CROSS-EXAMINATION

Stevenson's tone was conversational when he began with Erickson, but not friendly. No one in the Snell Courtroom would have mistaken them for friends.

"Let's start at the chalkboard." Andrew's team had brought it forward at the conclusion of Cartwright's brief direct examination, placing it just outside the witness box and facing the witness and the panel. "Will a chalkboard work for you, Mr. Erickson?"

Not waiting on an answer to the carefully-crafted rhetorical question, Andrew walked to the board and picked up the one piece of chalk that lay in the tray. Taking it as Erickson had in Jacob Matthew's class, sideways—its length against the slate—Andrew wrote out the word he wanted in very tall letters:

DEMEAN

Then he returned the chalk to the tray and took the few steps to his counsel table, picking up the book that was on the corner. "I believe we can agree on the meaning of this word, Mr. Erickson. *Webster's Collegiate Dictionary*, the book I am holding . . . ," Stevenson lifted the book so everyone in the courtroom might recognize its distinctive red dust jacket, "defines it this way: 'to lower in character or reputation.'

We'll begin with reputation: what other people think of you. When you were a KU freshman you were briefly a member of the debate team. You and your first colleague did poorly in your first tournament, and your colleague—a young woman—asked to be moved to a different team. Coach Daniel moved her, replacing her with Karen West, another first-year member of the team. Karen West is one of the students who moved the chalkboard up from the back. Perhaps you recognized her?

You and Ms. West debated as colleagues at a tournament at Emporia State University. At the conclusion of this second tournament your colleague—again a woman, this time Ms. West—asked to be moved to a different team. While I know all of this is familiar to you, Mr. Erickson, I will say for the panel's benefit that we're still dealing with background information.

This time the head debate coach asked you to come to his office, and you did. When you arrived, he told you of the accusations that had been made against you, both by Ms. West and by your first colleague, Ms. McKinney. Both said you were not prepared to give an effective speech as the first negative. In fact, they said you were entirely unprepared. They reported you had done no research, and they said you cited no research in any of the debates. Ms. West reported the only *authority* you offered in your entire first negative at Emporia State was the Bible.

At the conclusion of the Emporia State tournament, Ms. West confronted you. She was angry. She felt you had embarrassed her—and the entire team—by not preparing for the tournament, and she wanted to know why. And you answered her. You told her you had several *dates* in the time leading up to the tournament, and you had to do your *laundry*."

At the mention of "laundry," a number of the students in the court room who were watching Erickson made subdued but audible exclamations.

"By the way, Coach Daniel was willing to join us this morning, Mr. Erickson, in case you hadn't noticed him in the court room." Erickson hadn't; Erickson hadn't noticed much of anything to this point. Seth Daniel raised his hand from the back row.

"Everything I've said so far is correct, Mr. Erickson, is it not?"

Erickson said nothing. But he nodded affirmatively.

"Coach Daniel wanted to know whether Karen West's report on Emporia State—on the state of your preparation for it and on your explanation of why you hadn't prepared—was correct, and you told him it was. That's also true, isn't it?"

Erickson was now looking past Stevenson and directly at his former debate coach. Seth Daniel was looking directly back at him. Erickson nodded again.

Stevenson turned and directed his next question at Coach Daniel. "And because that level of commitment to debate, that kind of regard for one's colleague and for the entire debate team, is unacceptable to the debate program at Kansas, Coach Daniel dismissed you from the team. Isn't that also true? This time, Mr. Erickson, will you please make your answer out loud?"

Erickson considered a more elaborate response, thought better of it, and settled for "Yes."

Stevenson turned around, left the counsel table, and moved to the lectern, crossing from the panel's left to the panel's right as he did so. When he stopped, he pivoted back toward the witness and went on.

"Let's talk next about character. I want you to accept for the purpose of my questioning that 'integrity' is important to having a good character. Will you do that, please?"

Erickson's eyes had wandered to the panel. As he began to nod up and down, he spotted a frown forming between Professor Robert's eyes and lips. Catching himself he said, "Yes, sure."

"Will you also accept that academic integrity is important to The University of Kansas?"

Alert now, concerned with the direction of the examination but certain the only answer to the question hanging out there was "Yes," Erickson gave that answer.

With his left hand, Stevenson picked up the stack of papers on the lectern. He handed the page on top to Cartwright as he was walking past him and continued to the witness box, placing the second page on the flat surface in front of Erickson. Standing right next to the witness, Stevenson continued. "Mr. Erickson, do you recognize this as a copy of the University of Kansas' letter to you of last semester? It advises that as you had *admitted* to the accusation against you—you were accused of plagiarizing the work of another person for your own take-home, mid-term exam, the university found you had violated the Honor Code and placed you on academic probation."

Erickson had not worked much with Alex Cartwright in preparation for his testimony. They had gone over it last week, but quickly—maybe thirty minutes, tops. Never thinking to ask his young witness whether there were skeletons in his closet, Cartwright had not gone there. And the honors violation was hardly something Erickson used as a conversation starter with someone he just met, like Cartwright. Both were caught cold by the exhibit and the question that came with it, and neither could think of a response.

The immediate problem for Cartwright was the question: it seemed fair. No objection bubbled up on its own, and he could not think of one. For Erickson, the immediate problem was being outed in front of so many students. He did not embarrass easily, but he was embarrassed now.

Stevenson broke into the quiet: "Mr. Erickson—the letter; do you recognize it? That was my question."

"Y-y-yes," stuttered Erickson. "Yes, that's the letter."

"When the panel reads the letter, Mr. Erickson, they will see that the person who accused you of plagiarism—the person responsible for your being placed on academic probation and nearly losing your place as a student here—was none other than Professor Matthews. Isn't that correct?"

"That's right," said the witness.

"If I were to suggest, Mr. Erickson, that your confrontation with Professor Matthews earlier this semester had nothing to do with Mark Twain, or General Grant, or Huck Finn, or anything else from the nineteenth century but everything to do with your wanting revenge against Professor Matthews for what happened just last fall . . . what would you say to that?"

Erickson made a spirited and articulate answer. "No," he began. "That's not it at all. I was reacting to the class Professor Matthews was teaching this semester, not to anything that happened between us before. Rock Stars is a racist platform. It tries to make heroes out of two white guys from the nineteenth century who either made fun of slaves or owned them. We don't need that here."

But under cross-examination, timing is everything. Erickson had taken too long. When he did respond, he was too insistent; and his voice, which until then had been understated, was approaching shrill.

"I have one final topic for you, Mr. Erickson, which also touches on integrity. Before I get into it, though, I want to clarify something. Is the academic probation that was imposed on you by The University of Kansas last semester, in response to your plagiarism, still in effect?"

"Yes—until the end of this semester."

"All right. In that event, I will not require you to *answer* my next several questions. But I *am* going to ask them."

"In the spring of this year, *The Wall Street Journal* published an article on what it described as the 'surge' of cheating at the nation's universities. The article reported on what are called 'auction sites,' online sites where students who want homework or papers or take-home exams done for them by someone else can specify what grade was required—an 'A,' for example—and can provide a 'willing-to-pay' ceiling price for the work. Persons on the site who were willing to take on the work would then 'bid' for the opportunity to do it. Have you heard of such sites at KU?"

Erickson had gone to full alert at Stevenson' preface. But as the question went on, he realized he had not heard of any such auction site. He was at ease when the question concluded, and he responded with a prompt and relaxed "No."

Stevenson had one more question:

> Whether across an online auction site or in any other setting, have you ever accepted money to write a paper assigned to another student at KU?

The question was of course grounded on Erickson's Have Gun, Will Travel-patterned web site, which Jack Smith had found.

The question hung over Erickson like the spring snowpack on a high mountain ridge teeters over a back-country skier just before it becomes an avalanche. Try as he could, Erickson could not think of a way to outrun it. Time passed; he just sat there. Andrew Stevenson waited until even *he* became uncomfortable. Then he waited a moment longer. Then he spoke. His statement was for the witness, but he was looking at the panel.

"I said I would not require an answer of you, Mr. Erickson, and I won't."

Andrew went back to his own table, turned to the university's lawyer, and—still standing—said, "That was my last question, Mr. Cartwright. Your witness."

While Alex Cartwright did not appreciate the full extent of the wreckage lying in the witness box, he was not prepared to repair what he did recognize. He stood up. "Nothing, Mr. Chairman. We have no questions."

"Then, Mr. Erickson," said the Chairman, "you may be excused. We'll take a short recess, everyone. Let's try to be back in ten minutes."

Jacob Matthew's Defense

Jacob Matthews was his own first witness and took up the rest of the morning with ease. He was charismatic; Alex Cartwright had expected that. But he had not expected him to be funny. The morning ended on a belly laugh that even the panel broke up over, and the laughter carried everyone out of the courtroom and off to lunch.

Alex had prepared carefully for the direct examination he conducted during his own case. But he had only two witnesses—Erickson and the communications tech who introduced the video and then ran it. Alex used the noon recess to review his cross-examination outline for Professor Matthews. While he had never conducted a cross-examination before except in law school, he was at least proud of the outline. It bristled with detail, it covered the entire case, and he had a few surprises up his sleeve. Alex assumed Stevenson would take another hour after lunch, maybe ninety minutes, and then it would be his turn.

Not without his own surprises, Stevenson had taken but a moment after lunch to have Matthews authenticate a copy of his CV and the syllabus for the Rockstars course, both of which he introduced into the record. Then he announced he had concluded his questions and sat down. Way before he was ready to start, it was Alex's turn. He stood up, walked to the lectern, gripped it harder than he had intended to, and lifted his head.

Alex knew he had to maintain eye contact; his Litigation teacher at Tulsa had stressed how important that was to control the witness. As Alex's eyes bore into Matthews', Alex wondered how the philosophy professor could possibly withstand the intellectual pressure he was exerting. Matthews seemed not only unphased but perhaps a little bored.

Alex began: "You have been on the faculty at KU for fourteen years, is that correct?"

The first question was suggested by Julie Samford, the number three lawyer at KU and Alex's immediate supervisor. It was the first step to establishing Matthews' knowledge of the Faculty Code of Conduct. The University had charged him with violating the code; Julie felt it important to show Matthews knew the contents of the code or should have known them.

This would have been basic stuff for any trial lawyer, but Alex was no trial lawyer. Barely out of law school, Alex had taken the job at KU without a thought that he would one day—and soon, as it turned out—be selected as "lead counsel" for the most publicized legal event at the University of Kansas in years. Unsteady with the ever-shifting currents in the court room, Alex was equally unaware of the political currents flowing over and around this prosecution. There were lawyers on the staff of KU's general counsel who had tried cases, including the general counsel, herself. But none of them wanted anything to do with this hearing. And there was no money in the law department budget to retain experienced outside counsel. That left Alex.

"Yes," said Matthews, a picture of composure in the high witness box just left of the five members of the faculty panel, who were side-by-side atop the bench. Matthews' shoulders were even with Alex's eyes, and his head was a good twelve inches higher than Alex's.

Alex looked down for his next question. The lectern was empty: no notepad; no binder. Alex's trial notebook, his "must-have" for this witness, sat where he had left it on the table across the well of the courtroom. "Shit!" he said under his breath, instantly red-faced but grateful the microphone had not caught it and broadcast it from wall to wall. He said, "Excuse me for just a moment," fetched the black binder, opened it, and continued.

"You recall you were given a copy of the Faculty Code of Conduct when you were first hired at KU, correct?"

Again a "Yes" from Matthews.

"And you remember you received another copy of the Code of Conduct when you received tenure here at KU, isn't that right?"

Another "Yes."

"So, you are aware, Professor Matthews, that KU faculty are prohibited from demeaning their students, especially in a classroom setting, am I correct?"

"You are," Matthews replied from his superior position, still at ease.

Alex's Trial Tactics class flashed in front of him. He was actually doing cross-examination! Short questions, ones he knew the answers to, ones that required a "Yes" answer or the witness would be fairly subjected to criticism for evasion or equivocation. Alex could not help the smile that flickered across his face. He went on.

"So why was it, Professor Matthews, that in your disagreement with Mr. Erickson, which took place during your class, you used the F-word when addressing him?"

The sound of his question had barely reached the back row when Alex recognized he had violated the cardinal rule of cross-examination: *Never Ask "Why?"!* Until then he been pleased with himself, pleased at his surprising facility with this darkest of the dark arts of trial practice. Had he thought about it—and he hadn't—he would have known Matthews and Stevenson had spent hours preparing for this very question.

The classroom confrontation had been filmed by dozens of cell phones pulled hastily from pockets and duffels and backpacks as soon as it started. The F-word had come at the end, just before Matthews had left the lecture hall; everything else was crescendo. The *University Daily Kansan* had made Matthews' final question its headline—in the very same font it rolled out to announce the basketball team's national championship. Everybody knew this was coming, everybody knew Cartwright had to ask about it, and Alex had served it up on a platter.

Not for nothing had Jacob Matthews mastered the art of teaching in the University's largest classrooms. And not for nothing was he able to communicate past the hundreds of actual seats in Wescoe Hall to the thousands of virtual seats scattered across the internet. Jake knew what a pregnant pause was for, and when it had passed, he answered:

"Because he deserved it."

The court room erupted! High-fives everywhere. Shrill whistles leapt from countless fingers to crash against the walls of the hard-sided space. Quickly frustrated in his effort to call the courtroom to order, the Chair settled for a ten-minute recess.

Alex's attempts to "control" Matthews with leading questions after the recess had been a total failure. The low point came after Alex had established what he thought was a gaping hole in the professor's preparation for the Rock Stars course. He had listened carefully as Stevenson led Matthews from the idea for the course through trying it out on his colleagues to the university's main library, Watson, where he had honed his already-broad knowledge of Samuel Clemens and Ulysses S. Grant, "working late into the night in the dimly-lighted stacks at the back of the third floor." Every member of the panel knew that scene. They'd all been there: dusty books arrayed on narrow metal shelves, narrow metal desks with hard metal chairs, boiling in the summer and freezing in the winter, wishing KU would one day find the money to put it all online.

But missing from Matthews' tale of hard-scrabble scholarship was any mention of the contemporary rock stars, his foils for Mark Twain. Alex pounced.

"Professor Matthews, you have talked at length about your preparation for your class and about how you spent all this time at the university's main library, correct?"

Jake agreed he had.

"And you identified the people you felt it was important to read about, correct? To confirm what you already knew about them and, ideally, to learn something new, is that right?"

Jake agreed it was.

"This kind of work is really the foundation for academic integrity, isn't it, sir?"

"I suppose you could say that," Jake responded. "It would be at least presumptuous to try to teach someone else when you knew nothing about the subject, yourself."

"And you named Samuel Clemens—whom we know as Mark Twain, correct? He was one of the people you studied at Watson?"

"Yes," said the witness.

"And you named General Grant, correct?"

"Yes."

"But you did not name Madonna, or Taylor Swift, or Elton John, or Beyoncé, or Garth Brooks, or Lady Gaga . . . did you?"

"No, I didn't."

"And yet all of them are also featured in your class, isn't that right?"

"Yes, they are," Jake said more quietly.

Alex wished a hundred times since that he had stopped with that last answer. But he hadn't stopped because he did not know to stop. Just the opposite. He took a few steps to draw attention to himself, turned just a little too fast to face his witness, and asked just a little too sarcastically:

"So how *is* it, Professor Matthews, that you satisfied your *obligation* to academic *integrity* for all of these others?"

"I went to their concerts."

The students in the courtroom erupted again—applause first, then yelling. High-fives once again marched up and down the long tables. The chair called another recess, but only five minutes this time, barely time for milling around in the hallway and outside the front door of the law building.

When everyone had returned to the court room and the chair nodded to Alex to continue, Alex mumbled "Nothing further" and sat down.

Andrew Stevenson may well have had some questions for redirect. But Stevenson knew when to stop, and he did.

After Professor Matthews stepped down from the witness box and took his seat next to his lawyer, Stevenson called several other witnesses to establish Jake's academic bona fides and his character. As discouraged as he had been in a long while, Alex answered the testimony of each with "No questions."

By the time Stevenson had called his last character witness and Alex had passed on cross-examination for the last time, it was 4:40.

Noticing the break in the witnesses as well as the time, Professor Wojcek looked down over his wire-rims: "Professor Stevenson, do you have any other witnesses for this afternoon?" Stevenson was still standing, although looking down at his own trial notebook. He looked up at the Chairman and said, "Yes, we do." Then he turned to the back of the courtroom to find Karen West, one of the four students assisting Stevenson and his client.

Green Hall's courtroom had been a gift from the name partner of a prominent Phoenix firm who had graduated from KU's law school. It was initially designed by the same architect who designed the building, but it was modified by a Phoenix architect who specialized in courthouses. At the rear, just inside the double-doored entrance, was a kind of auditory breakwater—a tall, wooden barrier that separated the well of the courtroom and the jury box and the bench from the noise of the students as they entered from and left to the school's main entry hall. Karen West was standing next to the breakwater. She nodded at Stevenson, then reached down toward the young woman sitting beside her and touched her on the shoulder. The woman was tall; and when she stood, everyone in the room could see she was wearing a head scarf. It was beautiful, its soft fabric draping elegantly and its colors playing back and forth in a modern adaptation of a classic Persian design. It was a scarf of many colors, but two were unmistakable: crimson and blue. Without turning his back on her to face the panel, Andrew Stevenson announced his witness to the entire courtroom: "We call Ms. Farieh Bukhari."

Farieh Bukhari Takes the Stand

Farieh had been walked from just this seat to the witness box the week before, a small facet of Stevenson's witness preparation. Everyone had to see the courtroom before they testified; everyone had to approach the witness stand; everyone had to sit in the chair. Testifying was unsteadying enough; witnesses didn't need the extra pressure of not knowing where to go when their name was called, or of being confused by the awkwardness of the witness stand. Making her way to the front of the court room, Farieh stepped confidently up into the witness box and sat down. Almost immediately she made a graceful turn to the panel and smiled at them. Janek Wojcek had been reading his notes as Farieh approached them and did not really look at her until he raised his hand to swear her in. That's when he saw her eyes. "Do you swear . . . " became "Do you . . . do you . . . do you swear . . ." When at last he got the entire question out, Farieh answered "I do" and turned to face Andrew Stevenson.

Stevenson had carried his trial notebook to the lectern for every other witness. This time he walked the six paces without it. Only when he was facing her straight on did he begin.

"Will you please tell the panel your name?"

She did.

"Are you a student at KU?"

She was.

"What are you studying?"

"I have completed my degree in mathematics. I am studying petroleum engineering, English literature, and history."

"Are you a first-year student?"

She was.

"Did you enroll in Professor Matthews' class this spring, Philosophy 275?"

She did.

"Were you in Professor Matthews' class in Wescoe Hall on February 7 of this year?"

"Yes, I was."

"Were you there when another student, a Mr. Erickson, jumped up onto the stage of the classroom and began what I will call 'a conversation' with Professor Matthews about the class?"

"Yes, I was."

"Were you there for the entire conversation between Professor Mattthews and his student?"

"I was."

"Were you there until Professor Matthews left the classroom? To ask that another way, did you remain in the classroom until Professor Matthews walked all the way out?"

"Yes. I was still there when he left the room."

"Where were you seated when the class began?"

"I was in the second row, six or seven seats left of the center aisle."

"Did you have a clear view of Professor Matthews? And of Mr. Erickson? And of the chalkboard on the stage?"

"Yes. I could see Professor Matthews and the student, and I had a clear view of the chalkboard."

"Did the conversation become animated at some point?"

As Farieh began her answer it was plain that *she* was becoming animated.

"I thought the conversation was *animated* from the very beginning," she began. Leaning forward slightly, her voice rising in intensity, she continued. "I was not prepared for the student's *aggressiveness*. He was attacking Professor Matthews from the beginning. Professor Matthews stood his ground, but he did so politely, and that just made Erickson angry. And after that he was just a *bully*."

"Objection!" Cartwright had nearly jumped out of his chair to make his objection, but he was too excited to give a reason for it. That would have been a problem for Cartwright with a real judge in a real courtroom. But here it was a problem for the panel chair, Professor Wojcek, who had encountered no objections so far and did not know what to do with this one.

Andrew Stevenson let Professor Wojcek off the hook. "Ms. Bukhari, I understand you have feelings about what happened in class that day. And I know many other students do, too. But the panel is just interested in what you saw and heard." Turning his attention from his witness to the Chairman, Stevenson continued: "Mr. Chairman, we agree with Mr. Cartwright that Ms. Bukhari's calling Mr. Erickson a bully was beyond the scope of my question, and we have no objection to 'bully' being removed from the record."

Wearing a self-satisfied smirk that his objection had been conceded, and with no appreciation for what had actually just happened, Cartwright sat down.

"Ms. Bukhari, do you own a cell phone?"

"Yes, I do."

"Did you have it with you during the class we are talking about?"

"Yes, I did."

"Did you use it to make a video recording of what happened between Professor Matthews and his student?"

"Yes, I did."

"Have you looked at the video recording since you made it?"

"Yes."

"Do you believe your video recording fairly and accurately describes what happened in the classroom that day?"

"Yes, it does. It shows what happened."

"Did you give your recording to my assistant, Ms. West? Did the two of you bring it to the courtroom this afternoon? And are you prepared to play it for the panel?"

"Yes. We did all that."

"And is what I have marked as Matthews Exhibit 14 a copy of your cellphone video that you have been referring to?"

"Yes. That's the recording."

Stevenson turned his attention to Janek Wojcek. "Mr. Chairman, we have previously given a copy of this recording to Mr. Cartwright. We offer Exhibit 14 into evidence now, and we ask your permission to play it for the panel at this time."

Professor Wojcek looked over his glasses at the university's counsel. "Mr. Cartwright?"

Cartwright stood up, already speaking as he did so. "We have no objection to the recording being received as part of the record, Mr. Chairman. But we do object to playing it. The panel has already seen a video of what happened that day during the university's case; this would simply be repetitive, and it's already past five o'clock."

"May I respond," asked Stevenson.

"Yes, of course," said the Chairman.

"What the panel saw was not the entire encounter. The university's version of the recording was cut off immediately after Professor Matthews' last statement to Mr. Erickson—a question, actually." Students throughout the courtroom suppressed their laughter at Stevenson's clarification.

"The panel did not see Professor Matthews leave the classroom, and the panel did not see the reaction made to all of this by the rest of his students. We believe that reaction is important. In a courtroom, this principle is called the rule of completeness; it calls for the presentation of the entire recording—or document or whatever—when playing just a portion of it would be incomplete or misleading. Here, we believe the video recording shown you by the university was incomplete. We're prepared to show the entire encounter now, and we would like to do so."

Professor Wojcek looked straight ahead for a moment, then he turned to Cartwright. "Mr. Cartwright, we understand this encounter between Professor Matthews and Mr. Erickson was recorded by dozens of students, maybe more than that. Is what Professor Stevenson says correct? Did the recording you played yesterday end early, if you will—before Professor Matthews left the room, and before any reaction by the rest of the students?"

There was only one right answer to the question. Cartwright knew what it was, and he knew there was no way to prevent what was about to happen—only mitigate it. He stood up, cleared his throat, and answered: "The charge the university is bringing has to do with what Professor Matthews said to Mr. Erickson before he left the stage, not what happened after that. That is why the recording we played yesterday ended when it did." He cleared his throat again. "But we have no objection to Professor Stevenson's playing the video recording he brought this afternoon, even though the panel has seen virtually all of it before." He sat down.

"Very well," said Professor Wojcek. "Please play your tape, Professor Stevenson."

Cartwright had played his video recording at the start of the day, just after 9:00 a.m., when the morning sun that breached the courtroom's east windows had dulled every image projected on the screen. It was now just after 5:00; the sun had nearly set on the west side of Green Hall; and Stevenson's team, which had measured the windows the week before, had just covered them in carefully-cut black-out shades. When Karen West cued up the video on her laptop, Erickson fairly jumped onto the screen opposite the jury box—every color bright, every muscle taut. For Erickson, it had been game-on from the moment he vaulted the stage, and this time the panel could see that clearly.

Stevenson stood to the side as the panel watched the scenes again. While there had been only a single day of evidence so far, what evidence there was had dealt with the two antagonists and their character. What the panel had heard was that Erickson was a jerk, and a lazy one, and that Matthews was brilliant, innovative, funny, and hugely popular. Viewed in a context entirely absent that morning, this afternoon's video presented an ambush—carefully laid and unrelenting—and the determined efforts of a fine teacher to withstand it. Stevenson asked Karen to stop the video after Matthews had flung his final question at Erickson. With the screen frozen around Matthews' folding his notebook, just before he left the stage, Stevenson moved from where he had been standing and watching to his now-familiar spot in front of the panel.

"You will remember this is where the university's version ended. There are another fifty-seven seconds to watch. As we said a few minutes ago, you will see Professor Matthews leave the classroom. And you will see how his students responded. Karen, please go ahead."

The screen came back to life. On screen again, Jacob Matthews picked up his notebook, stepped down the stairs to his right, and made his way to the center. Then he turned and took his first slow steps up the slope of the aisle toward the door at the top. He had cleared the third row when the first student stood and began to applaud. By the time Matthews reached the center of the classroom, every student in every row behind him was standing and clapping, and the ones in front of him were leaving their seats. When he opened the door and walked out of sight the video showed only the backs of the students—*all* were standing, and the only sound was their applause.

"May we have the lights again?" asked Stevenson. The team had them on immediately.

"Ms. Bukhari, I have two more questions for you. The university's charge is a written document. At the end of it, even though Professor Matthews is not charged with any sort of racial insensitivity, the university criticizes him for not erasing what Mr. Erickson had written on the chalkboard." Stevenson stopped, walked back to counsel table, reached down for a single piece of paper, picked it up, and continued—now reading.

"The charge says, in fact: 'Professor Matthews, although aware of the offensive nature of the material written on the chalkboard in his classroom, failed to erase it. As a consequence, it was there for his students to see as they left the class.'"

Andrew put the paper back on the table and returned to the lectern.

"Was the offensive material that Mr. Erickson wrote on Professor Matthews' chalkboard there for his students to see as they left the class that day?"

"No, it wasn't."

"How do you know that, Ms. Bukhari?"

Andrew taught all of his witnesses what had been taught to him: they were to look at him when they answered his questions—not at the judge or the jury or, in this instance, the hearing panel. His years of trying cases had confirmed that was the better approach. Farieh may have remembered his instruction, but if she did she ignored it. She turned and faced the panel. That evening, Janek Wojcek would tell his wife the young woman's green eyes had "flashed" when she answered.

"***I*** erased the board. The moment Professor Matthews left the classroom I walked up on the stage, and ***I*** erased it."

Andrew counted to five, staring straight at his witness. Then he walked back to his table, turned to the panel, said "Your witness," and sat down.

Cartwright was on his feet immediately. He just as quickly said "No questions" and he just as quickly sat down.

"You may be excused, then," said the Chairman, and the witness stepped down onto the floor of the courtroom and moved toward her seat in the back. As Farieh made her way past him, Andrew looked at her and said, "Thank you." He allowed her to walk all the way to the back. When she had taken her seat—which another team member had held for her by sitting in it during her testimony, Stevenson stood, straightened his shoulders, and stepped toward the bench. He very nearly "rested." But remembering where he was at the last minute he said instead: "Mr. Chairman, that concludes the case for Professor Matthews." Professor Wojcek noted the time for the record, then adjourned the hearing until the next morning.

Alex Cartwright stood up with the panel and waited for them to leave the way a third-grade boy waits for recess. He already had his materials in his briefcase. He could not get out of Green Hall fast enough.

Evening of the First Day: Jake & Andrew

Y*ou really tore 'em up!*

Jake waited until they had cleared the front doors of Green Hall—but just—before he was fairly shouting at Andrew Stevenson. "Do you think they'll quit tomorrow—'dismiss,' I think you said?!"

They were approaching Andrew's cherry-red F-150. The truck was almost an affront to the woke members of the law faculty; but Andrew had always driven pickups, and he wasn't about to trade for a Subaru Outback whose roof barely cleared his wheel wells.

"Slow down there, Jake. We've had one good day. As the great cowboy philosopher Yogi Berra used to say, 'It ain't over 'til it's over.' We're gonna get one beer to celebrate this opening dust-up. Then, you're gonna get some sleep—you haven't had much lately, and I'm going back to work. Get in."

Jake opened the door and found himself shoulders-even with the top of the passenger seat. He had to do a little hop-step off the running board to get all the way into the big Ford, but he made it.

Andrew pulled out of the lot on the east side of Green Hall, drove around the building to Bob Billings, and turned left. The

Lawrence Beer Company had plenty of outdoor seating and Andrew was confident they could find a table with some privacy between the building and its large stone fireplace. They were there in five minutes.

“I’ll buy,” said Jake; "You earned it. The lager?”

“Yep,” responded Andrew. “And give me a minute, I want to check in with our team before it gets any later.” Jake went inside; Andrew and his cell phone disappeared behind the fireplace. When Jake came back with the beers Andrew was already seated at the small two-top next to the side door.

“I had no idea timing was so important,” said Jake, still excited. “To sit there and watch all of this stuff unfold in real time and realize there was nothing that little piss-ant Cartwright could do about it—that was fantastic!”

“Cartwright’s not a piss-ant, Jake. He’s young, and he’s doing a job nobody else in the legal shop at Strong Hall had the guts to do. His case has been damaged, and maybe he’s a little embarrassed, but he’s more dangerous now than he ever was. And . . . . he’s got the whole night to do something about it.”

Jake came back instantly: “What’s he gonna *do*? Pray I’m a closet member of the Ku Klux Klan and that somebody will bring him a white robe with my name on it? Come on, Andrew; he’s toast.”

“He may be toast. But like I said, this isn’t over until it’s over. I’ve seen a lot of desperate lawyers pull a rabbit out of the hat in closing argument. You have to stay with it ‘til that panel comes back with its decision. That’s when it’s over—not a minute before.”

“OK, OK.” Jake took another drink of his beer and changed his position in the narrow metal chair, signaling his acquiescence as well as his discomfort. “What will happen tomorrow? You told the panel we were finished; what’s KU gonna do?”

“That’s what I asked the team to work on. I don’t know. Cartwright put on a bare-bones case, and I think that was smart; he wasn't going to make you any less popular by dragging it out. He didn't know what we were going to do, and now he's seen it. We called several character witness. Maybe he's got his own witness in the wings."

Andrew shifted his considerable weight, took another drink, then broke into a big grin. "Lord knows enough people around here think you're an asshole. Maybe Cartwright found one of 'em!"

Jake's response was immediate: "God *damn* it, Andrew, this is serious!" But Jake was laughing too before he got all the words out.

They just sat for a while, taking in the evening. They had finished their beers, the sun would not go down for another thirty minutes, and it was a nice time to be doing nothing. But Andrew interrupted. "I'm going back to my office to review what we did today with the team. We'll brainstorm what Cartwright might do with it. If there is something, we'll find it. What you need to do is go home and chill out and then get some sleep. You ready?"

They stood up together and walked to Andrew's pickup, got in, and drove back. Jake's house was just up the hill from the law school, a beautifully-proportioned Tudor that had actually looked out over Green Hall until the steady expansion of Learned Hall, the school of engineering, had stolen its view. Andrew slowed at the driveway and stopped. "Remember, Jake—sleep. I want you alert tomorrow. We don't know what they're going to do; we need to be able to react rapidly and intelligently. Meet me at my office at 8:30. If I need you sooner than that I'll call you. Got it?"

Jake had dismounted this very high ride and was looking back at Andrew. "Got it."

Andrew put the truck in gear as he watched Jake turn and walk up his driveway. His friend had some of his swagger back.

Evening of the First Day: Alex Cartwright

Alex shouldered past several students as he hurried into the entry hall and out the front door of Green Hall. Stopping at McLain's Market for a coffee and a sandwich, both to go, Alex took the south side of the Chi Omega fountain, crossed Jayhawk Boulevard to the sidewalk on the north side, and walked the remaining 150 yards to Strong Hall, the university's administration building. The Chancellor had her office there, and the Provost. So did the university's General Counsel, Margaret Thompson, who was just down the second-floor hall from the Chancellor. Her newly-refinished, cherry-paneled suite included an anteroom for her administrative assistant and a small conference room that looked out over Jayhawk Boulevard through the windows on the south wall.

Alex's office, such as it was, was on Strong's third floor. The lecture hall that had for decades prolonged the sleep of undergraduates in the College of Liberal Arts and Sciences who had drawn it for a 7:30 class had been cut up into small, walled spaces for the university's newest lawyers and cubicles for her paralegals and her computer techs. Alex walked up the narrow staircase, gently kicked open the door to his office as his arms were full of case files and food, and walked in. The office was dark.

"SHIT! SHIT! SHIT! SHIT! ***SHIT***!" he yelled for the benefit of himself and maybe Tommie Radcliffe, the redheaded computer geek who had started the same week as Alex and whom he had passed as he made his way down the hall from the stairs.

He put the coffee on the shelf behind his desk chair where he kept the coaster, let the files slump onto the seat of his one guest chair, turned to the door and closed it, and stood there in the dark.

"***SHIT***!"

He turned on the light, cleared last night's papers off his desktop, dropped his food where the papers had been, sat in his desk chair, spun around to retrieve the coffee and the coaster, spun back, and opened the paper bag from McLain's. He had barely taken a bite of the BLT and was reaching for the coffee when he heard the knock on his door. Julie Samford had already helped herself into his office. She walked up to his desk, dropped a manila file folder into the middle of it—nearly spilling the coffee—and stared at him.

"What's that?" Alex asked, steadying his grande-size cup.

"That's your rebuttal exhibit," Julie said. "You're going to need something. You can't let the hearing end at the close of Professor Matthew's presentation."

"Why not?" Alex was genuinely curious. He had never tried a case before, not a real one in a real courtroom. This academic hearing had already been plenty real enough. As Stevenson had announced he was finished, Alex assumed the whole thing was done, except for final argument, which the chair said they could make if they wanted to. Alex's was going to be short.

He turned back the top of the folder. Inside were heavy sheets of paper with official-looking writing on them. But the paper wasn't nearly as compelling as the gift wrap. A wide blue ribbon surrounded the pages. Perched dead-center on the ribbon was a gigantic gold medallion that had been imprinted by some kind of seal. It looked to Alex like the paper version of a medal awarded by the pasha to whoever had saved Constantinople from the Golden Horde.

When Alex looked back at Julie, it was clear he had no idea what he had in front of him.

"The ribbon and the seal are what lawyers used to call your 'Act of Congress.' In most state courts, it would render the documents that came with it self-authenticating. I don't think you're going to have any trouble getting the documents admitted tomorrow, but we don't want to take any chances."

"But what are the documents?" asked Alex, almost in protest.

"They are official records from Cape Girardeau County, Missouri."

Alex had picked up the packet and had begun reading the document on top of the very thin stack. "These are from 1854!" he exclaimed. "What does a hearing about twenty-first century rock stars have to do with the boot heel of Missouri before the Civil War?"

"Do you remember Stevenson's last character witness?"

"Sure," said Alex. "The faculty member from the medical school—Barnes, I think, in St. Louis—who had known Matthews and his wife since college. He said something like, 'There's not a racist bone in Matthews' body,' or words to that effect."

"Just right," said Julie.

"OK," said Alex. "So where are we with all this ancient stuff?"

"Just read it," Julie answered.

Alex read it. The court records reported the sale of slaves to one John Abernathy of Cape Girardeau in 1854.

Alex looked up again. "OK, I've read it. What does this have to do with Jacob Matthews?"

"Matthews' wife is an Abernathy. She grew up in Cape Girardeau. Her family owned slaves. That's what it has to do with."

Alex looked down at the packet again. His eyes took in the ribbon and the medallion and the heavy pages underneath while his brain unwound what his supervising attorney wanted him to do. He knew what the next question was; he had to be careful how he asked it.

"This stuff happened generations ago. I doubt even Matthews' wife is aware of this, and I'd bet my own money Matthews isn't. And even if he and his wife *are* aware of it, that doesn't mean they are proud of that history, or are themselves racists, or even less that they support the idea of slavery. Are you saying you want me to offer these papers into evidence tomorrow morning?!"

"You're not as stupid as you look, Alex," she said.

Julie Samford continued. "You are going to stand up tomorrow morning and tell the panel you have a very short rebuttal presentation. You are going to hand them these documents. You are going to explain what they are, how they are self-authenticating, and what self-authenticating means. You will tell them that means they are genuine—the real thing.

You are going to tell them the Abernathys continue to live in Cape Girardeau County—right up until today. And you are going to tell them Professor Matthews is married to a member of a family that used to own slaves.

Then you are going to announce you have concluded the presentation by the university. And then you are going to sit down.

Do you have any more questions?"

Alex did not. He was looking straight ahead, not even seeing Julie Samford, unaware he was seeing anything. And as he was looking ahead and seeing nothing his supervising attorney left his office. He never saw her go.

Second Day of Trial: Early Morning

Tuesday broke hard even for Andrew Stevenson, who was once again in the law school parking lot at 7:15. This was more than an April shower, and the gusts that pushed it across the campus had nearly blown his umbrella inside-out as he stepped down out of his truck and hurried into Green Hall. He stopped to brew his cup of coffee in the battered Keurig that sat in the faculty coffee bar—Starbucks Pike Place Roast was what they had that week, which worked for him; then he walked to the elevator.

Andrew had drunk strong coffee since he was a small boy. His grandfather Amos was in the kitchen at the farmhouse whenever Andrew visited, didn't matter how early or how late, coffee mug on the table in front of him. His grandfather made it in a percolator that Andrew called "Granddad's tin pot," learning only later it was made of stainless steel with a Bakelite handle and a matching knob for the lid. His grandfather would fill the pot, position the tube, add the basket, and measure the coffee—exactly six rounded teaspoons. He would count them out: "One, two, four, three, five for the pot and six for me!" Then came what Granddad called "the magic." He would break an egg over the coffee and shake in a little salt before pushing down the lid and putting the pot on the stove for the water to boil. Andrew's grandmother would never touch the stuff, and Andrew thought the result was undrinkable the first few times he tried it. But he loved his grandfather, his grandfather loved his coffee, and soon enough Andrew was drinking it right along with him. Andrew still had the "tin pot." It was the only thing he wanted when his grandfather died, and it sat on the shelf in his office behind his desk. Seeing it as he walked into his office, and thinking about his grandfather, were important parts of his morning.

Andrew and the team had met at the law school for several hours after he dropped off Jake. They reviewed what little there had been of the university's case, and they reviewed every witness and every exhibit that Andrew had presented for their client, looking for a crack that Cartwright might exploit. Finding none, they brainstormed ideas for possible rebuttal evidence. Once again they came up empty. Sure, they had had ideas, but most were simply "out there." Jake currently counted no female students among his TAs, for example, and he might be labeled "sexist." But he had relied on female TAs in previous semesters, and the undercurrent of the actual charges of losing control of the classroom and demeaning Erickson was racism, not sexism. So that didn't make any sense, and neither did anything else they threw back and forth at each other. They had called it a night before 11:00.

Andrew got up from his desk, walked out the door and past the stacks, and ended up by the carrels against the east wall of the building. Watching the last of the squalls climb over Slawson Hall, he silently conceded he had no idea where Cartwright might go that morning. It was within the realm of possibility the young man would do nothing—just say the university was finished. But Andrew's instincts told him that wasn't happening. He'd just have to see. He turned around and walked back to his office, wanting to be there when Jake arrived, not looking aimlessly out the window.

Second Day of Trial

Andrew and Jake had arrived in the courtroom at 8:45 following a very brief and upbeat meeting in Andrew's office. Andrew told Jake the team had carefully gone over everything, had concluded they were in good shape, and had gone to bed rather than hyperventilating over the what-ifs. That was just what Jake wanted to hear.

"Good morning, Mr. Chairman." Andrew stood before he spoke to Professor Wojcek, prompting the bespectacled scholar to look up briefly as he made his way to the bench. Wojcek had come in ahead of the rest of the panel intending not to speak with anyone but to look over his notes of yesterday's session. He was no jurist, but he was taking his assignment seriously. Recognizing Andrew's voice, he was genuinely pleased to see his faculty colleague and grateful for the deference of the greeting.

Andrew had not thought consciously about the formality of his greeting; the words had formed themselves. His decades in courtrooms and judges' chambers and legislative committee hearings had taught him how to address a presiding officer. The formality was especially helpful here as he and Wojcek knew each other, having served side by side on the most recent faculty committee to select the Dean of the College of Liberal Arts. That was just three years ago.

When he wasn't teaching, preparing for class, working on his own scholarship, or chasing cattle with his brother on the family ranch in the Flint Hills, Andrew read history. But he had not lived history. Wojcek had lived history. The gaunt Pole could talk about the events of World War II (which his mother and father had fought in), the Cold War (which he had resented as a boy and resented even more as a faculty member at the University of Warsaw), and Solidarity and the rise of Lech Walesa like Andrew could talk about barbed-wire fences and branding. Their two-hour committee meetings had often been a prelude to longer dinners on Massachusetts Street. Andrew would choose the steaks. After Janek would choose the subject, Andrew was more than content to pour the wine and listen. But their evenings lasted only as long as it took to choose the new Dean. Wojcek began his sabbatical the next semester at Charles University in the Czech Republic; Andrew went west for his to the law school at Berkeley. When they came back, they were tasked with more assignments than they had time for, they rarely saw one another, and there were no more dinners. But Andrew remembered the dinners, and he was confident Janek did too.

The Provost had given them a far better panel than Andrew had predicted. Professor Wojcek was not merely a positive; having him as the Chair was a blessing. And none of the others seemed antagonistic to Jake. One, Paul Roberts, was someone Jake knew well, and liked.

The courtroom was full when the rest of the panel came in and climbed the steps to the bench and took their seats. In fact, it was packed; every space along the back walls was filled with students staring at their cell phone. New this morning was the satellite dish in the parking lot courtesy of FOX News and its Kansas City affiliate, WDAF. Professor Wojcek looked out over the crowd and said, "Good morning." Many people responded. Then the panel

Chair looked down at the university's counsel and asked, "Mr. Cartwright, does the university have anything further it wishes to present?"

Cartwright seemed to take a very deep breath as he stood up. "Yes, Mr. Chairman, we do."

Unlike the day before, when the university counsel's table was awash with legal pads and memos and Post-it notes and the wayward trial notebook, that same surface had a single stack on it this morning. There were eight documents in the stack, and they were identical. Long pages backed with a heavy, sky-blue paper were joined at the top with rivets and circled with a broad, navy ribbon. Glued to the top of each ribbon was a serrated paper disc the size of a hockey puck. Shiny gold, the disc bore the unmistakable imprint of an old-fashioned seal. Cartwright handed one to Stevenson, then turned to the bench with a question. "May I approach the panel?"

The Chair said he could.

Cartwright took the few steps and handed the next six copies to Professor Wojcek—one for the record, one each for the members of the panel.

Closing Argument

A FALSE START

To say Andrew Stevenson's objection to the university's rebuttal exhibit was "vigorous" did not begin to capture it. For the first time in anyone's memory, Stevenson was red in the face and had raised his voice in a courtroom. It was only when his client gestured him over and quietly told him he was repeating himself that Stevenson finally stopped talking. The Chair received the exhibit, the university had nothing more to offer, and Stevenson had nothing more to offer on behalf of Professor Matthews.

It was now only ten o'clock. Troubled by the nature of the university's rebuttal and by the intensity of Andrew Stevenson's objection to it, the Chair announced he wanted the panel to have time to review the evidence—"all of the evidence," he had said—before they would have closing argument. Professor Wojcek asked whether the two sides had any objection to making their arguments the next morning. When neither did he adjourned the hearing.

The people in the courtroom had been ready for the conclusion, and FOX News had only just set up. Everyone was disappointed. But everyone would be back the next day.

WEDNESDAY

It was now Wednesday morning. Having satisfied himself the parties had no questions for the panel, Professor Wojcek said they were ready for the lawyers' closing remarks. Cartwright went first and was finished in ten minutes. The Chair turned to Andrew Stevenson. Janek Wojcek took off his glasses as though to clean them; he spoke so quietly the students in the back of the courtroom did not hear him. "Mr. Stevenson?"

Andrew was up every morning at 5:00 whether he had a case to try or not. He was up this morning at 5:00, his mind turning over and over what he would say about Cape Girardeau. He had anticipated the rest of the evidence that had been presented, his own and the university's; he just needed a moment to make sure the panel had made sense of it. But he had not anticipated Cape Girardeau. And while he had several ways to go with the university's rebuttal and had run them all to ground last night with his team, he had not decided which one to take. He stood up. He would figure it out when he got to it.

"Mr. Cartwright," he said, looking down from his six feet and two inches. His tone was pleasant, but distant.

He made the quarter turn to the bench, took a step forward, and smiled. "Ladies and gentlemen of the panel." This time there was warmth in his voice. He paused only a moment. "Professor Matthews and I thank you for hearing our side of this matter."

He turned his body slightly away from the bench and toward the audience—but he was still speaking to the panel. "You have been more than patient," he continued. Then he turned fully to the audience, walking away from the bench and toward the students who filled the chairs of the jury box, who filled the chairs behind the counsel tables, and who had crammed into the standing spaces against the back wall of the courtroom. This time he spoke directly to them.

"I have been in a few courtrooms, but I guess I've never seen the hootin' and hollerin' we've seen here these last few days!" The mostly undergraduates laughed immediately. But this time their interruption was a short one; they did not want to miss any part of what was coming next.

Still smiling, encouraged by the laughter, Andrew turned again and walked to his position directly in front the bench. Had the Chair reached out his hand in Andrew's direction, Andrew could have extended his and touched him. He began slowly, hands at his side, his head moving slowly left to right across the five faces of the professors who would decide this case.

"It occurred to me we are nearly all faculty here. Each of you is a distinguished faculty representative of your own college and of the university, as well. Professor Matthews, whom the University has accused of violating its Code of Conduct, is himself a distinguished faculty member. You have heard about many of his achievements. Just this spring he was named a Faculty Fellow of the KU Honors Program. I teach at the school of law. Only Mr. Cartwright, who represents the university in this proceeding, is not a member of our faculty."

He turned slightly, picked up a piece of paper from the table where he had been sitting, and held it at shoulder level so he could read from it while maintaining eye contact with the panel.

"Nearly all of us are also a little older. The university's website, which I made a copy of," he explained, tilting the paper slightly in the panel's direction, "says each of you has at least ten years teaching experience since you received your Ph.D. Professor Matthews' experience is similar."

Andrew went on. "That Mr. Cartwright is not quite a year out of law school is hardly his fault. But it may explain one part of the university's case that certainly needs explaining. We'll get to that a little later."

With that, Andrew moved to the lectern where his notes were waiting. He would not need them. For the next fifteen minutes, aided by several strategic clips from Farieh's cell-phone video, Andrew took the panel through Jacob Matthews' encounter with his student in Wescoe Hall. He would get to a spot, pause the video by pointing his hand-held control at the screen, then look at the panel as he asked them a question. As he asked it, the question would appear on a second screen in a bold font. Andrew would move on, but the second screen would hold that question, and then the next one. When he had finished, the second screen presented nine questions to the panel, including:

- **Why would a student who merely had a question about a lecture not only get out of his seat to ask it, but vault the stage?**
- **Why would a student who merely had a question about a lecture walk immediately to the chalkboard—as though he were going to take over the class?**
- **Why would a student who merely had a question about a lecture take an accusatory tone with the teacher, from the very first moment?**
- **Why would a student who merely had a question about a lecture demand a response about a book that was never mentioned in the lecture and was not part of the syllabus?**
- **Why would a student who merely had a question about a lecture use the chalkboard to broadcast the most inflammatory, most unwelcome word in our language?**
    - **(a) a word that appears nowhere in the readings that are part of the syllabus?**
    - **(b) a word that was never used in the course?**
    - **(c) a word that, used by a student in almost any other setting at the University of Kansas, would get the student suspended?**

He told the panel he was finished with the video by turning it off and placing the control on counsel table in front of Jake. He left the questions on the second screen, where they would remain visible to the panel. But he did not return to the bench. Instead, he walked to the far end of the jury box, smiling at the young student sitting in the last seat as he approached her. Once at the end he turned back to the panel.

"There may be several explanations, I suppose. Maybe young Mr. Erickson got excited. Maybe he hated Samuel Clemens? Or Ulysses S. Grant? Maybe he hated the entire class?" He paused again as he walked the length of the jury box, moving close to the panel member sitting at the far right. As he anticipated, the rest of the panel turned to face him.

"But maybe this was a set-up? Maybe young Mr. Erickson—either on his own or, more likely, in league with someone else—was out to get Professor Matthews? Maybe they came up with this phony confrontation to bait him, to create such a preposterous display of disrespect that even someone as learned and as courteous as Professor Matthews would lose his temper.

Set-up or not, Jacob Matthews was subjected to the kind of disrespect no faculty code is intended to tolerate. Even though the word used by Mr. Erickson's classmate, Ms. Bukhari, in her testimony is not a part of the record, you are free to reach your own conclusions about the nature of his behavior. It *was* bullying—naked, persistent, angry, and unapologetic. *Bullying.* That's just what it was.

Did Professor Matthews finally lose his temper? Did he yell at his student? Yes, he did.

Was this a violation of the Code of Conduct? No."

He returned to the center of the bench. When he resumed, he spoke directly to the panel's Chair.

"But no matter what Mr. Erickson said and did to provoke Professor Matthews, and no matter how impossible it is to demean someone who deserves no respect, some of you may still be troubled by what Professor Matthews said at the end. If you are, we want you to consider this:

Entrapment is no less a defense to the charge against Professor Matthews than it is to a criminal charge. If a person is subjected to such powerful and unfair forces by the alleged victim that he commits a violation he would otherwise not have committed, that is entrapment—and the violation is excused.

That is what happened here. Professor Matthews has taught this course for years, just as he has taught an Honors Seminar, just as he has mentored hundreds of undergraduate and graduate students, just as he has done his own research and published his own papers and books, and just as he has served the university community and the community of Lawrence. Never—not once!—has he exhibited behavior that even remotely resembles what Tom Erickson goaded him into on that Tuesday afternoon this spring. This was entrapment. And for that reason as well, you should find Professor Matthews did not violate the university's Code of Conduct."

Stevenson moved again, this time to counsel table, where he poured a half glass of water and drank it. Then he returned to his spot directly in front of the bench.

"I said at the beginning there was a part of the university's case that needs explaining. I want to talk with you about that last.

You will remember Professor Matthews and I objected to the introduction of materials from Cape Girardeau. The point of our objection was not that the events were untrue. Professor Matthews' wife's family did own slaves in the boot heel of Missouri. But that happened roughly 180 years ago. It was only twenty years before that that Thomas Jefferson was still alive, and was himself a slave owner. And while we can debate how our society should deal with Thomas Jefferson, and with other persons who actually owned slaves, there is no debate over whether their descendants born a century and a half later should be condemned because of the actions of their long-dead ancestors.

Yet sadly, that is what the university is trying to do here: condemn Professor Matthews from the grave, a grave that belongs to a family not even his own. We believe its conduct in this entire proceeding is unfair. But the Cape Girardeau exhibit is more than unfair. It is mean-spirited, and it is ugly." He picked up the document, held it to his nose, and tossed it back on the table. "There's a stench to it.

So, what needs explaining? That's the question we've saved for the end. What needs explaining is why Alex Cartwright, a young lawyer not even a year out of law school, would stoop to offering this ugliness into evidence against Professor Matthews.

While I can't tell you I know the answer to a moral certainty, I have a pretty good idea.

I have been a law professor at KU for a dozen years. I'm proud of that: proud of the school of law, proud of its faculty, and proud of Kansas University. Most *all* of the people at KU are good people. But someone at KU is not a good person. Someone here is determined to hurt Professor Matthews—to make an example of him."

Stevenson reached over, picked up the beribboned Cape Girardeau exhibit once again, and held it up for the entire courtroom to see. "And they became so concerned for how this case was going that they resorted to *this*!

This isn't about Professor Matthews. And it's not about his wife, or her parents, or her grandparents, or anyone else close in time or in spirit to what she and her husband stand for today. This is about winning—winning at any cost. That to me is the explanation for this disgusting exhibit.

Is this Alex Cartwright's fault? I don't think so. In fact, I would bet a thousand dollars right now he had no idea this document even *existed* when we started this case on Monday. If Alex Cartwright had this document at the beginning of this hearing he would have showed it to me. Law students are taught to do that; lawyers are *required* to do that. That Alex Cartwright did not give me the document until yesterday morning tells me he did not *know about it* until yesterday morning.

And I would bet another thousand dollars that if it were his decision to make, he would never have offered it into evidence, no matter when he got it. No, this is the work of other people, people who are out to get Professor Matthews.

Ferreting out who these people are is not your concern. But you can take into account what they *did* when deciding how to respond to the university's charges.

Stevenson moved again, but only slightly: maybe a foot or two toward his client, looking at him as he did so, but no farther from the bench. Then he looked back at the panel.

In just a few minutes you will leave this courtroom and go to the Rice Room upstairs. That's where you will talk about what you've seen and heard; that's where you will decide whether there was any violation of the university's Code of Conduct on that Tuesday afternoon in February.

If you believe Tom Erickson's behavior exemplifies the character, the search for knowledge, and the academic spirit you want to see in your *own* students at the University of Kansas, then you should consider finding there was a violation.

In the same vein, if you believe digging up documents such as the one from Cape Girardeau and using them as a weapon against a distinguished scholar . . . if you believe *that* is the kind of behavior the University of Kansas should engage in . . . if *this* makes you proud of your university, then you should consider finding there was a violation."

Stevenson moved again, this time directly behind his client. Resting his hands on the back of Jake's chair he continued, "But if your university means all of the things to you that it means to me—all of the good things, all of the things that *do* make you proud, all of the things that let you say 'Jayhawk' with a smile on your face and let you stand a little straighter when you say it, then you will decide there was *no* violation. And you will end this long night for Professor Matthews.

That's the decision we ask you to make."

Stevenson pulled back his own chair, placed his other hand on his client's shoulder, and sat down.

The Panel Reaches a Decision

The five panel members made their separate ways to the Rice Room. Some stopped at the restroom; some stopped for coffee in the coffee bar across the hall from the courtroom; some checked e-mail. One—Gwendolyn Stewart, the African-American Chair of American Studies—called the Chancellor's Office to report the hearing had concluded and the panel was about to begin its deliberations. Nearly fifteen minutes had passed before they all reached the fourth floor and took seats around the long table that paralleled the west wall. As it was immediately apparent the seats they had taken were too far apart—Gwendolyn, at one end of the table, was at least twenty feet from Paul Roberts, the Clark Bricker Distinguished Professor of Chemistry at the other end, the Chair suggested everyone move to the middle. Relocated and now seated across from one another, they were more at ease with both their surroundings and their task.

Janek Wojcek, the elegant Regents Professor of European History whose scholarship focused on World War II and post-war Germany, had presided over the hearing and would lead the discussion. Years earlier, when he left the University of Warsaw to join the faculty at Kansas, one of his students told him he looked like Albert Einstein. He didn't, but he had kept his steadily-graying hair long ever since. He brushed it back past his glasses and cleared his throat. "Shall we begin?"

There was no one around the table who did not know Jacob Matthews. Some had served on committees with him; some taught in the Honors Program with him; one—Paul Roberts—was as big a Jayhawk basketball fan as Matthews and saw him at the "Hawk Talk" events held at Johnny's West during the season. Much more so than the others, Roberts might be considered Matthew's friend, but all five knew him. None of this was grounds for disqualification; there was no way to convene a panel whose members did not know him.

It was Roberts who spoke next. "I think we should take a vote now and see whether anyone here honestly believes Jake Matthews demeaned the lily-livered coward who hijacked his class!"

Wojcek looked over his glasses at Roberts and addressed him like he was a freshman late for class. "Professor Roberts, please! While each of us may have their own strong feelings about what we have heard over the last two days, it is important—no, imperative—that we conduct ourselves in a patient, cooperative way during these deliberations."

"I will be glad to be cooperative," joined Afamefana Okafor, professor of petroleum engineering and a native of Nigeria. He was "Fahmie" to his friends, of which there were hundreds both in and out of his department. "But it is hard for me to be patient. I agree with Paul. The behavior of the student, Mr. Erikson, was shameful. I don't know how Professor Matthews tolerated it as long as he did. It makes me uncomfortable even to participate in a conversation that works from the premise Professor Matthews may have violated the University Code of Conduct by demeaning him. Erickson surrendered whatever entitlement he had to courtesy and respect from his teacher when he jumped up on the stage and began taunting him. As for losing control of the classroom, Professor Matthews did not lose it—Mr. Erickson stole it."

No one spoke in the silence that followed Professor Okafor's remarks; no one made eye contact, either. Finally, Professor Wojcek posed another quiet question: "Does anyone here believe differently?"

"No," said Alia Bol, the native Sudanese who taught in African and African-American Studies.

"I agree with Alia." This time it was Gwendolyn Stewart. "I have a hard time believing anyone at Strong Hall watched the entirety of this on YouTube before they allowed this charge to proceed."

Janek Wojcek spoke again, this time more forcefully. "And I agree, as well. I was appalled at Erickson's behavior in Professor Matthews' class. And I was more appalled at the so-called 'rebuttal' evidence offered Tuesday morning by Mr. Cartwright. I felt it was my obligation to receive it, in order to allow the university to make as complete a record as it believed necessary. But it was pure scapegoating—the worst I have ever witnessed."

Janek looked at each of his colleagues and continued. "As we seem to be in agreement, I propose a short break to allow us to satisfy ourselves that is, in fact, how we feel. Then we will reconvene here and take a formal vote. Say, ten minutes?"

The release felt by every jury once they reach a verdict spread to each of the five. They pushed back their chairs as one and were immediately upright and talking as they made their way to the door.

No one needed ten minutes; they were back and seated in five. Roberts in particular was fired up, his intellectual energy bordering on the kinetic. After they voted 5-0 in favor of a finding of "No violation," Roberts was unable to restrain himself. He stood up.

"A finding on the charges is not enough! This was nothing short of a witch hunt. We have to communicate to the Chancellor, to our colleagues, to our students, and to the public that Jake

Matthews did absolutely nothing wrong and that he is a valued, important member of this academic community. We should read a statement to that effect just after we announce the vote, and I will be more than happy to write it."

Paul plainly expected this to be a rallying cry, yet no one rallied. When several dropped their gaze to the table, Paul demanded even more emphatically, "What's wrong with you?! We all agree this was an outrage. Let's have the courage to say so!"

It was Alia Bol who responded. She was older than Paul Roberts, and she looked up at him as she might have looked up at her son. "Professor Roberts . . . Paul. Everyone should have colleagues as passionate as you.

We were asked to determine whether a violation of the Code of Conduct occurred, whether Professor Matthews behaved improperly. We have done that, and we will report that. But we were not asked to determine whether the *university* behaved improperly.

We could announce such a determination. We are here; the courtroom is waiting for us; so is the media. Yet I believe such an announcement is poison. If we announce the university was *within* its rights to bring this charge, we dilute the power of the finding we are about to make in favor of Professor Matthews. If we announce the university was *wrong* to bring the charge, then we discredit the university. The former will accomplish nothing for Professor Matthews; the latter will set off a media storm that could do serious damage to KU.

We have completed our assignment. In my opinion, that is enough."

Still standing, Paul looked past her to Professor Okafor, who was nodding in agreement. So was Professor Stewart, and so was Janek Wojcek. Moving to the door, Paul Roberts added for anyone still listening, "Give me a minute. I'll be right back. Then we can go down and announce our decision."

Looking for Salina

F*arieh, it's Richie!*

It was April 11. The cool mornings of middle March had needed only a few showers to strip off the dirty sheets of snow and wash them across the sidewalks to the storm drains. Since then, warmer days had done their part and Jayhawk Boulevard was bursting with color. Dogwoods and redbuds led the way, battalions of daffodils lined up behind the white and pink guidons, and the trees of Marvin Grove and their sisters along Jayhawk Boulevard competed to see which would leaf out first.

Farieh and Richie had continued their walks that spring. But his getting in touch with her to arrange them required that he call WheatFields, and the increasing frequency of his calls had become awkward. She had given him her cell number only a week ago in self-defense, half expecting to be barraged by texts. There had been none—nothing—until now, and this was a phone call. Richie wanted to know whether she had an hour late in the afternoon. He would pick her up at Miller and they would walk. She had asked where they were going. "It's not far at all," he had said. He was right about their ultimate destination, it was not far at all. But he did not reveal it when he opened the front door for her. First the walk.

Farieh stepped off her porch into a day so bright its sky might have been polished for the funeral procession of Queen Elizabeth. They crossed Jayhawk Boulevard at Danforth Chapel, turned left past Lippincott, walked to the corner, and turned downhill.

"The Grove?" said Farieh. It was more a statement than a question as Richie always wanted to start there. They went to its west edge by the Campanile, then down Campanile Hill and through the Spencer Art Museum's parking lot to the tunnel that took them to the Union. Richie wanted a vanilla latte, and he knew Farieh would drink a tea, and he knew they could find both at the coffee shop on the main level. They talked about school and basketball—Richie was still working his way through the team's not making the Final Four. About her family—she would return to Iran later that summer and would see them for the first time in almost a year. And about her seminar trip to England and Scotland with Professor Lochlear—the Honors 190 teacher whom she had become close to first semester and who was now her major advisor. Professor Lochlear's instantly-subscribed excursion to the British Isles would take up the start of Farieh's summer. She was particularly excited about England because Professor Lochlear had assured her she would have time to see her older sister, who was chasing a D.Phil. in Engineering and living at Magdalen College. Farieh loved Magdalen. Like her sister, she was not sure one's college made much difference to how one did with their academic work in an era of PCs and cell phones and the Internet. But the beauty of the place made a difference to how one felt about the experience. And when it came to the beauty of Oxford's many colleges, Magdalen was *primus inter pares*.

When Richie had finished his latte he stood up, put on his jacket, and waited for Farieh to stand and join him. "I guess we're done here!" she said sharply. She took her cup from her lips and put it down slowly enough for Richie to notice she had not finished her tea, then she pushed back from the table. *What is the hurry?!* she thought. They walked out the south door and through the circle of bronze Jayhawks and ended up in front of Dyche. That's when Richie told her where they were going—to Fraser Hall. "It's such a gorgeous day," he said, "I thought we'd see what it looks like from the highest place on campus. That OK?"

"Sure," said Farieh. Though she had lived across the street from Fraser for nearly a year, she had never set foot in the stone-faced building that stole the sun from Lilac Lane around 2:30 each afternoon.

They walked in through the doors on the east side of the long structure whose twin red towers sustained the memory of "old" Fraser. Nodding to the students who had finished class and were leaving the building, they stepped into the elevator and rode to the top, the seventh floor. There wasn't much to see on stepping out. The classrooms had stopped on the third floor; with one exception, only narrow passageways into faculty and TA offices led off the hallway on seven. The exception was the small conference room at the southwest corner. Richie headed for it, walked in, and moved to the three windows looking out west over the top of Jayhawk Boulevard. The blinds were closed against a sun that hit this side of the building hard in the afternoon. Richie took a moment to untangle the cords on the center window and pull them up. Then he just stood there. Farieh walked across the room and took up the same stance on his left side. They were far above the trees, far above Watson and Flint and Wescoe and Strong and all the other buildings, just looking west. As the seconds turned into a minute, and then another, Farieh began to wonder what they were looking for.

Richie spoke to her like a KU player would address the grade schoolers at Gene Bennett's Basketball Camp when announcing they would have pancakes for breakfast: "In the morning, if it's not cloudy and you look hard enough, you can see Salina!"

Farieh liked Richie. He was one of the smartest young men she had met, he was unquestionably the finest athlete, he was the tallest person she had ever spent time with, and he was good-looking. He was courteous, he was respectful of her and her faith, and he was as attentive as an Azarbaijan mastiff. The affection building inside her for her impossibly-young man from Salina was undeniable. But either because of the physical barriers she had imposed on them from the first or because of his overall lack of experience with women, whenever Richie's feelings for her burbled up he turned as silly as a middle-school first-year. Farieh knew he was trying to be endearing, and funny. But Farieh had learned about horizons and the curvature of the earth as a child during trips to the mountains with her parents. Salina was 140 miles away! Beyond that, Lawrence was enjoying a riotous spring. The leaves that had already formed on the trees west of the bypass would have obscured Salina had it changed places with Stull, the tiny community on the western edge of Lawrence that had far more occupants in its supposedly-haunted cemetery than it did in the few buildings on its main street.

But even with all the silliness, Richie was gaining on Farieh. She appreciated the consistent though often-awkward way in which Richie maintained the physical distance she had asked for. As he stood next to her staring out the seventh-floor window across the canopies bordering Jayhawk Boulevard, he was again maintaining that distance even though it was hard for him. Farieh guessed, in fact, that Richie wanted to put his arm around her; she had sensed the tension in his left arm before it had actually moved. But Richie had remembered and relaxed, and now he just stood there, arm at his side, looking out the window.

Her next sensation was of her own creation: without telling herself to do so she had closed the small space between them. As the right side of her body leaned in lightly against Richie's chest, she could feel the tension returning to his body, but it faded as she held her position. She had never thought about this before in the context of their relationship, but she was also tall. Richie was a nice height for her.

Farieh had checked her phone on the way into the building and knew it was getting close to 5:30. She closed her eyes. She liked the closeness and the warmth. She could miss dinner, glad to replace it with a futile search for Salina. When she felt his heart beating against her shoulder she looked up. Her amusement of a moment ago displaced by stronger feelings, she wondered what she might do if Richie looked down at her in the same way she was looking up at him. No painter could match what the late sun was doing to the cleft of his chin, to his eyes, and to the hollows and the edges of the rest of his face, and Farieh hoped he would turn them all to her. But Richie shared his face only with the sun. She leaned in against him once more before shifting her weight to the left, reopening the small space between them she had momentarily bridged. She had given him as much of an embrace as she could offer.

Lights Out

Gene Bennett's personal copy of the Big 12 Conference Championship Trophy had arrived at his office that morning, its ten-week delay addressed in the brief accompanying note from the Commissioner: supply-chain problems. It came an even eight weeks since the Kansas head coach had turned off his lights on his way to Dallas for the Sweet 16, seven weeks since his return from the Final Four—where he had been feted as both a former championship coach and a commentator and where he had burned privately that his team was not playing, and six weeks since he had again thrown himself into recruiting. Despite the challenges of the transfer portal and the vexations of NIL, Kansas had gotten some good players. "We'll be able to field a team next year," Gene would say to people when he was tired, which he was.

He had opened a packing crate so over-engineered it could have carried the Hope Diamond, had removed and dusted off the trophy, and had placed it in line with the others with all the emotion he might have spent on ordering a cheeseburger at Dempsey's. Dallas wasn't the first place they had had a tournament game in their hands and lost it, but it was the most recent. Even two months later there was a hurt that had not let go.

By 11:00 he realized he did not want to see anybody, so he called his admin and asked her to order a chef's salad for lunch, and a vanilla malt. His favorite ice-cream treat wouldn't help his diet, but it might help his spirits. And then he went back to the hundreds of e-mails that had piled up since Selection Sunday. He had a system for this, and he stuck to it even though making "a real response" to the people he liked—that was his years' old commitment—took real time. The rest he would either forward to his admin, with a request that she respond to them, or delete. By 10:30 that evening he had finished the e-mail and he was ready to leave.

He logged off, stood up from his desk, and checked to see he hadn't left anything he'd need in the bathroom. He would not be back for several weeks; he and his wife Betsey needed some time off, and they were taking it. Then he turned off his desk lamp and walked into the front part of his office where the team's trophies and plaques and medals and citations were displayed alongside the several awards that were personal to him. Gene was proud of all of this. He never minimized it, never showed any false modesty about it.

Most nights the light that washed across the threshold from the hallway seemed to settle on one of the objects, allowing it to sparkle back at Gene as he approached the door. And when he turned around that one last time he would smile as he saw it. But there were other moments when neither the collected gloss of all of the awards nor the determined effort of one of them could lift his mood. Perhaps sensing the duty that settled on the junior member, the newly-arrived Big 12 Trophy did her best to capture and redirect the shafts from the hallway, but Gene wasn't looking. He shrugged into his jacket, pulled the door closed, and turned left into the corridor that would take him to the north stairwell. From there, the night that waited down the stairs and just beyond the Wagnon Center's entrance doors was only twenty feet away. But Gene didn't need the darkness that a Kansas night might offer; he was still carrying a saddlebag full from Texas.

Rock Chalk, Baby!

It was a perfect May afternoon: high sun, seventy-eight degrees, no wind. Every sorority patio and roof deck was filled with sunbathers, the golfers were golfing—both traditional and frisbee, and the members of KU's faculty who had completed their courses and their final exams were on holidays spread across the country. But not Andrew and Jake. As they were still in Lawrence, Andrew proposed a leisurely lunch at his favorite campus restaurant. Jake accepted, and Andrew said he would pick him up at his office at 11:30.

Andrew turned the ten-minute walk from the law school to Wescoe into a thirty-minute meander, stopping first at the Dickinson Fountain just outside the lower-level door to Green Hall, then walking up the hill to McLain's Market, where he picked up an iced coffee. He turned north at the Chi Omega Fountain so he could double back on Memorial Drive and take in the Vietnam War Memorial, then he climbed back up to Jayhawk Boulevard to admire the tulips preening in front of Budig. Jake's building came next after the Gothic shell that housed the Hoch Auditoria. Already outside and leaning against one of the west-side columns, Jake walked down the steps and slid into his friend's pace.

When Andrew's hearty greeting went unanswered he was surprised. Still, the day was too lovely to dwell on it so Andrew just kept walking. As they made their way past Flint and crossed to Watson, the university's main library, Andrew was struck again by his friend's mood, which remained deeply introspective. They crossed Jayhawk Boulevard to Lippincott, formerly the school of law and still home to the university's most important work of art, the Daniel Chester French statue of the first law dean. Those who had taken this walk with Andrew more than once knew he always crossed here, his genuflection to the beauty and the emotionality of the statue. Dyche Hall was just beyond the Daniel Chester French, and Andrew spoke up as they got there. "What do you think of the grotesques?"

Barely aroused from the torpor he had brought along as their third companion, Jake lamely asked, "The grotesques?"

"The new gargoyles around the frieze. They were just installed last week. What do you think?"

Jake never even looked up. "They're fine, I guess. I was never much drawn to Dyche, anyway."

That was too much for Andrew. "Not drawn to it? It's the most magnificent building on campus and one of the most magnificent buildings west of the Mississippi River. How can you not be drawn to it? And the new grotesques are fantastic!"

"If you say so," said Jake, eyes still straight ahead.

"We need to get you something to eat! Good thing we're almost there."

They entered the Union through the main entrance on the east side and walked through the long entry hall to the stairs on the west side. One floor up, just inside the building proper, was one of Andrew's favorite restaurants in the country. It was small, no more than eight tables. And it was open only for lunch and an occasional dinner, never on weekends. But it was run by Sarah Rasmussen, a welcoming soul who knew how to run a kitchen and who had been pursued by one restaurant after another in Lawrence until she was recruited to turn Impromptu into something special. She had. The service was excellent: Sarah had trained her student servers thoroughly, far beyond what a visiting parent might expect. And the food was amazing. The standard fare—the brisket, the veggie burger, the truffle fries, the mac and cheese—was all best in town. But each day Sarah's chef prepared a soup, a salad, and two entrees, one of them a fish flown in daily to a Lawrence restaurant consortium she had made the Union join. These items would have dazzled at the finest restaurants in Kansas City. That someone could find a restaurant this good in a student union was hard for Andrew to get his arms around. But he wasn't complaining; he ate there every chance he got.

Andrew walked past the skeletal lectern that served as the hostess' stand and into the open arms of Sarah, who always greeted him like a long-lost brother, another reason Andrew liked to come here.

"You're early," she said as she held him for a moment at arms' length before releasing him.

"Jake's starving," responded Andrew. "He almost fell asleep walking over here!"

"I have your table," said Sarah, and led them both to the west wall. The table sat beneath the window, its two perfect tulips—one red, one yellow—vying to be tallest in their tapered glass vase. Sarah stopped, Jake sat down. Andrew thanked Sarah, then he too took his seat, unfolded his blue linen napkin, and picked up the small menu. Andrew was looking at it when he spoke to his friend: "I'm not sure where you are, Jake, but it doesn't seem to be Lawrence, Kansas. What's up?"

Andrew had thought a direct question might be the right approach. But the seconds that ticked off while Jake said nothing became yet another trouble sign. Finally, Jake lifted his head from his own menu and responded.

"I'm leaving Lawrence."

"So am I!" said Andrew. "Back to the ranch to see my brother, but only for the weekend. Then I'm taking a month and going to England and Scotland. It's been years since I've walked London and seen the museums and gone to the theatre. I'll be there ten days. Friends will join up along the way, then we'll take the fast train to Edinburgh. We'll have four days chasing the restaurants and the pubs around the castle, then to the Highlands for some fishing. We'll go to Inverness, then Oban for the amazing seafood they serve in restaurants right on the docks, then to Glasgow for the flight home.

Where are *you* going?"

"When I said, 'I'm leaving Lawrence,' Andrew, I meant I'm leaving KU. I gave my notice last week. I'll be here through the end of June. This is probably our last lunch at Impromptu for a while."

Jake had his full attention now, and Andrew looked at his friend's eyes. Jake wasn't crying, exactly, but he seemed to be on the edge of it. Andrew reached across the table and put his large hand on Jake's arm. "I guess we didn't slay all the dragons after all."

They just looked at each other. It was Jake who broke the silence. "I just couldn't get past the Provost. The encounter with Erickson was ridiculous. *Nobody* believed I demeaned that little prick. But he allowed Erickson's complaint to go forward! People assume it was over when the panel announced their decision, but it wasn't, I guarantee you. That little attack on my reputation cost me much more than a month of my life. I still wake up to it.

There have been a lot of nice things that have happened since then; I'm not ignoring that. Most of the faculty have been great, especially the Honors faculty. Geoff even threw a party for me at his house. But do you know what I heard from my own department chair? You know what I've received from *him* since the panel decision was printed in the *UDK*? One thing. One *FUCKING* thing! Not a congratulatory phone call; not an invitation to his office or, God forbid, to his house. Not a party at Wescoe Beach. One thing. Know what it was? My teaching schedule for next fall. He sent me my **TEACHING SCHEDULE!**

You know I visited at Notre Dame two years ago. Rick Jeffries was my contact there and he was great. Rock Stars was a huge hit in South Bend and the faculty made me an amazing offer to stay. But I love KU, and I came back. When the Provost handed down his indictment against me this spring Rick called me the minute he heard about it. He never said a thing about my leaving KU. He wanted me to know he was sad about what was coming down, and he wanted me to know he was on my side. That was it. He checked in with me every week from then on. When FOX NEWS reported the decision three minutes after the panel announced it, Rick was the first person to text me. Know what he said? 'ROCK CHALK, BABY!'

I waited a few days, then I called him. Rick said Notre Dame still wanted me, and he said he believed they'd pay me $100,000 more in salary than they offered the last time. I thought he was kidding. But the note he sent a week later confirmed it. Notre Dame had received a large gift in support of religious studies and philosophy, large enough to support new, fully-endowed chairs in both departments. He had met with his colleagues, and with the donor, and they all agreed to offer the philosophy chair to me.

I will be The Samuel Langhorne Clemens Distinguished Professor of Philosophy at the University of Notre Dame."

Jake lowered his head, took a deep breath, and sighed. When he looked up at his friend his eyes were still gleaming.

"Wow," whispered Andrew. It was the only thing he could think of.

Sun Sets on Marvin Grove

The reality of their looming summer separation had set in, so they agreed to meet at the Campanile and talk about it. They chose 8:00 p.m. on a Monday; neither had class that day, and Farieh would have finished her work at WheatFields. You couldn't see the sun setting from the base of the Campanile, the Chi Omega house was in the way. But the painted sky was pretty from the top of the hill where the graduates would begin their walk down into the stadium. It had become a good place for them to meet.

At some moment after that Thanksgiving morning six months ago, Farieh had decided she liked this boy from Salina, Kansas, even if he was goofy. He was athletic, he was handsome, he was confident—about some things at least, and he was crazy about her. Her feelings for him had grown well past the fondness she had experienced in their early walks. But their time together was only days from ending, and both were apprehensive of what the summer might do to their relationship.

Richie got to the north side of the bell tower at 7:45 and started pacing. She had told him she had an errand to run at the

Union and would come up from the art museum parking lot, and he wanted to watch for her as she made her way past the grove and up the hill. He was OK until he spotted the yellow head scarf through the trees.

The walking helped Farieh—she felt purposeful. But the steps were still hard and she had to make herself take them. She had thought all weekend about how they had arrived here, how their feelings were arcing about like fireflies, how she was about to leave for a series of summer destinations that would have them on opposite sides of the planet. But it wasn't just their feelings that demanded the meeting, it was the courtesy. Both had been born to courtesy, and raised in it. They had to say "Goodbye" and they had to say it face-to-face.

Having stayed the sun's rays as Farieh walked toward them, the walnuts and hackberries let them loose once she passed. The day was already late. But there was light enough still to borrow it, and that let their branches cast sharp shadows against the Spencer's west façade and its brilliant round window, and they liked that. Their thick trunks had allowed the hide-and-seek Farieh and Richie had played one carefree afternoon not even a month ago.

As it neared the bell tower, the sidewalk rising in front of her passed the place where Richie had fallen over laughing into the winter's afternoon snowfall. She remembered how he had made himself into a snow angel, and how she had knelt down and touched him and claimed him for her own.

They were only paces apart when their eyes met. Farieh smiled. Stumbling at first, Richie moved. But he was moving downhill, his second step was long and assured, and in those next moments he forgot everything she had taught him about the strictures of her culture. He took her hands as he rushed past her and swung her out over the slope, her suede boots flying into space. He set her down and reached beneath her arms and lifted her—high into the air at first and then just lower so he could press his cheek against the place where her head scarf met the collar of her red jacket and breathe in the notes of the yeast and the honey that floated between them. Then he swung her again.

Had they been liquid, Farieh's blossoming emotions might have drenched him. But Richie did not notice them. The restraint that had kept him from taking Farieh in his arms had surrendered. His eyes were closed.

Acknowledgments

I had written things before I met my wife, Dru, but I was not a writer. Without her support, her urging me to look at the world through the eyes of others, her patience, and her love, this book would never have happened.

Thea Rademacher, Flint Hills Publishing's CEO, delivered the technical support the project required and the professional guidance her author required. She also provided the encouragement her author needed. I am indebted to her and to my long-time friend, Clyde Toland, who introduced us.

Louis Copt, whose prairie fire greets me whenever I look up from my desk, provided the splendid painting for the cover.

I was fortunate to have a group of friends willing to read portions of the book as it developed. Their feedback, which was as instructive as it was positive, pointed out inaccuracies and helped get the story back on track. Anything that remains inaccurate is my responsibility. Thank you David Brown, Tom Carmody, Walt Cofer, Mary Fay, Nicola Heskett, Matt Hoy, Phil McKnight, Marie Pickard, Peggy Raish, Mike Stout, Matt Wiltanger, and Todd Woods.

It was the technical skill of my former administrative assistant, Julie Schonhoff, that enabled me to transition from messy first drafts to professional Word documents.

Hamideh Gerami was critical to my attempt to introduce a compelling young Iranian woman to a Midwestern university. Here, especially, any missteps in that introduction are mine alone. Ted Juneau gave me insight after insight into the world of Jayhawk basketball while shaping the entire basketball narrative. And Matt Biscan's counsel made every chapter better. Special thanks to all three of you.

About the Author

BILL SAMPSON served as a Judge Advocate with the United States Navy before returning to Kansas for private practice. After a legal career trying and managing cases, teaching, and leading professional organizations throughout the country, he retired from the courtroom and now lives in Lawrence with his wife, Dru. Their three children and seven grandchildren live in Philadelphia, San Francisco, and Moscow, Idaho. *Wheat Fields* is his first novel.

www.billsampson.us

CPSIA information can be obtained
at www.ICGtesting.com
Printed in the USA
LVHW042035040323
740947LV00006B/69/J

9 781953 583444